Ready® | 4

Mathematics
PRACTICE AND
PROBLEM SOLVING
Teacher Guide

Teacher Advisors

Rachel Adelstein, Assistant Principal, Briggs Avenue Academy, Bronx, NY

Crystal Bailey, Math Impact Teacher, Eastern Guilford Middle School, Guilford County Schools, Gibsonville, NC

Max Brand, Reading Specialist, Indian Run Elementary, Dublin City School District, Dublin, OH

Dinah Chancellor, Professional Development Mathematics Consultant, Southlake, TX

Helen Comba, Supervisor of Basic Skills & Language Arts, School District of the Chathams, Chatham, NJ

Cindy Dean, Classroom Teacher, Mt. Diablo Unified School District, Concord, CA

Leah Flynn, Classroom Teacher, Brockton Public Schools, Brockton, MA

Randall E. Groth, Ph.D, Associate Professor of Mathematics Education, Salisbury University, Salisbury, MD

Bill Laraway, Classroom Teacher, Silver Oak Elementary, Evergreen School District, San Jose, CA

Jennifer Lerner, Classroom Teacher, PS 57, New York City Public Schools, New York, NY

Susie Legg, Elementary Curriculum Coordinator, Kansas City Public Schools, Kansas City, KS

Sarah Levine, Classroom Teacher, Springhurst Elementary School, Dobbs Ferry School District, Dobbs Ferry, NY

Nicole Peirce, Classroom Teacher, Eleanor Roosevelt Elementary, Pennsbury School District, Morrisville, PA

Donna Phillips, Classroom Teacher, Farmington R-7 School District, Farmington, MO

Maria Rosati, Classroom Teacher, Harwood Elementary School, Warren Consolidated Schools, Warren, MI

Kari Ross, Reading Specialist, MN

Sunita Sangari, Math Coach, PS/MS 29, New York City Public Schools, New York, NY

Eileen Seybuck, Classroom Teacher, PS 57, New York City Public Schools, New York, NY

Mark Hoover Thames, Research Scientist, University of Michigan, Ann Arbor, MI

Shannon Tsuruda, Classroom Teacher, Mt. Diablo Unified School District, Concord, CA

Acknowledgments

Editorial Director: Cynthia Tripp
Cover Designers, Illustrators: Julia Bourque, Matt Pollock
Book Designer: Scott Hoffman

Executive Editor: Kathy Kellman
Supervising Editors: Pamela Halloran, Grace Izzi
Director–Product Development: Daniel J. Smith
Vice President–Product Development: Adam Berkin

Table of Contents

Student Book includes a Family Letter for every lesson and Unit Vocabulary pages.

Student Book includes a Family Letter for every lesson and Unit Vocabulary pages.

Unit 4: Number and Operations—Fractions *(continued)*

Unit 5: Measurement and Data

Student Book includes a Family Letter for every lesson and Unit Vocabulary pages.

Teacher Resource Blacklines

Teacher Resource blackline masters are provided for use with the collaborative practice games in *Ready Practice and Problem Solving*. Full instructions for use of these teacher resources can be found in the Step by Step for each unit game.

Student Book includes a Family Letter for every lesson and Unit Vocabulary pages.

Ready® Program Overview

Ready is an integrated program of assessment and data-driven instruction designed to teach your students rigorous national and state standards for college and career readiness, including mathematical practice standards. You can use the program as a supplement to address specific standards where your students need instruction and practice, or more comprehensively to engage students in all standards.

Built for the new standards. Not just aligned.

For Students

Ready Instruction provides differentiated instruction and independent practice of key concepts and skills that build student confidence. Interim assessments give frequent opportunities to monitor progress.

Ready Practice and Problem Solving complements ***Ready Instruction***, through rich practice, games, and performance tasks that develop understanding and fluency with key skills and concepts.

Ready Assessments provides three full-length assessments designed to show student mastery of standards.

For Teachers

The ***Ready Teacher Resource Book*** and ***Ready Practice and Problem Solving Teacher Guide*** support teachers with strong professional development, step-by-step lesson plans, and best practices for implementing rigorous standards.

Ready Teacher Toolbox provides online lessons, prerequisite lessons from previous grades, center activities, and targeted best-practice teaching strategies.

Ready *Program* Features

 Built with **all-new content** written specifically for rigorous national and state standards for college and career readiness

 Uses a research-based, **gradual-release** instructional model

 Requires **higher-order thinking** and complex reasoning to solve problems

 Integrates **Standards for Mathematical Practice** throughout every lesson

 Embeds thoughtful **professional development**

 Encourages students to develop **deeper understanding** of concepts and to understand and use a variety of mathematical strategies and models

 Promotes **fluency** and connects hands-on learning with clearly articulated models throughout

What's in *Ready*® *Practice and Problem Solving*

Building on *Ready Instruction, Ready Practice and Problem Solving* encourages students to reason, use strategies, solve extended problems, and engage in collaborative learning to extend classroom learning. Designed for flexibility, *Ready Practice and Problem Solving* can be used for homework, independent classroom practice, and in after-school settings.

Lesson Practice Pages

Practice specific to each part of every *Ready Instruction* lesson gives students multiple opportunities to reinforce procedural fluency and synthesize concepts and skills learned in the classroom.

- Lesson practice pages can be used at the end of a lesson or after completing each part of a lesson.

- For ease of use, each part of a *Ready Practice and Problem Solving* lesson includes a *Ready Instruction* page reference indicating when they could be assigned.

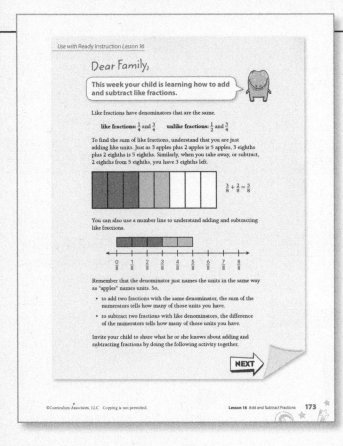

Family Letters

- Family Letters can be sent home separately before each lesson, or as part of a family communication package. They include a summary statement, vocabulary definitions, and models that help adult family members support their child's mathematical learning.

- Each letter concludes with a simple activity that encourages students to share their math knowledge with family members while practicing skills or concepts in a fun, engaging way.

- A Spanish version of each letter is available on the Teacher Toolbox.

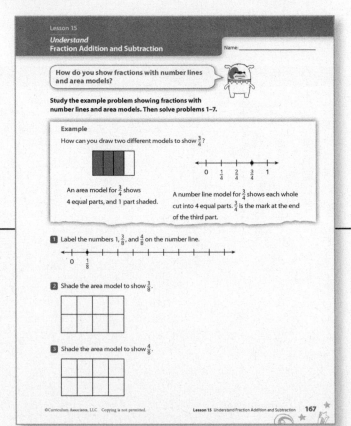

Prerequisite Skill Practice

- Students apply lesson **prerequisite concepts or skills** as they work with models that support those in the *Ready Instruction* lesson Introduction.

- This serves as a review of previous understandings and prepares students for the next section of the *Ready Instruction* lesson.

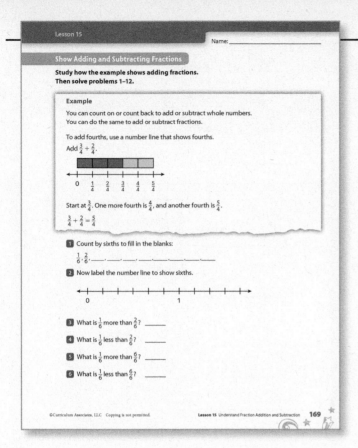

- **Worked-out examples** support and reinforce students' classroom learning, and can also serve as an explanation of the math content for adult family members if the practice pages are used as homework.

- Problems are **differentiated** to provide maximum flexibility when assigning practice as independent classwork or homework. The differentiation is marked in the Teacher Guide as basic **B**, medium **M**, or challenging **C**.

- **Vocabulary** is defined at the point where terms are used in the practice problems.

- Students are encouraged to show their work and use models and strategies they learned in the *Ready Instruction* lesson.

- Lessons conclude with **mixed practice** problems that vary in type, including multiple choice, yes-no formats, and open-ended questions.

Solve.

7. Label the number line to show fourths.

8. Now use the number line in problem 7 to show $\frac{2}{4} + \frac{2}{4}$.

9. Label the number line to show fourths again.

10. Now use the number line in problem 9 to show $\frac{4}{4} - \frac{2}{4}$.

11. Use the number line and area model below to show $\frac{2}{8} + \frac{1}{8} + \frac{3}{8}$.

12. Look at the three area models. Which one would you choose to show $\frac{1}{8} + \frac{2}{7}$? Explain how the denominator of the fraction helps you choose the model.

Vocabulary

denominator the number below the line in a fraction. It tells how many equal parts are in the whole.

→ $\frac{3}{4}$ 4 equal parts

numerator the number above the line in a fraction. It tells how many equal parts are described.

→ $\frac{3}{4}$ 3 parts described

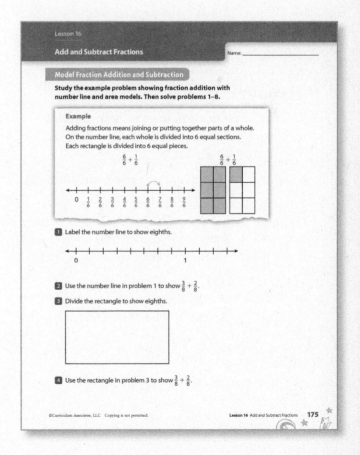

A9

Unit Practice Pages

Unit materials cover multiple skills and concepts, helping students make connections across standards.

Unit Game

- Unit Games are engaging collaborative experiences, designed to encourage students to use **strategic thinking** as they play the game with a partner.

- Students record the mathematics of each game to **promote fluency** and reinforce learning. The recording sheet also serves as an opportunity for informal assessment by providing a written record for teachers to monitor students' work.

- These partner games can be used at classroom centers and/or sent home for play with an adult family member.

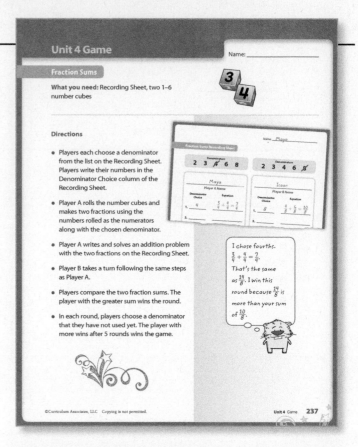

Unit Practice

- The Unit Practice provides **mixed practice** of lesson skills and concepts, and includes visual or stepped-out support for students.

- Unit Practice problems **integrate multiple skills**.

- These pages present problems with a **variety of formats**, including multiple choice and constructed response, to help students become familiar with items they will encounter on their state tests.

- The unit practice pages can be assigned as homework, used as independent or small group practice, or for whole class discussion.

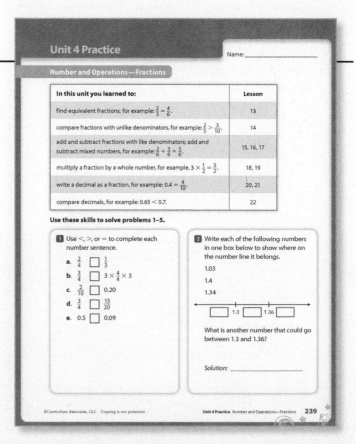

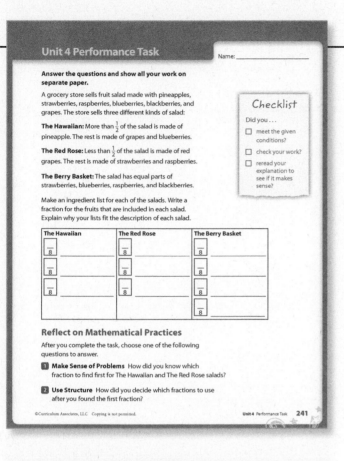

Unit Performance Task

- Real-world Unit Performance Tasks require students to **integrate skills and concepts**, apply higher-order thinking, and explain their reasoning.

- Engaging real-world tasks encourage students to become active participants in their learning by requiring them to organize and manage mathematical content and processes.

- **Performance Task Tips** help students organize their thinking.

- Students are asked to reflect on **Mathematical Practices** after they have concluded their work.

Unit Vocabulary

- The Unit Vocabulary is a way for students to integrate vocabulary into their learning. Vocabulary pages provide a **student-friendly definition** for each new and review vocabulary term in the unit.

- Students are given space to write **examples** for each term to help them connect the term to their own understanding.

- After students have completed these pages, they can use them as a reference.

- Throughout the units, students are given opportunities to further personalize their acquisition of mathematics vocabulary by selecting terms they want to define.

Fluency Practice Pages

Skills Practice

- Fluency facts practice and multi-digit computation worksheets in multiple formats provide flexibility and promote the use of grade-appropriate strategies and algorithms.

- These worksheets for grade-level facts and operations can be used any time after the skill has been taught.

Repeated Reasoning Practice

- Repeated Reasoning practice worksheets encourage students to make use of **structure** and look for **regularity** as part of their development of grade-level fluency.

- In this type of fluency practice, students identify and describe patterns in the relationship between the answers and the problems. This develops their abstract reasoning skills, mental math skills, and a deeper understanding of fractions and base ten numbers.

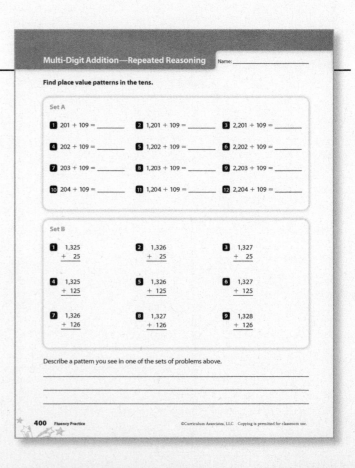

Correlation Chart

Common Core State Standards Practice in *Ready® Practice and Problem Solving*

The table below shows the standards addressed in lesson practices, unit practices, games, and performance tasks, all of which correspond to **Ready Instruction** lessons and units. Use this information to plan and focus meaningful practice.

Common Core State Standards for Grade 4 — Mathematics Standards		Content Emphasis	*Ready® Practice and Problem Solving*
Operations and Algebraic Thinking			
Use the four operations with whole numbers to solve problems.			
4.OA.A.1	Interpret a multiplication equation as a comparison, e.g., interpret 35 = 5 × 7 as a statement that 35 is 5 times as many as 7 and 7 times as many as 5. Represent verbal statements of multiplicative comparisons as multiplication equations.	Major	Lesson 5 Practice Unit 2 Practice
4.OA.A.2	Multiply or divide to solve word problems involving multiplicative comparison, e.g., by using drawings and equations with a symbol for the unknown number to represent the problem, distinguishing multiplicative comparison from additive comparison.	Major	Lesson 6 Practice Unit 2 Practice
4.OA.A.3	Solve multistep word problems posed with whole numbers and having whole-number answers using the four operations, including problems in which remainders must be interpreted. Represent these problems using equations with a letter standing for the unknown quantity. Assess the reasonableness of answers using mental computation and estimation strategies including rounding.	Major	Lesson 9 Practice Lesson 10 Practice Unit 2 Practice Unit 2 Performance Task Unit 3 Performance Task
Gain familiarity with factors and multiples.			
4.OA.B.4	Find all factor pairs for a whole number in the range 1–100. Recognize that a whole number is a multiple of each of its factors. Determine whether a given whole number in the range 1–100 is a multiple of a given one-digit number. Determine whether a given whole number in the range 1–100 is prime or composite.	Supporting/Additional	Lesson 7 Practice Unit 2 Game: Factor Finder Unit 2 Practice Unit 2 Performance Task
Generate and analyze patterns.			
4.OA.C.5	Generate a number or shape pattern that follows a given rule. Identify apparent features of the pattern that were not explicit in the rule itself. *For example, given the rule "Add 3" and the starting number 1, generate terms in the resulting sequence and observe that the terms appear to alternate between odd and even numbers. Explain informally why the numbers will continue to alternate in this way.*	Supporting/Additional	Lesson 8 Practice Unit 2 Practice
Number and Operations in Base Ten			
Generalize place value understanding for multi-digit whole numbers.			
4.NBT.A.1	Recognize that in a multi-digit whole number, a digit in one place represents ten times what it represents in the place to its right. *For example, recognize that 700 ÷ 70 = 10 by applying concepts of place value and division.*	Major	Lesson 1 Practice Unit 1 Practice Unit 3 Game: Multiplication Products
4.NBT.A.2	Read and write multi-digit whole numbers using base-ten numerals, number names, and expanded form. Compare two multi-digit numbers based on meanings of the digits in each place, using >, =, and < symbols to record the results of comparisons.	Major	Lesson 1 Practice Lesson 2 Practice Unit 1 Game: How Close Can You Get? Unit 1 Practice
4.NBT.A.3	Use place value understanding to round multi-digit whole numbers to any place.	Major	Lesson 4 Practice Unit 1 Practice Unit 1 Performance Task

The Standards for Mathematical Practice are integrated throughout the lesson practices, unit practices, and unit games.

Common Core State Standards © 2010. National Governors Association Center for Best Practices and Council of Chief State School Officers. All rights reserved.

Common Core State Standards for Grade 4 — Mathematics Standards	Content Emphasis	Ready® Practice and Problem Solving
Number and Operations in Base Ten (continued)		
Use place value understanding and properties of operations to perform multi-digit arithmetic.		
4.NBT.B.4 Fluently add and subtract multi-digit whole numbers using the standard algorithm.	Major	Lesson 3 Practice Unit 1 Game: How Close Can You Get? Unit 1 Practice Unit 1 Performance Task
4.NBT.B.5 Multiply a whole number of up to four digits by a one-digit whole number, and multiply two two-digit numbers, using strategies based on place value and the properties of operations. Illustrate and explain the calculation by using equations, rectangular arrays, and/or area models.	Major	Lesson 11 Practice Unit 2 Performance Task Unit 3 Game: Multiplication Products Unit 3 Practice Unit 3 Performance Task
4.NBT.B.6 Find whole-number quotients and remainders with up to four-digit dividends and one-digit divisors, using strategies based on place value, the properties of operations, and/or the relationship between multiplication and division. Illustrate and explain the calculation by using equations, rectangular arrays, and/or area models.	Major	Lesson 12 Practice Unit 3 Practice Unit 3 Performance Task
Number and Operations—Fractions		
Extend understanding of fraction equivalence and ordering.		
4.NF.A.1 Explain why a fraction $\frac{a}{b}$ is equivalent to a fraction $\frac{(n \times a)}{(n \times b)}$ by using visual fraction models, with attention to how the number and size of the parts differ even though the two fractions themselves are the same size. Use this principle to recognize and generate equivalent fractions.	Major	Lesson 13 Practice Unit 4 Practice
4.NF.A.2 Compare two fractions with different numerators and different denominators, e.g., by creating common denominators or numerators or by comparing to a benchmark fraction such as $\frac{1}{2}$. Recognize that comparisons are valid only when the two fractions refer to the same whole. Record the results of comparisons with symbols $>$, $=$, or $<$, and justify the conclusions, e.g., by using a visual fraction model.	Major	Lesson 14 Practice Unit 4 Game: Fraction Sums Unit 4 Practice Unit 4 Performance Task
Build fractions from unit fractions.		
4.NF.B.3 Understand a fraction $\frac{a}{b}$ with $a > 1$ as a sum of fractions $\frac{1}{b}$.	Major	Lesson 15 Practice Lesson 16 Practice Lesson 17 Practice Unit 4 Game: Fraction Sums Unit 4 Practice Unit 4 Performance Task
4.NF.B.3a Understand addition and subtraction of fractions as joining and separating parts referring to the same whole.	Major	
4.NF.B.3b Decompose a fraction into a sum of fractions with the same denominator in more than one way, recording each decomposition by an equation. Justify decompositions, e.g., by using a visual fraction model. *Examples:* $\frac{3}{8} = \frac{1}{8} + \frac{1}{8} + \frac{1}{8}; \frac{3}{8} = \frac{1}{8} + \frac{2}{8}; 2\frac{1}{8} = 1 + 1 + \frac{1}{8} = \frac{8}{8} + \frac{8}{8} + \frac{1}{8}.$	Major	
4.NF.B.3c Add and subtract mixed numbers with like denominators, e.g., by replacing each mixed number with an equivalent fraction, and/or by using properties of operations and the relationship between addition and subtraction.	Major	
4.NF.B.3d Solve word problems involving addition and subtraction of fractions referring to the same whole and having like denominators, e.g., by using visual fraction models and equations to represent the problem.	Major	

Common Core State Standards for Grade 4 — Mathematics Standards	Content Emphasis	Ready® Practice and Problem Solving
Number and Operations—Fractions (continued)		
Build fractions from unit fractions. (continued)		
4.NF.B.4 Apply and extend previous understandings of multiplication to multiply a fraction by a whole number.	Major	Lesson 18 Practice Lesson 19 Practice Unit 4 Practice
4.NF.B.4a Understand a fraction $\frac{a}{b}$ as a multiple of $\frac{1}{b}$. *For example, use a visual fraction model to represent $\frac{5}{4}$ as the product $5 \times \left(\frac{1}{4}\right)$, recording the conclusion by the equation $\frac{5}{4} = 5 \times \left(\frac{1}{4}\right)$.*	Major	
4.NF.B.4b Understand a multiple of $\frac{a}{b}$ as a multiple of $\frac{1}{b}$, and use this understanding to multiply a fraction by a whole number. *For example, use a visual fraction model to express $3 \times \left(\frac{2}{5}\right)$ as $6 \times \left(\frac{1}{5}\right)$, recognizing this product as $\frac{6}{5}$. (In general, $n \times \left(\frac{a}{b}\right) = \frac{(n \times a)}{b}$.)*	Major	
4.NF.B.4c Solve word problems involving multiplication of a fraction by a whole number, e.g., by using visual fraction models and equations to represent the problem. *For example, if each person at a party will eat $\frac{3}{8}$ of a pound of roast beef, and there will be 5 people at the party, how many pounds of roast beef will be needed? Between what two whole numbers does your answer lie?*	Major	
Understand decimal notation for fractions, and compare decimal fractions.		
4.NF.C.5 Express a fraction with denominator 10 as an equivalent fraction with denominator 100, and use this technique to add two fractions with respective denominators 10 and 100.4 *For example, express $\frac{3}{10}$ as $\frac{30}{100}$, and add $\frac{3}{10} + \frac{4}{100} = \frac{34}{100}$.*	Major	Lesson 20 Practice
4.NF.C.6 Use decimal notation for fractions with denominators 10 or 100. *For example, rewrite 0.62 as $\frac{62}{100}$; describe a length as 0.62 meters; locate 0.62 on a number line diagram.*	Major	Lesson 21 Practice Unit 4 Practice
4.NF.C.7 Compare two decimals to hundredths by reasoning about their size. Recognize that comparisons are valid only when the two decimals refer to the same whole. Record the results of comparisons with the symbols >, =, or <, and justify the conclusions, e.g., by using a visual model.	Major	Lesson 22 Practice Unit 4 Practice
Measurement and Data		
Solve problems involving measurement and conversion of measurements.		
4.MD.A.1 Know relative sizes of measurement units within one system of units including km, m, cm; kg, g; lb, oz.; l, ml; hr, min, sec. Within a single system of measurement, express measurements in a larger unit in terms of a smaller unit. Record measurement equivalents in a two-column table. *For example, know that 1 ft is 12 times as long as 1 in. Express the length of a 4 ft snake as 48 in. Generate a conversion table for feet and inches listing the number pairs (1, 12), (2, 24), (3, 36), . . .*	Supporting/ Additional	Lesson 23 Practice Unit 5 Practice Unit 5 Performance Task
4.MD.A.2 Use the four operations to solve word problems involving distances, intervals of time, liquid volumes, masses of objects, and money, including problems involving simple fractions or decimals, and problems that require expressing measurements given in a larger unit in terms of a smaller unit. Represent measurement quantities using diagrams such as number line diagrams that feature a measurement scale.	Supporting/ Additional	Lesson 24 Practice Lesson 25 Practice Unit 5 Practice
4.MD.A.3 Apply the area and perimeter formulas for rectangles in real world and mathematical problems. *For example, find the width of a rectangular room given the area of the flooring and the length, by viewing the area formula as a multiplication equation with an unknown factor.*	Supporting/ Additional	Lesson 26 Practice Unit 5 Practice Unit 5 Performance Task

Common Core State Standards for Grade 4 — Mathematics Standards	Content Emphasis	Ready® Practice and Problem Solving
Measurement and Data (continued)		
Represent and interpret data.		
4.MD.B.4 Make a line plot to display a data set of measurements in fractions of a unit $\left(\frac{1}{2}, \frac{1}{4}, \frac{1}{8}\right)$. Solve problems involving addition and subtraction of fractions by using information presented in line plots. *For example, from a line plot find and interpret the difference in length between the longest and shortest specimens in an insect collection.*	Supporting/ Additional	Lesson 27 Practice
Geometric measurement: understand concepts of angle and measure angles.		
4.MD.C.5 Recognize angles as geometric shapes that are formed wherever two rays share a common endpoint, and understand concepts of angle measurement:	Supporting/ Additional	Lesson 28 Practice Unit 5 Practice
4.MD.C.5a An angle is measured with reference to a circle with its center at the common endpoint of the rays, by considering the fraction of the circular arc between the points where the two rays intersect the circle. An angle that turns through $\frac{1}{360}$ of a circle is called a "one-degree angle," and can be used to measure angles.	Supporting/ Additional	
4.MD.C.5b An angle that turns through *n* one-degree angles is said to have an angle measure of *n* degrees.	Supporting/ Additional	
4.MD.C.6 Measure angles in whole-number degrees using a protractor. Sketch angles of specified measure.	Supporting/ Additional	Lesson 29 Practice Unit 5 Game: Angle Sums Unit 5 Practice
4.MD.C.7 Recognize angle measure as additive. When an angle is decomposed into non-overlapping parts, the angle measure of the whole is the sum of the angle measures of the parts. Solve addition and subtraction problems to find unknown angles on a diagram in real world and mathematical problems, e.g., by using an equation with a symbol for the unknown angle measure.	Supporting/ Additional	Lesson 30 Practice Unit 5 Game: Angle Sums
Geometry		
Draw and identify lines and angles, and classify shapes by properties of their lines and angles.		
4.G.A.1 Draw points, lines, line segments, rays, angles (right, acute, obtuse), and perpendicular and parallel lines. Identify these in two-dimensional figures.	Supporting/ Additional	Lesson 31 Practice Unit 6 Practice Unit 6 Performance Task
4.G.A.2 Classify two-dimensional figures based on the presence or absence of parallel or perpendicular lines, or the presence or absence of angles of a specified size. Recognize right triangles as a category, and identify right triangles.	Supporting/ Additional	Lesson 32 Practice Unit 6 Game: Shape Round Up Unit 6 Practice Unit 6 Performance Task
4.G.A.3 Recognize a line of symmetry for a two-dimensional figure as a line across the figure such that the figure can be folded along the line into matching parts. Identify line-symmetric figures and draw lines of symmetry.	Supporting/ Additional	Lesson 33 Practice Unit 6 Practice

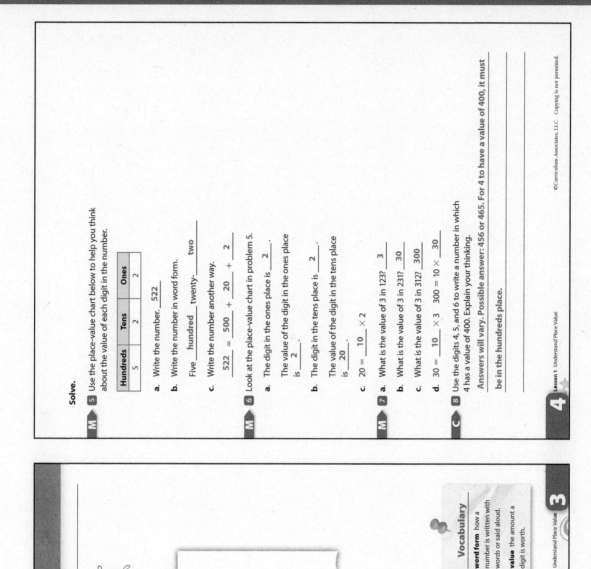

Name: _____

Lesson 1

Understand Place Value

How do you know the place value of each digit in a number?

Study the example that shows how a place-value chart shows the value of each digit in a number. Then solve problems 1–8.

Example

The place-value chart shows the number 435.

Hundreds	Tens	Ones
4	3	5

Word form: *four hundred thirty-five*

The 4 in the hundreds place has a value of 400.
The 3 in the tens place has a value of 30.
The 5 in the ones place has a value of 5.

So, another way to write 435 is 400 + 30 + 5.

B 1 Show the number 762 in the following place-value chart.

Hundreds	Tens	Ones
7	6	2

B 2 What is the value of 7 in 762? __700__

B 3 What is the value of the digit in the tens place in 762? __60__

M 4 Use place value to show another way to write 762.

762 = __700__ + __60__ + __2__

Vocabulary
word form how a number is written with words or said aloud.
value the amount a digit is worth.

Solve.

M 5 Use the place-value chart below to help you think about the value of each digit in the number.

Hundreds	Tens	Ones
5	2	2

a. Write the number. __522__

b. Write the number in word form.

Five __hundred__ twenty- __two__

c. Write the number another way.

522 = __500__ + __20__ + __2__

M 6 Look at the place-value chart in problem 5.

a. The digit in the ones place is __2__ .

The value of the digit in the ones place is __2__ .

b. The digit in the tens place is __2__ .

The value of the digit in the tens place is __20__ .

c. 20 = __10__ × 2

M 7 a. What is the value of 3 in 123? __3__

b. What is the value of 3 in 231? __30__

c. What is the value of 3 in 312? __300__

d. 30 = __10__ × 3   300 = 10 × __30__

C 8 Use the digits 4, 5, and 6 to write a number in which 4 has a value of 400. Explain your thinking.

Answers will vary. Possible answer: 456 or 465. For 4 to have a value of 400, it must be in the hundreds place.

_____

⭐ **4**

3 Lesson 1 *Understand Place Value*

Key

B Basic   **M** Medium   **C** Challenge

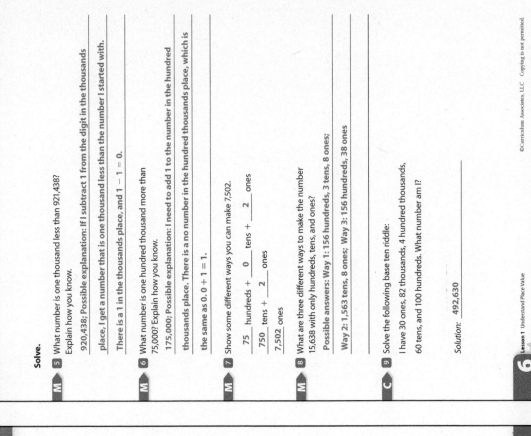

Lesson 1

Name: _____

Use Place Value

Study how the example uses a place-value chart to show the value of the digits in a number. Then solve problems 1–8.

Example

Look at the place-value chart below. What is the value of the 3?

Then, use place value to explain the value of 3 if it were in the ten thousands place.

Hundred Thousands	Ten Thousands	Thousands	Hundreds	Tens	Ones
2	0	3	5	5	4

Standard form: 203,554
Expanded form: 200,000 + 3,000 + 500 + 50 + 4
Word form: _two hundred three thousand, five hundred fifty-four_

The 3 is in the thousands place, so it has a value of 3,000.
If 3 were in the ten thousands place, its value would be 30,000.

B **1** Write 70,681 in the following place-value chart.

Hundred Thousands	Ten Thousands	Thousands	Hundreds	Tens	Ones
	7	0	6	8	1

B **2** Write 70,681 in expanded form and word form.

Expanded form: 70,000 + 600 + 80 + 1

Word form: seventy thousand, six hundred eighty-one

B **3** What would be the value of 8 if it were in the thousands place? ___8,000___

M **4** What is the value of the 6 in 70,681? Explain how you know.

600; Possible explanation: The 6 is in the hundreds

place. _____

Vocabulary

value the amount a digit is worth.

©Curriculum Associates, LLC   Copying is not permitted.

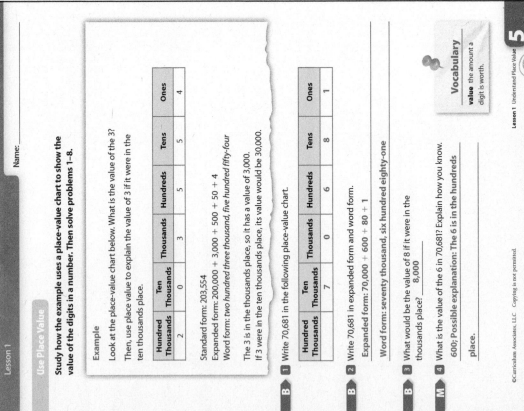

Solve.

M **5** What number is one thousand less than 921,438? Explain how you know.

920,438; Possible explanation: If I subtract 1 from the digit in the thousands

place, I get a number that is one thousand less than the number I started with.

There is a 1 in the thousands place, and 1 − 1 = 0.

M **6** What number is one hundred thousand more than 75,000? Explain how you know.

175,000; Possible explanation: I need to add 1 to the number in the hundred

thousands place. There is no number in the hundred thousands place, which is

the same as 0. 0 + 1 = 1.

M **7** Show some different ways you can make 7,502.

75 hundreds + __0__ tens + __2__ ones

750 tens + __2__ ones

7,502 ones

M **8** What are three different ways to make the number 15,638 with only hundreds, tens, and ones?

Possible answers: Way 1: 156 hundreds, 3 tens, 8 ones;

Way 2: 1,563 tens, 8 ones; Way 3: 156 hundreds, 38 ones

C **9** Solve the following base ten riddle:

I have 30 ones, 82 thousands, 4 hundred thousands, 60 tens, and 100 hundreds. What number am I?

Solution: ___492,630___

©Curriculum Associates, LLC   Copying is not permitted.

©Curriculum Associates, LLC   Copying is not permitted.

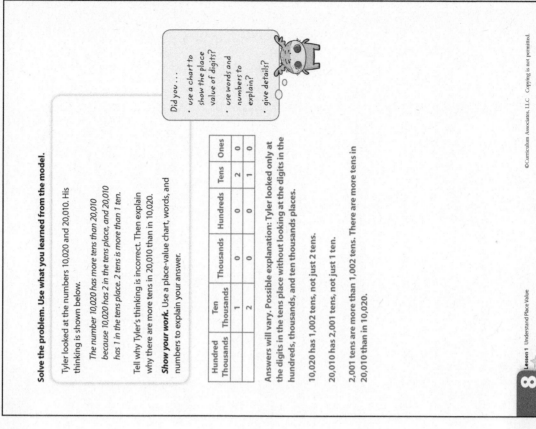

Solve the problem. Use what you learned from the model.

Tyler looked at the numbers 10,020 and 20,010. His thinking is shown below.

The number 10,020 has more tens than 20,010 because 10,020 has 2 in the tens place, and 20,010 has 1 in the tens place. 2 tens is more than 1 ten.

Tell why Tyler's thinking is incorrect. Then explain why there are more tens in 20,010 than in 10,020.

Show your work. Use a place-value chart, words, and numbers to explain your answer.

Hundred Thousands	Ten Thousands	Thousands	Hundreds	Tens	Ones
	1	0	0	2	0
	2	0	0	1	0

Answers will vary. Possible explanation: Tyler looked only at the digits in the tens place without looking at the digits in the hundreds, thousands, and ten thousands places.

10,020 has 1,002 tens, not just 2 tens.

20,010 has 2,001 tens, not just 1 ten.

2,001 tens are more than 1,002 tens. There are more tens in 20,010 than in 10,020.

Did you . . .
- use a chart to show the place value of digits?
- use words and numbers to explain?
- give details?

Lesson 1

Name: _____

Reason and Write

Study the example. Underline two parts that you think make it a particularly good answer and a helpful example.

Answers will vary. Note whether students incorporate the features they chose in their answer on the next page.

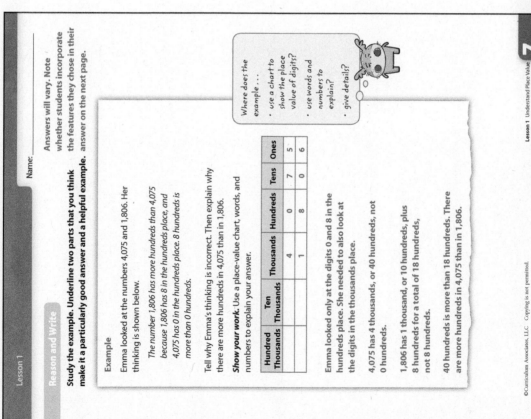

Example

Emma looked at the numbers 4,075 and 1,806. Her thinking is shown below.

The number 1,806 has more hundreds than 4,075 because 1,806 has 8 in the hundreds place, and 4,075 has 0 in the hundreds place. 8 hundreds is more than 0 hundreds.

Tell why Emma's thinking is incorrect. Then explain why there are more hundreds in 4,075 than in 1,806.

Show your work. Use a place-value chart, words, and numbers to explain your answer.

Hundred Thousands	Ten Thousands	Thousands	Hundreds	Tens	Ones
		4	0	7	5
		1	8	0	6

Emma looked only at the digits 0 and 8 in the hundreds place. She needed to also look at the digits in the thousands place.

4,075 has 4 thousands, or 40 hundreds, not 0 hundreds.

1,806 has 1 thousand, or 10 hundreds, plus 8 hundreds for a total of 18 hundreds, not 8 hundreds.

40 hundreds is more than 18 hundreds. There are more hundreds in 4,075 than in 1,806.

Where does the example . . .
- use a chart to show the place value of digits?
- use words and numbers to explain?
- give details?

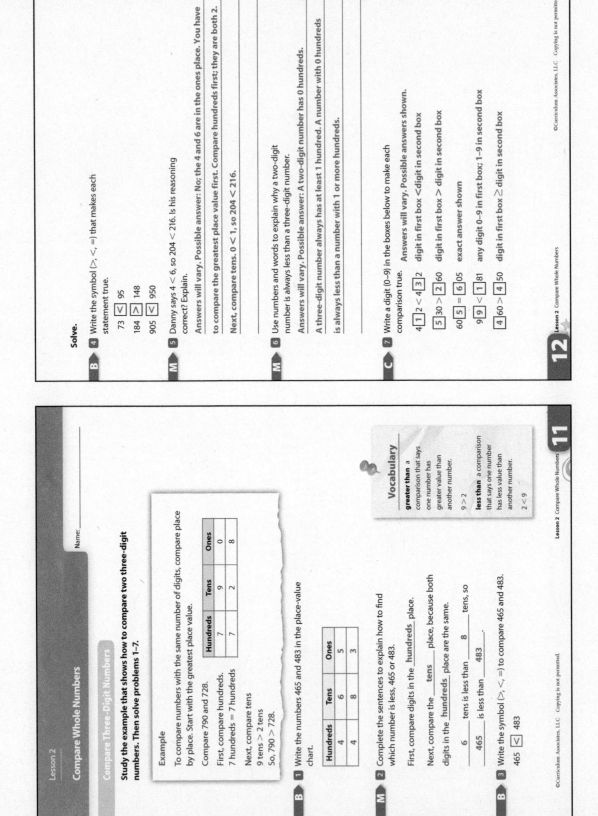

Lesson 2

Compare Whole Numbers

Compare Three-Digit Numbers

Study the example that shows how to compare two three-digit numbers. Then solve problems 1–7.

Example

To compare numbers with the same number of digits, compare place by place. Start with the greatest place value.

Compare 790 and 728.

Hundreds	Tens	Ones
7	9	0
7	2	8

First, compare hundreds.
7 hundreds = 7 hundreds

Next, compare tens
9 tens > 2 tens
So, 790 > 728.

B 1 Write the numbers 465 and 483 in the place-value chart.

Hundreds	Tens	Ones
4	6	5
4	8	3

M 2 Complete the sentences to explain how to find which number is less, 465 or 483.

First, compare digits in the __hundreds__ place.

Next, compare the __tens__ place, because both digits in the __hundreds__ place are the same.

6 __tens is less than__ 8 tens, so

465 __is less than__ 483.

B 3 Write the symbol (>, <, =) to compare 465 and 483.
465 < 483

Vocabulary

greater than a comparison that says one number has greater value than another number.
9 > 2

less than a comparison that says one number has less value than another number.
2 < 9

Solve.

B 4 Write the symbol (>, <, =) that makes each statement true.
73 < 95
184 > 148
905 < 950

M 5 Danny says 4 < 6, so 204 < 216. Is his reasoning correct? Explain.
Answers will vary. Possible answer: No; the 4 and 6 are in the ones place. You have to compare the greatest place value first. Compare hundreds first; they are both 2.
Next, compare tens. 0 < 1, so 204 < 216.

M 6 Use numbers and words to explain why a two-digit number is always less than a three-digit number.
Answers will vary. Possible answer: A two-digit number has 0 hundreds. A number with 0 hundreds is always less than a number with 1 or more hundreds.
A three-digit number always has at least 1 hundred. A number with 0 hundreds is always less than a number with 1 or more hundreds.

C 7 Write a digit (0–9) in the boxes below to make each comparison true. Answers will vary. Possible answers shown.
4 [1] 2 < 4 [3] 2   digit in first box < digit in second box
5 [30] > 2 [60]   digit in first box > digit in second box
60 [5] = 6 [05]   exact answer shown
9 [9] > [1] 81   any digit 0–9 in first box; 1–9 in second box
4 [60] > 4 [50]   digit in first box ≥ digit in second box

11 Lesson 2 Compare Whole Numbers
©Curriculum Associates, LLC   Copying is not permitted.

12 Lesson 2 Compare Whole Numbers
©Curriculum Associates, LLC   Copying is not permitted.

Key

B Basic   **M** Medium   **C** Challenge

Lesson 2

Name: _____

Compare Multi-Digit Numbers

Study the example that shows how to compare multi-digit numbers. Then solve problems 1–6.

Example

Cara piloted two flights. On her first flight, she flew the airplane 30,825 feet high. On her second flight, she flew 30,750 feet high. Compare how high Cara flew on her two flights.

Hundred Thousands	Ten Thousands	Thousands	Hundreds	Tens	Ones
	3	0	8	2	5
	3	0	7	5	0

The ten thousands and thousands digits are the same.

The hundreds digits are different.

8 hundreds > 7 hundreds

30,825 > 30,750

1 In 2013, 50,266 runners finished the New York City Marathon and 38,879 runners finished the Chicago Marathon. Compare these numbers by lining up the place value. Explain which number is greater.

50,266
38,879

Answers will vary. Possible explanation: Write the numbers one above the other.

Start with the greatest place value, the ten thousands. 5 ten thousands > 3 ten thousands, so 50,266 > 38,879.

2 Two numbers are shown in expanded form. Explain and show how to compare these numbers.

60,000 + 2,000 + 500 + 80 + 3
60,000 + 7,000 + 200 + 40 + 5

Answers will vary. Possible explanation: The numbers are 62,583 and 67,245.

Compare the numbers place by place. The ten thousands are the same. The thousands are different. 2 thousands < 7 thousands, so 62,583 < 67,245.

13

Solve.

3 Circle all the numbers that are greater than 98,765.

a. (100,100) *(circled)*
b. 89,975
c. (99,132) *(circled)*
d. (987,650) *(circled)*

4 Walnut Elementary raised $1,950 for new technology in their school. Grove Elementary raised $1,890. Which school raised more money? Explain how you know.

Walnut Elementary raised more money. Possible explanation: 1,950 > 1,890. Both numbers have 1 thousand, so I compared the hundreds. 9 hundreds > 8 hundreds, so 1,950 is greater than 1,890.

5 Write the symbol (>, <, =) that makes the statement true.

8,035 [>] 894

62,999 [<] 63,000

142,073 [<] 143,750

501,348 [>] 500,348

6 Tell whether each number sentence is *True* or *False*.

a. 33,003 = 33,030   ☐ True   ☒ False
b. 524,980 > 52,498   ☒ True   ☐ False
c. 270,615 < 270,569   ☐ True   ☒ False
d. 100,000 < 99,999   ☐ True   ☒ False

Lesson 2 Compare Whole Numbers

14

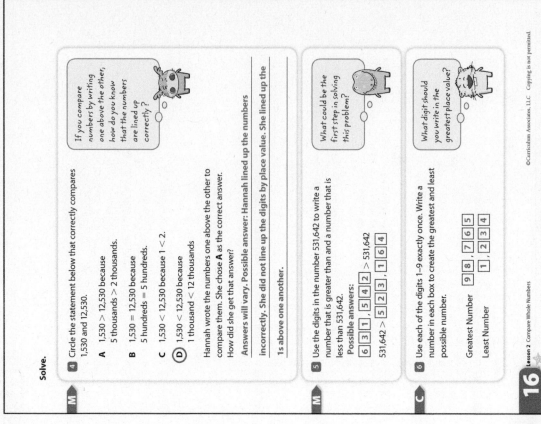

Lesson 2

Compare Whole Numbers

Solve the problems.

B 1. Ethan read 901 pages this month. Henry read 1,002 pages. Maria read 1,020 pages. Kylie read 1,012 pages. Who read the least number of pages?

    A Ethan   **C** Maria

    B Henry   **D** Kylie

What place-value position do you need to compare?

B 2. A photographer has picture files saved in three online albums. The Wedding album has 2,073 files. The Birthday album has 1,860 files. The Pets album has 2,370 files. Which album has the most files?

You might want to use a place-value chart to compare these numbers.

Show your work.

Possible student work: Place-value chart shown. Students may also line up the numbers by place value or write the numbers in expanded form.

	Thousands	Hundreds	Tens	Ones
Wedding	2	0	7	3
Birthday	1	8	6	0
Pets	2	3	7	0

Solution: The Pets album has the most files.

M 3. Which of these is equal to 25,973?

    A 25 thousands, 973 hundreds

    B 259 hundreds, 7 tens, 3 ones

    C 25 hundreds, 97 tens, 3 ones

    D 25 ten thousands, 9 hundreds, 7 tens, 3 ones

How could you write this number with only hundreds, tens, and ones?

Lesson 2 Compare Whole Numbers   **15**

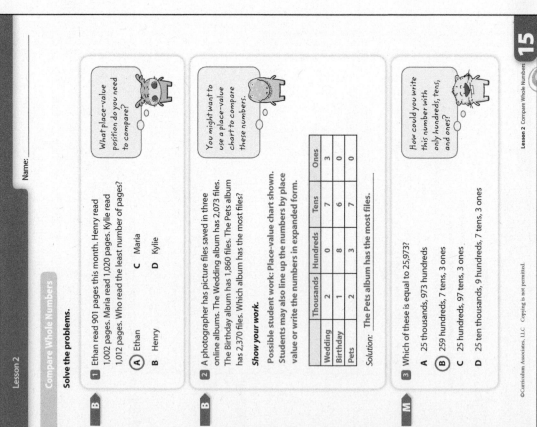

Solve.

M 4. Circle the statement below that correctly compares 1,530 and 12,530.

    A 1,530 > 12,530 because 5 thousands > 2 thousands.

    B 1,530 = 12,530 because 5 hundreds = 5 hundreds.

    C 1,530 < 12,530 because 1 < 2.

    (D) 1,530 < 12,530 because 1 thousand < 12 thousands

If you compare numbers by writing one above the other, how do you know that the numbers are lined up correctly?

Hannah wrote the numbers one above the other to compare them. She chose **A** as the correct answer. How did she get that answer?

Answers will vary. Possible answer: Hannah lined up the numbers incorrectly. She did not line up the digits by place value. She lined up the 1s above one another.

M 5. Use the digits in the number 531,642 to write a number that is greater than and a number that is less than 531,642.

Possible answers:

6 3 1 , 5 4 2 > 531,642

531,642 > 5 2 3 , 1 6 4

What could be the first step in solving this problem?

C 6. Use each of the digits 1–9 exactly once. Write a number in each box to create the greatest and least possible number.

What digit should you write in the greatest place value?

Greatest Number   9 8 , 7 6 5

Least Number   1 2 , 3 4

16   **Lesson 2** Compare Whole Numbers

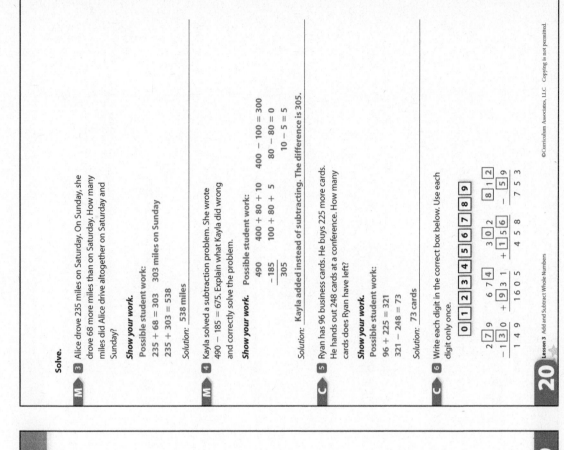

Name: _____

Lesson 3

Add and Subtract Whole Numbers

Add and Subtract Three-Digit Numbers

Study the example showing how to subtract by breaking apart and combining numbers. Then solve problems 1–6.

Example

Solve 852 − 623.

Use place value to write each number as hundreds, tens, and ones.

$852 = 800 + 50 + 2$ or **800 + 40 + 12**
$623 =$ **600 + 20 + 3**

Subtract hundreds. $800 − 600 = 200$
Subtract tens. $40 − 20 = 20$
Subtract ones. $12 − 3 = 9$

Combine the differences. $200 + 20 + 9 = 229$
$852 − 623 = 229$

B **1** Show how to use place value to subtract 947 − 586.

$947 = 900 + 40 + 7$ or $800 + 140 + 7$
$586 = 500 + 80 + 6$

$800 − 500 = 300$
$140 − 80 = 60$
$7 − 6 = 1$
$300 + 60 + 1 = 361$ so $947 − 586 = 361$

B **2** Show how to use place value to add 354 + 271.

$354 = 300 + 50 + 4$
$271 = 200 + 70 + 1$
$ 500 + 120 + 5$ or 625
$354 + 271 = 625$

Solve.

M **3** Alice drove 235 miles on Saturday. On Sunday, she drove 68 more miles than on Saturday. How many miles did Alice drive altogether on Saturday and Sunday?

Show your work.
Possible student work:
$235 + 68 = 303$ 303 miles on Sunday
$235 + 303 = 538$

Solution: __538 miles__

M **4** Kayla solved a subtraction problem. She wrote $490 − 185 = 675$. Explain what Kayla did wrong and correctly solve the problem.

Show your work. Possible student work:

490	$400 + 80 + 10$	$400 − 100 = 300$
− 185	$100 + 80 + 5$	$80 − 80 = 0$
305		$10 − 5 = 5$

Solution: __Kayla added instead of subtracting. The difference is 305.__

C **5** Ryan has 96 business cards. He buys 225 more cards. He hands out 248 cards at a conference. How many cards does Ryan have left?

Show your work.
Possible student work:
$96 + 225 = 321$
$321 − 248 = 73$

Solution: __73 cards__

C **6** Write each digit in the correct box below. Use each digit only once.

0 1 2 3 4 5 6 7 8 9

```
  2 7 9       6 7 4      3 0 2      8 1 2
- 1 3 0     + 9 3 1    + 1 5 6    -   5 9
  1 4 9       1 6 0 5    4 5 8      7 5 3
```

Key

B Basic   **M** Medium   **C** Challenge

Lesson 3

Add Whole Numbers

Study the example showing how to use addition to solve a word problem. Then solve problems 1–6.

Example

On Friday, 1,150 people saw the school play. On Saturday, 987 people saw the play. How many people saw the play on those two days?

```
        1 1
  1,150      1,150
+   987    +   987
              2,137
```

```
     7  →  0 ones + 7 ones = 7 ones
   130  →  5 tens + 8 tens = 13 tens or 1 hundred + 3 tens
 1,000  →  1 hundred + 9 hundred = 10 hundreds or 1 thousand
 1,000  →  1 thousand + 0 thousand = 1 thousand
 2,137
```

2,137 people saw the play.

B 1 Show two ways to add 7,315 + 1,890.

```
          1 1
  7,315        7,315
+ 1,890      + 1,890
               9,205
```

```
      5  →  5 ones + 0 ones = 5 ones
    100  →  1 ten + 9 tens = 10 tens or 1 hundred
  1,100  →  3 hundreds + 8 hundreds = 11 hundreds or 1 thousand 1 hundred
+ 8,000  →  7 thousands + 1 thousand = 8 thousands
  9,205
```

M 2 Find the sum.

```
   1 1
  1,025
+ 4,589
  5,614
```

Possible student work shown. Students might also use place value to add.

Solve.

M 3 Last summer, Mia's family drove 1,024 miles from Grand Canyon National Park to Mount Rushmore National Memorial. Then they drove 1,389 miles from Mount Rushmore to Yosemite National Park. How many miles did they drive in all?

Show your work.

```
    1 1
  1,024
+ 1,389
  2,413
```

Solution: _2,413 miles_

M 4 Use the tiles to create a number that makes each addition problem true. You may use a tile more than once.

[1] [2] [3] [4] [5]

```
    1 1 1
+ 3, 2 5 4
  3, 3 6 5
```

```
  5, 3 1 9
+ 4, 5 2 1
  9, 8 4 0
```

C 5 On Monday, Calvin ran 4,250 meters. On Tuesday, he ran 4,980 meters. How many meters did he run altogether on Monday and Tuesday?

Show your work.

```
    1 1
  4,250
+ 4,980
  9,230
```

Solution: _9,230 meters_

C 6 Sam added 6,152 and 379 and got a sum of 9,942. Explain why Sam's addition is incorrect and find the sum of 6,152 + 379.

```
    1 1
  6,152
+   379
  6,531
```

Answers will vary. Possible answer: Sam did not line up the numbers by place value. The sum is 6,531.

Name: _____

Lesson 3

Subtract Whole Numbers

Study the example showing how to use subtraction to solve a word problem. Then solve problems 1–6.

Example

In one day, Pete took 7,192 steps. Joe took 5,210 steps. How many more steps did Pete take than Joe?

Regroup.

Thousands	Hundreds	Tens	Ones
7	1	9	2
6	10 + 1 = 11	9	2

Subtract.

	Thousands	Hundreds	Tens	Ones
	6	11	9	2
−	5	2	1	0
	1	9	8	2

$$\begin{array}{r} \overset{6\ 11}{7\!\!\!/1\!\!\!/92} \\ -\ 5{,}210 \\ \hline 1{,}982 \end{array}$$

Pete took 1,982 more steps than Joe.

B **1** Subtract.

$$\begin{array}{r} 3{,}008 \\ -\ 1{,}265 \\ \hline 1{,}743 \end{array}$$

B **2** Find the difference.

$$\begin{array}{r} 1{,}640 \\ -\ 952 \\ \hline 688 \end{array}$$

Solve.

M **3** The table below shows the number of seats in two basketball arenas. How many more seats does Arthur Arena have than Griffin Fieldhouse?

Number of Seats	
Griffin Fieldhouse	22,826
Arthur Arena	44,750

Show your work.

$$\begin{array}{r} \overset{3\ 17\ 4\ 10}{44{,}7\!\!\!/5\!\!\!/0} \\ -\ 22{,}826 \\ \hline 21{,}924 \end{array}$$

Solution: _____21,924 more seats_____

M **4** A city has a population of 289,000 people. Ten years ago, the population was 259,500 people. How many more people does the city have now?

Solution: _____29,500 more people_____

M **5** Use the tiles below to create a number that makes each subtraction problem true. You may use a tile more than once.

[1][2][3][4][5]

$$\begin{array}{r} 8\ 7,\ 0\ 0\ 5 \\ -\ \boxed{2}\ \boxed{5}\ \boxed{1}\ \boxed{4}\ \boxed{3} \\ \hline 6\ 1,\ 8\ 6\ 2 \end{array}$$

$$\begin{array}{r} 6\ 5,\ 9\ 0\ 0 \\ -\ \boxed{1}\ \boxed{3}\ \boxed{2}\ \boxed{5} \\ \hline 6\ 4,\ 5\ 7\ 5 \end{array}$$

C **6** Peter listed his car for sale at $21,550. After a week, he dropped the sale price by $1,650. When the car sold, the sale price was another $1,955 less. What was the final sale price of the car?

Show your work.

21,550 − 1,650 = 19,900

19,900 − 1,955 = 17,945

Solution: _____The final sale price was $17,945._____

Name: _____

Lesson 3

Add and Subtract Whole Numbers

Solve the problems.

1 Jake has 1,326 songs on his music player. Kyle has 795 more songs than Jake. How many songs does Kyle have?

A 2,021   C 2,121 ⟵ circled

B 631   D 531

Do you add or subtract to solve this problem?

2 A school's goal is to raise $5,000 to donate to charity. The school has raised $2,157. How much more money does the school need to raise?

A $2,843 ⟵ circled   C $2,953

B $7,157   D $3,843

What do you need to do before you can subtract ones?

Sonya chose **C** as the correct answer. How did she get that answer?

Answers will vary. Possible answer: She regrouped the tens and hundreds incorrectly.

3 Tell whether each number sentence is *True* or *False*.

What symbols tell you whether to add or subtract?

a. 908 + 1,725 = 2,633   [X] True   [ ] False

b. 17,625 − 2,460 = 5,245   [ ] True   [X] False

c. 112,950 + 32,408 = 45,358   [ ] True   [X] False

d. 43,900 − 17,825 = 26,075   [X] True   [ ] False

Solve.

4 Use the information below to fill in the missing data in the table.

The height of Willis Tower is 325 feet *less* than the height of One World Trade Center.

The height of Trump Tower is 139 feet *more* than the height of the Empire State Building.

The height of Bank of America Tower is 576 feet *less* than the height of One World Trade Center.

How do you know when to add and when to subtract?

Five Tallest Buildings in the U.S.

Rank	Name	Location	Height (ft)
1	One World Trade Center	New York City	1,776
2	Willis Tower	Chicago	1,451
3	Trump Tower	Chicago	1,389
4	Empire State Building	New York City	1,250
5	Bank of America Tower	New York City	1,200

5 Use the information in the table below to answer the riddle. Write the the missing data in the table.

I am the tallest building in the world. If you add my height to the height of the next three tallest buildings, the total is 8,132 feet. How tall am I?

What operation do you need to do first?

Four Tallest Buildings in the World

Rank	Name	Location	Height (ft)
1	Burj Khalifa	United Arab Emirates	2,717
2	Makkah Royal Clock Tower	Saudi Arabia	1,972
3	One World Trade Center	New York City	1,776
4	Taipei 101	Taipei, Taiwan	1,667

Show your work.

Possible work: 1,972 + 1,776 + 1,667 = 5,415

8,132 − 5,415 = 2,717

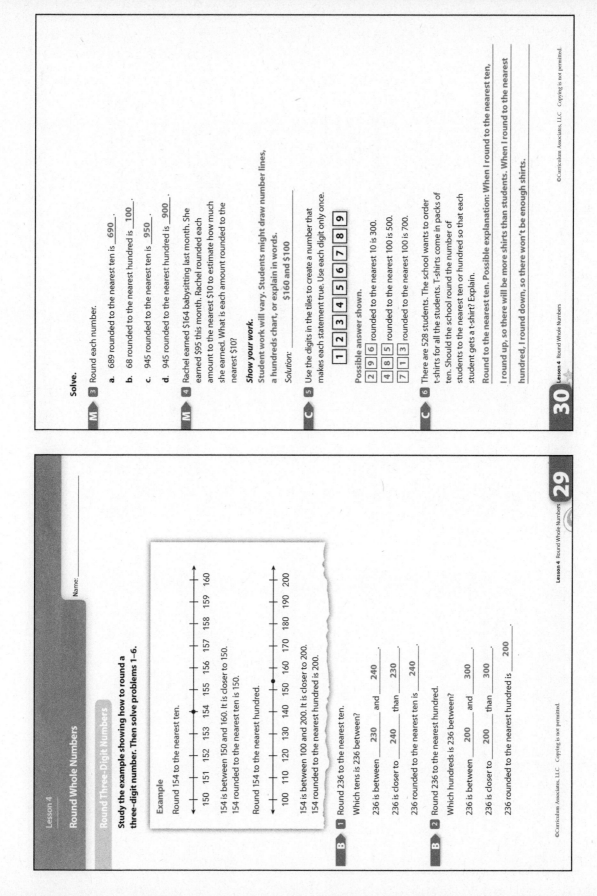

Name: _____

Lesson 4
Round Whole Numbers

Round Three-Digit Numbers

Study the example showing how to round a three-digit number. Then solve problems 1–6.

Example
Round 154 to the nearest ten.

150 151 152 153 154 155 156 157 158 159 160

154 is between 150 and 160. It is closer to 150.
154 rounded to the nearest ten is 150.

Round 154 to the nearest hundred.

100 110 120 130 140 150 160 170 180 190 200

154 is between 100 and 200. It is closer to 200.
154 rounded to the nearest hundred is 200.

B 1 Round 236 to the nearest ten.
Which tens is 236 between?

236 is between __230__ and __240__.

236 is closer to __240__ than __230__.

236 rounded to the nearest ten is __240__.

B 2 Round 236 to the nearest hundred.
Which hundreds is 236 between?

236 is between __200__ and __300__.

236 is closer to __200__ than __300__.

236 rounded to the nearest hundred is __200__.

©Curriculum Associates, LLC   Copying is not permitted.

Lesson 4 Round Whole Numbers **29**

Solve.

M 3 Round each number.
a. 689 rounded to the nearest ten is __690__.
b. 68 rounded to the nearest hundred is __100__.
c. 945 rounded to the nearest ten is __950__.
d. 945 rounded to the nearest hundred is __900__.

M 4 Rachel earned $164 babysitting last month. She earned $95 this month. Rachel rounded each amount to the nearest $10 to estimate how much she earned. What is each amount rounded to the nearest $10?

Show your work.
Student work will vary. Students might draw number lines, a hundreds chart, or explain in words.

Solution: _____ $160 and $100 _____

C 5 Use the digits in the tiles to create a number that makes each statement true. Use each digit only once.

1 2 3 4 5 6 7 8 9

Possible answer shown.

2 9 6 rounded to the nearest 10 is 300.

4 8 5 rounded to the nearest 100 is 500.

7 1 3 rounded to the nearest 100 is 700.

C 6 There are 528 students. The school wants to order t-shirts for all the students. T-shirts come in packs of ten. Should the school round the number of students to the nearest ten or hundred so that each student gets a t-shirt? Explain.

Round to the nearest ten. Possible explanation: When I round to the nearest ten, I round up, so there will be more shirts than students. When I round to the nearest hundred, I round down, so there won't be enough shirts.

©Curriculum Associates, LLC   Copying is not permitted.

30 **Lesson 4** Round Whole Numbers

Key
B Basic   **M** Medium   **C** Challenge

Lesson 4

Round Whole Numbers

Study the example showing how to round multi-digit numbers to estimate a sum. Then solve problems 1–6.

Example

Round each number to the nearest thousand to estimate the sum.

246,135 + 651,970

Round 246,135 to the nearest thousand.

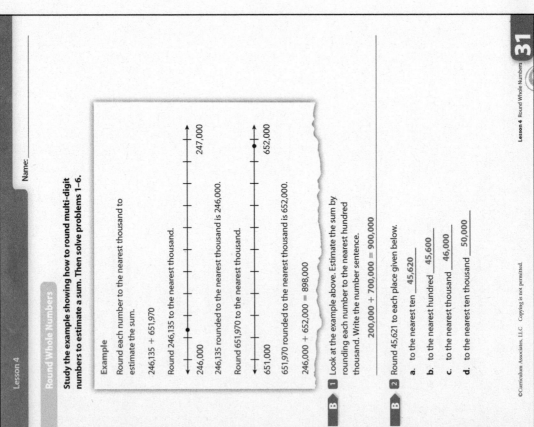

246,135 rounded to the nearest thousand is 246,000.

Round 651,970 to the nearest thousand.

651,970 rounded to the nearest thousand is 652,000.

246,000 + 652,000 = 898,000

B 1 Look at the example above. Estimate the sum by rounding each number to the nearest hundred thousand. Write the number sentence.

200,000 + 700,000 = 900,000

B 2 Round 45,621 to each place given below.

a. to the nearest ten ___45,620___

b. to the nearest hundred ___45,600___

c. to the nearest thousand ___46,000___

d. to the nearest ten thousand ___50,000___

Solve.

M 3 Round 452,906 to each place given below.

a. to the nearest hundred thousand ___500,000___

b. to the nearest ten thousand ___450,000___

c. to the nearest thousand ___453,000___

d. to the nearest hundred ___452,900___

e. to the nearest ten ___452,910___

B 4 The table below shows driving distances between U.S. cities. Round each number to the nearest hundred.

	Actual distance (mi)	Rounded distance (mi)
Atlanta, GA to Los Angeles, CA	2,173	2,200
Los Angeles, CA to Seattle, WA	1,135	1,100
Atlanta, GA to Chicago, IL	716	700
Chicago, IL to San Francisco, CA	2,131	2,100

M 5 Look at the table in problem 4. Lisa drove from Atlanta to Los Angeles to Seattle. Alex drove from Atlanta to Chicago to San Francisco. Use the rounded numbers to show who drove farther and by about how many miles.

Show your work.

Lisa: 2,200 + 1,100 = 3,300

Alex: 700 + 2,100 = 2,800   3,300 − 2,800 = 500

Solution: __Lisa drove about 500 miles more than Alex.__

C 6 Write numbers in the boxes below to show rounding on a number line. What place value are you rounding to?

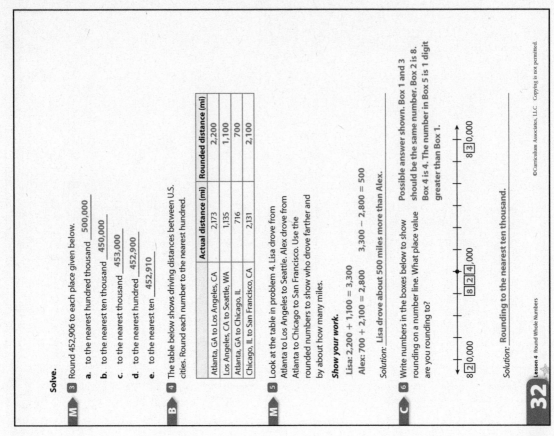

8 2 0,000   8 2 4,000   8 3 0,000

Possible answer shown. Box 1 and 3 should be the same number. Box 2 is 8. Box 4 is 4. The number in Box 5 is 1 digit greater than Box 1.

Solution: __Rounding to the nearest ten thousand.__

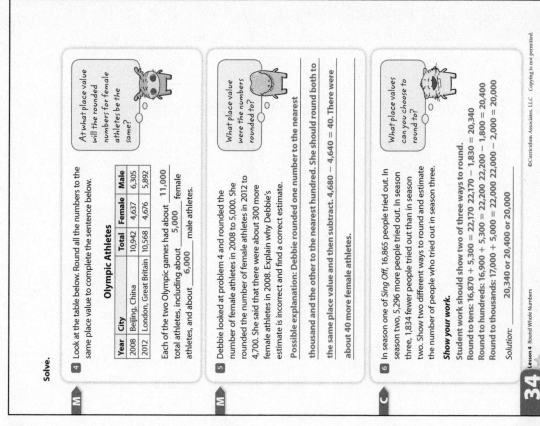

Lesson 4

Round Whole Numbers

Solve the problems.

1 (B) Choose *Yes* or *No* to tell whether to round up to the greater hundred thousand.

a. 949,500   [ ] Yes   [X] No
b. 503,817   [ ] Yes   [X] No
c. 180,000   [X] Yes   [ ] No
d. 352,625   [X] Yes   [ ] No

Which place value should you look at?

2 (M) Which numbers have been rounded correctly to the nearest hundred? Circle the letter for all that apply.

(A) 38,753 ⟶ 38,800
B   38,503 ⟶ 39,000
(C) 38,910 ⟶ 38,900
(D) 38,960 ⟶ 39,000
E   38,109 ⟶ 38,110

Which digit do you look at in each number to round to the nearest hundred?

3 (M) A company spent $850,290 on advertising last year. The company spent $872,650 this year. Which of the following is the best estimate of how much more the company spent this year?

A $100,000   C $22,000
B $30,000   (D) $22,400

Tyson chose **D** as the correct answer. Explain how he got his answer.

Answers will vary. Possible answer: Tyson rounded each number to the nearest hundred and subtracted. 872,700 − 850,300 = 22,400.

What do you do first to solve this problem?

Lesson 4   Round Whole Numbers

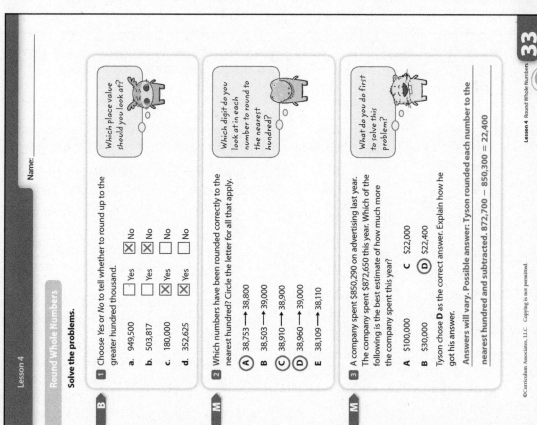

Solve.

4 (M) Look at the table below. Round all the numbers to the same place value to complete the sentence below.

Olympic Athletes

Year	City	Total	Female	Male
2008	Beijing, China	10,942	4,637	6,305
2012	London, Great Britain	10,568	4,676	5,892

Each of the two Olympic games had about 11,000 total athletes, including about 5,000 female athletes, and about 6,000 male athletes.

At what place value will the rounded numbers for female athletes be the same?

5 (M) Debbie looked at problem 4 and rounded the number of female athletes in 2008 to 5,000. She rounded the number of female athletes in 2012 to 4,700. She said that there were about 300 more female athletes in 2008. Explain why Debbie's estimate is incorrect and find a correct estimate.

Possible explanation: Debbie rounded one number to the nearest thousand and the other to the nearest hundred. She should round both to the same place value and then subtract. 4,680 − 4,640 = 40. There were about 40 more female athletes.

What place value were the numbers rounded to?

6 (C) In season one of *Sing Off*, 16,865 people tried out. In season two, 5,296 more people tried out. In season three, 1,834 fewer people tried out than in season two. Show two different ways to round and estimate the number of people who tried out in season three.

Show your work.
Student work should show two of three ways to round.
Round to tens: 16,870 + 5,300 = 22,170   22,170 − 1,830 = 20,340
Round to hundreds: 16,900 + 5,300 = 22,200   22,200 − 1,800 = 20,400
Round to thousands: 17,000 + 5,000 = 22,000   22,000 − 2,000 = 20,000

Solution: 20,340 or 20,400 or 20,000

What place values can you choose to round to?

Lesson 4   Round Whole Numbers

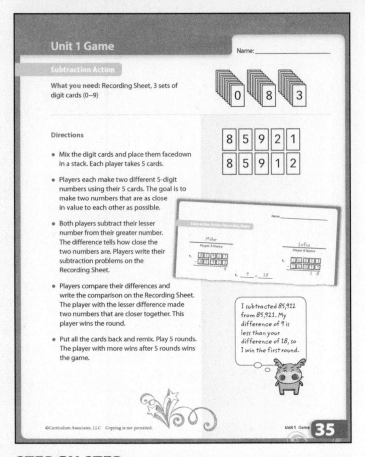

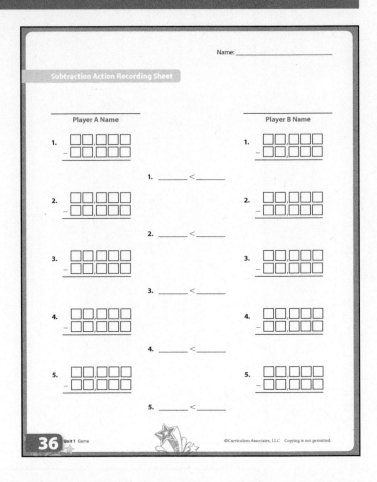

STEP BY STEP

CCSS Focus - 4.NBT.A.2, 4.NBT.B.4 *Embedded SMPs* - 6, 7, 8 **Objective:** Subtract multi-digit numbers. Compare multi-digit numbers.	**Materials** For each pair: Recording Sheet (TR 1), 3 sets of 0–9 Digit Cards (TR 2)

- Display the digit cards and recording sheet. Read through the directions with students. Be sure students understand that the goal is to get the smallest difference between two numbers.

- Demonstrate how to make two different 5-digit numbers with the digit cards. Discuss ways you might decide how to arrange the digits in each number. Ask students how they can use place value to make numbers that are close together.

- Model subtracting the numbers to find the difference. Discuss how changing the place value of a number in a subtraction problem changes the difference.

- Model recording two different subtraction problems on the recording sheet. Write the comparison. Tell students that the player with the lesser difference made two numbers that are closer together. This player wins the round.

- Have students play the game. Remind them to remix all the cards after each round of play.

- When students have finished the game, ask them to share the strategies they used. How did they decide where to place the digits to make numbers that were close together?

Vary the Game Change the goal by asking students to to find the greater difference between two numbers. Have students make two 5-digit numbers that are as far apart from each other as possible. The winner of each round is the player with the greater difference.

Challenge Use rounding to play the game. Have students round each of their 5-digit numbers to the nearest 1,000 and then subtract to find the difference. Have students describe how their strategies change and what place value is affected by the rounding.

Unit 1 Practice

Name: _____

Number and Operations in Base Ten, Part 1

In this unit you learned to:

	Lesson
read and write numbers using number names, for example: 495 is *four hundred ninety-five.*	1
read and write numbers using expanded form, for example: 352 = 300 + 50 + 2.	1
compare two multi-digit whole numbers, for example: 6,131 > 6,113.	2
add multi-digit whole numbers, for example: 3,966 + 7,550 = 11,516.	3
subtract multi-digit whole numbers, for example: 25,082 − 11,919 = 13,163.	3
round multi-digit whole numbers, for example: 528 rounded to the nearest ten is 530.	4

Use these skills to solve problems 1–6.

B 1 Use <, >, or = to complete each number sentence.

a. 790,599 (<) 791,043

b. 52,180 (>) 50,000 + 2,000 + 10 + 8

c. 99,999 (<) 100,000

d. 55 hundreds + 2 tens (=) 5,520

e. 200,000 + 10,000 + 300 + 50 (>) 210,305

M 2 A publishing company printed 920,500 copies of a book. The company sold 843,255 copies. How many books did not sell?

Show your work.

920,500 − 843,255 = 77,245

Solution: **77,245 books**

Solve.

M 3 The second longest bridge in the world, the Tianjin Grand Bridge, is 373,000 feet long. Its length is 167,700 feet less than the length of the longest bridge in the world. What is the length of the longest bridge?

Show your work.

373,000 + 167,700 = 540,700

Solution: **540,700 feet**

M 4 Use the clues below to guess the mystery number.

• The number is less than 190,000 and greater than 180,000.

• 5,000 more than the number has 187 thousands.

• 200 less than the number has 4 hundreds.

Solution: **182,600**

M 5 Round each number in the table to the given place value. Then, write <, >, or = to compare the rounded numbers.

Round to . . .	95,498	Compare (>, <, or =)	95,607
Tens	95,500	<	95,610
Hundreds	95,500	<	95,600
Thousands	95,000	<	96,000
Ten Thousands	100,000	=	100,000

C 6 Juan's company spent $2,350 on an event. They spent about $1,500 on food and about $900 on entertainment. What could the actual cost of the food and entertainment be?

Show your work.

Answers will vary. The sum of the two items must equal $2,350. When rounded to the nearest hundred, the cost of food should round to $1,500 and the cost of entertainment should round to $900.

Possible answers:

Solution: food **$1,480** entertainment **$870**

Key

B Basic M Medium C Challenge

TEACHER NOTES

Common Core Standards: 4.NBT.A.3, 4.NBT.B.4
Standards for Mathematical Practice: 1, 2, 3, 4, 6
DOK: 3
Materials: none

About the Task

To complete this task, students use their understanding of place value to round multi-digit numbers and add multi-digit numbers. Students analyze the information provided in a table, interpret their calculations, make a prediction, and provide a written explanation of their work.

Getting Students Started

Read the problem out loud with students and go over the checklist. Have them identify the goal: the 4th grade needs to collect 20,000 box tops. Point out the phrases "to the nearest hundred" and "about how close" to be sure students understand that the science teacher is looking for an estimate, not an exact number, of how many box tops have been collected so far. Ask students how they could estimate the number of box tops shown in the chart for each class. If students do not come up with the idea of rounding the numbers, introduce the idea, pointing out the phrase "to the nearest hundred" in the problem. Ask students which class has collected the most box tops so far. **(SMP 1)**

Completing the Task

Students should first round the numbers in the table. Ask students how they could round each number to the nearest hundred. Students can add a row to the bottom of the table to record their rounded numbers. **(SMP 2)**

Students should add the rounded numbers to get an estimate of the total number of box tops collected. Ask students to explain why an estimate is an appropriate number to use for the total box tops collected so far. **(SMP 3)**

Students should include in their email a greeting, an answer to the science teacher's question, and an explanation of how they came up with the amounts. Ask students if their emails include all of the information and whether there is additional information they could include. **(SMP 3, 6)**

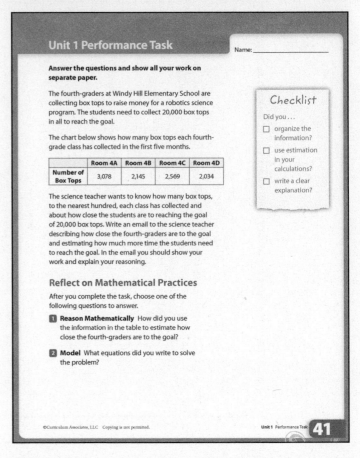

Extension

If some students have more time to spend on this problem, you can have them solve this extension:

Find the actual numbers of box tops collected so far. Explain whether this information would change the prediction you made about how much longer it will take the 4th grade to reach its goal.

SAMPLE RESPONSES AND RUBRIC

4-Point Solution

Dear Science Teacher,
The fourth grade classes have collected about
9,800 box tops in the first five months. This is
almost halfway to the goal of 20,000 box tops.
I rounded the number of box tops that each of
the 4 classes has collected to the nearest hundred.
Then I added together the rounded numbers
to get a total of 9,800 box tops collected so far.
3,100 + 2,100 + 2,600 + 2,000 = 9,800

	Room 4A	Room 4B	Room 4C	Room 4D
Number of Box Tops	3,078	2,145	2,569	2,034
Rounded Number	3,100	2,100	2,600	2,000

It took the classes five months to almost reach the halfway mark, so it will take about five more months to reach the goal, as long as they continue to collect box tops at about the same pace.

Sincerely,
Colin

REFLECT ON MATHEMATICAL PRACTICES

1. Look for an explanation that the numbers in the table can be rounded and then added to find an estimated total. **(SMP 2)**

2. Look for addition equations to find the total and a subtraction equation to find the difference between the number collected so far and the goal. **(SMP 4)**

SCORING RUBRIC

4 points The student's answer is accurate and the explanation given in the email is complete and understandable. Numbers for each class are rounded correctly and added correctly. The student wrote a clear explanation of how estimation was used and described how to use the estimated total to make a prediction. The email includes a greeting and a signature.

3 points The student's answer is accurate. Numbers were correctly rounded and added. The explanation may be unclear and may not show how the calculations support the reasoning in the explanation. Ambiguous wording may not make clear whether the numbers used are estimates or exact numbers.

2 points The student's answer is incorrect. The rounding or addition has errors. The email contains some of the required elements.

1 point The student has made errors in rounding and addition. There may be no work shown. The prediction of when the goal may be met is incorrect or missing. The explanation is incomplete and/or incorrect. The response is not written in the form of an email or the email does not contain an explanation.

SOLUTION TO THE EXTENSION

Possible Solution

3,078 + 2,145 + 2,569 + 2,034 = 9,826

The actual number of box tops collected so far is 9,796. Since 9,826 is close to 9,800, this information would not change my prediction. It shows that the fourth grade is almost halfway to its goal, so the classes would still need about five more months to reach the goal.

Lesson 5
Understand
Multiplication

Name: _____

How do you show and write multiplication?

Study the example showing multiplication with an array and a number sentence. Then solve problems 1–5.

Example
In art class, 4 students each painted 6 tiles.
Draw an array to show the tiles.

4 rows of 6 tiles
is 24 tiles in all.

Write a multiplication sentence. $4 \times 6 = 24$

Vocabulary
multiplication an operation used to find the total number of items in equal-sized groups.

B 1 Look at the arrays. Complete the sentences.

a. 3 rows of __9__ tiles
is __27__ tiles in all.
$3 \times 9 = 27$

b. __2__ rows of 8 triangles
is __16__ triangles in all.
$2 \times 8 = 16$

c. __5__ rows of __5__ stars
is __25__ stars in all.
$5 \times 5 = 25$

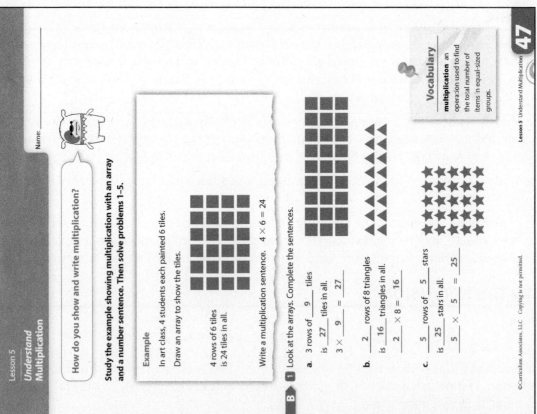

Lesson 5 Understand Multiplication **47**

Solve.

M 2 Each of 3 students in a book club read 7 books. Draw an array and write a multiplication sentence to show the number of books read.

Student models may vary but should show an array with 3 rows and 7 objects in each row.

Multiplication sentence: $3 \times 7 = 21$

M 3 Write a word problem that could be modeled by the multiplication sentence $6 \times 8 = 48$.

Answers will vary. Students should write a real-world problem that tells about a situation with 6 groups of 8, for a total of 48.

M 4 Leila's bookshelf has 4 shelves. Each shelf has 9 books. Write a multiplication sentence to tell about the books. Explain what each number in the multiplication sentence means.

$4 \times 9 = 36$. **Possible explanation: The 4 tells how many shelves there are. The 9 tells how many books are on each shelf. The 36 tells how many books there are altogether.**

C 5 Look at problem 4. Suppose Leila moves her books onto a bookshelf with 6 shelves. She puts an equal number of books on each shelf. Describe what the array for this problem looks like and write a multiplication sentence.

The array has 6 rows and 6 objects in each row. $6 \times 6 = 36$

48 Lesson 5 Understand Multiplication

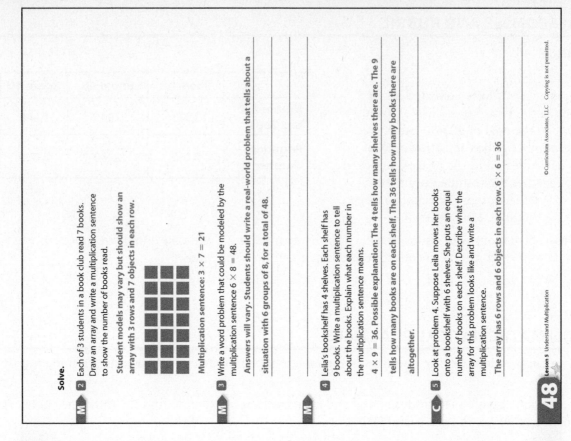

Key

B Basic   **M** Medium   **C** Challenge

Lesson 5

Name: _____

Show Multiplication

Study the example showing how a bar model is used to show multiplication as a comparison. Then solve problems 1–7.

Example

Harris rides his bike 5 blocks to school. Daniel rides his bike 3 times as far as Harris. How far does Daniel ride his bike to school?

You can use a bar model to show multiplication as a comparison.

Harris [5]
Daniel [5][5][5] = 15

15 is 3 times as many as 5.
$15 = 3 \times 5$

B 1 Use the bar model to the right to describe the comparison and write an equation.

[6]

48 is __8__ times as many as __6__.

__48__ = __8__ × __6__

6 6 6 6 6 6 6 6 = 48

B 2 Draw and label a bar model to show a number that is 5 times as many as 7.

[7]

7 7 7 7 7 = 35

M 3 Write a word problem that the bar model in problem 2 could represent.

Possible answer: Mr. Chu drove 7 miles. Mr. Smith drove 5 times as many miles as Mr. Chu. How many miles did Mr. Smith drive?

©Curriculum Associates, LLC Copying is not permitted.
Lesson 5 Understand Multiplication **49**

Solve.

M 4 Tara scored 6 times as many soccer goals as Leah during one season. Leah scored 3 goals. Draw a bar model and write an equation that represents the number of goals Tara scored.

Leah [3]
Tara [3][3][3][3][3][3] = 18

$18 = 6 \times 3$

M 5 What two comparisons does the equation $4 \times 2 = 8$ show?

a. __8__ is __4__ times as many as __2__.

b. __8__ is __2__ times as many as __4__.

M 6 Draw two different bar models to represent $2 \times 4 = 8$.

[2][2][2][2] = 8

[4][4] = 8

C 7 A pet caretaker walks dogs 9 times a day. He walks dogs from Monday to Friday, 5 days a week. Draw and label a bar model to show the total number of times the caretaker walks dogs in a week.

Number of times caretaker walks dogs in 1 day [9]

Number of times caretaker walks dogs in 5 days [9][9][9][9][9] = 45

50 Lesson 5 Understand Multiplication
©Curriculum Associates, LLC Copying is not permitted.

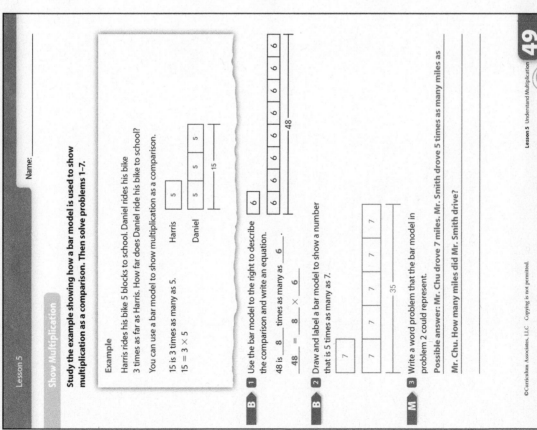

Lesson 5

Name: _____

Reason and Write

Study the example. Underline two parts that you think make it a particularly good answer and a helpful example.

Example

Sylvie needs 2 cups of flour to make one loaf of bread. She wants to make 3 loaves of bread. She says she needs 5 cups of flour.

Is Sylvie correct? What did she do right? What did she do wrong?

Show your work. Use a bar model, an equation, and words to explain.

Sylvie is not correct. She used the numbers 2 and 3, but she added 2 + 3 instead of multiplying 2 × 3.

Sylvie needs 2 cups of flour for one loaf of bread, so she needs 3 times as many cups of flour for 3 loaves of bread.

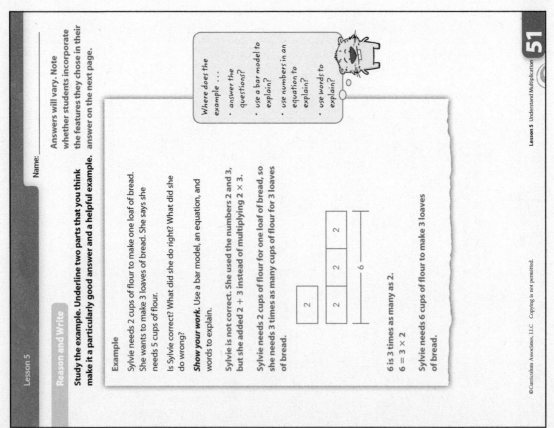

6 is 3 times as many as 2.

6 = 3 × 2

Sylvie needs 6 cups of flour to make 3 loaves of bread.

Where does the example . . .
• answer the questions?
• use a bar model to explain?
• use numbers in an equation to explain?
• use words to explain?

Answers will vary. Note whether students incorporate the features they chose in their answer on the next page.

Solve the problem. Use what you learned from the model.

Victor needs 3 teaspoons of salt to make dough for one pizza. He wants to make dough for 8 pizzas. Victor says he needs 24 teaspoons of salt.

Is Victor correct? What did he do right? What did he do wrong?

Show your work. Use a bar model, an equation, and words to explain.

Possible answer:

Victor is correct. He used multiplication to find 3 × ? = 24.

Victor needs 3 teaspoons of salt to make dough for one pizza, so he needs 8 times as many teaspoons of salt to make dough for 8 pizzas.

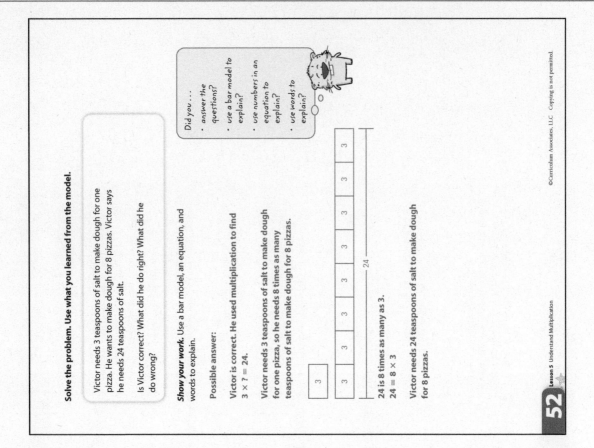

24 is 8 times as many as 3.

24 = 8 × 3

Victor needs 24 teaspoons of salt to make dough for 8 pizzas.

Did you . . .
• answer the questions?
• use a bar model to explain?
• use numbers in an equation to explain?
• use words to explain?

Lesson 6
Multiplication and Division in Word Problems

Name: _____

Model Multiplication

Study the example showing how to use a model to solve a multiplication problem. Then solve problems 1–6.

Example

Lauren worked 4 hours last week. She worked 3 times as many hours this week as last week. How many hours did Lauren work this week?

Last week | 4 |

This week | 4 | 4 | 4 | = 12

12 is 3 times as many as 4.

$12 = 3 \times 4$

Lauren worked 12 hours this week.

Vocabulary

multiplication an operation used to find the total number of items in equal-sized groups.

B 1 Nina picked 8 tomatoes last month. She picked 4 times as many tomatoes this month. How many tomatoes did Nina pick this month?

Label the bar model and complete the sentences.

Last month | 8 |

This month | 8 | 8 | 8 | 8 | = 32

32 is __4__ times as many as __8__.

$32 = \underline{4} \times \underline{8}$

Nina picked __32__ tomatoes this month.

B 2 Ben has 6 marbles. Tom has 3 times as many marbles as Ben. How many marbles does Tom have?

0   6   6   6   6   12   6   18

$\underline{6} \times \underline{3} = 18$

Tom has __18__ marbles.

Solve.

For problems 3–5, students might use a bar model, skip count on a number line, or use another model to solve the problem.

M 3 Yesterday Ruth scored 2 points at the game. Today she scored 8 times as many points as she did yesterday. How many points did Ruth score today?

Show your work.

Possible work:

16 is 8 times as many as 2.

$2 \times 8 = 16$

Solution: __16 points__

M 4 Matt planted 5 times as many flowers on Sunday as he planted on Saturday. Matt planted 7 flowers on Saturday. How many flowers did Matt plant on Sunday?

Show your work.

Possible work:

35 is 5 times as many as 7.

$7 \times 5 = 35$

Solution: __35 flowers__

M 5 Mr. Ash has 7 students in art class. Mr. Trent has double the number of students in his class as Mr. Ash. How many students does Mr. Trent have in his class?

Show your work.

Possible work:

14 is 2 times as many as 7.

$7 \times 2 = 14$

Solution: __14 students__

C 6 Which is more: 2 times as many as a number or 5 times as many as the same number? Explain. Choose any number to show how you know.

5 times as many as a number is more than 2 times as many as the number.

Possible explanation: I chose the number 1: $5 \times 1 = 5$ and $2 \times 1 = 2$.

$5 > 2$, so 5 times the number is more than 2 times the number.

Key

B Basic   **M** Medium   **C** Challenge

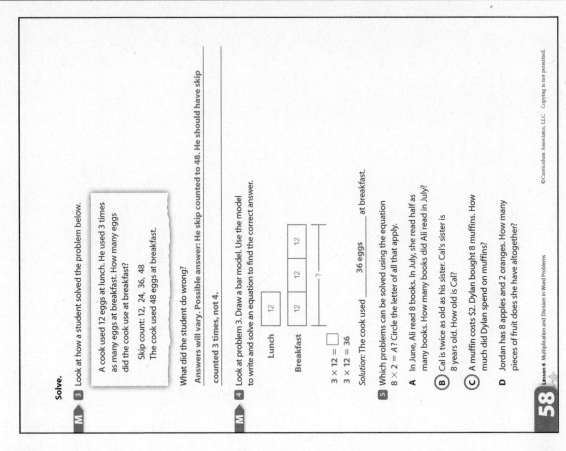

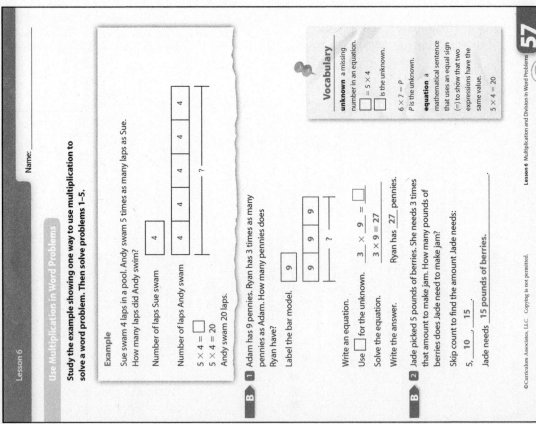

Page 57

Lesson 6

Name: _____

Use Multiplication in Word Problems

Study the example showing one way to use multiplication to solve a word problem. Then solve problems 1–5.

Example

Sue swam 4 laps in a pool. Andy swam 5 times as many laps as Sue. How many laps did Andy swim?

Number of laps Sue swam   [4]

Number of laps Andy swam   [4][4][4][4][4] ?

$5 \times 4 = \square$
$5 \times 4 = 20$
Andy swam 20 laps.

Vocabulary

unknown a missing number in an equation.
$\square = 5 \times 4$
$\square$ is the unknown.

$6 \times 7 = P$
P is the unknown.

equation a mathematical sentence that uses an equal sign (=) to show that two expressions have the same value.
$5 \times 4 = 20$

1 Adam has 9 pennies. Ryan has 3 times as many pennies as Adam. How many pennies does Ryan have?

Label the bar model.

[9]

[9][9][9] ?

Write an equation.

Use $\square$ for the unknown. $3 \times 9 = \square$

Solve the equation. $3 \times 9 = 27$

Write the answer.   Ryan has __27__ pennies.

2 Jade picked 5 pounds of berries. She needs 3 times that amount to make jam. How many pounds of berries does Jade need to make jam?

Skip count to find the amount Jade needs:

5, __10__, __15__.

Jade needs __15 pounds of berries.__

Page 58

Solve.

3 Look at how a student solved the problem below.

A cook used 12 eggs at lunch. He used 3 times as many eggs at breakfast. How many eggs did the cook use at breakfast?

Skip count: 12, 24, 36, 48
The cook used 48 eggs at breakfast.

What did the student do wrong?

Answers will vary. Possible answer: He skip counted to 48. He should have skip counted 3 times, not 4.

4 Look at problem 3. Draw a bar model. Use the model to write and solve an equation to find the correct answer.

Lunch   [12]

Breakfast   [12][12][12] ?

$3 \times 12 = \square$
$3 \times 12 = 36$

Solution: The cook used __36 eggs__ at breakfast.

5 Which problems can be solved using the equation $8 \times 2 = A$? Circle the letter of all that apply.

A In June, Ali read 8 books. In July, she read half as many books. How many books did Ali read in July?

B Cal is twice as old as his sister. Cal's sister is 8 years old. How old is Cal?

C A muffin costs $2. Dylan bought 8 muffins. How much did Dylan spend on muffins?

D Jordan has 8 apples and 2 oranges. How many pieces of fruit does she have altogether?

Name: _____

Lesson 6

Use Division in Word Problems

Study the example showing a way to use division to solve a word problem. Then solve problems 1–5.

Example

The Tigers scored 36 points. They scored 4 times as many points as the Lions. How many points did the Lions score?

Lions | ? |

Tigers | ? | ? | ? | ? | —— 36

$36 \div 4 =$ ☐
$36 \div 4 = 9$
The Lions scored 9 points.

B **1** Charlie and Gabe collected cans to recycle. Charlie collected 5 times as many cans as Gabe. Charlie collected 50 cans. Draw a bar model you could use to compare the number of cans each boy collected.

Gabe | ? |

Charlie | ? | ? | ? | ? | ? | —— 50

B **2** Look at the model you drew in problem 1. Write and solve an equation to show how many cans Gabe collected.

Show your work.

$50 = 5 \times$ ☐ or $50 \div 5 =$ ☐

$50 \div 5 = 10$

Solution: **Gabe collected 10 cans.**

Solve.

M **3** Choose *Yes* or *No* to tell whether each equation is solved correctly.

a. $6 = 2 \times$ ☐   ☐ $= 12$ ☐ Yes ☒ No

b. $7 \times H = 28$ $H = 4$ ☒ Yes ☐ No

c. $2 = p \div 5$ $p = 10$ ☒ Yes ☐ No

M **4** James and Chris are in the school play. James has 42 lines to memorize. That is 6 times as many lines as Chris. Write and solve an equation to find the number of lines Chris has to memorize.

Show your work.

$42 = 6 \times L$ or $42 \div 6 = L$

$L = 7$

Solution: **Chris needs to memorize 7 lines.**

C **5** Choose numbers from the tiles below to fill in the bar model. Then write and solve an equation using the model.

| 24 | 12 | 8 | 6 | 4 | 3 | 2 | 1 |

| 8 |

| 8 | 8 | 8 | —— 24

Possible answer shown. Answers should show the same number in each box of the model and a product beneath the model that is 3 times the number in the model.

Equation: **Possible answer: $24 = 3 \times a$ or $24 \div 3 = a$**

Solution: **Possible answer: $a = 8$**

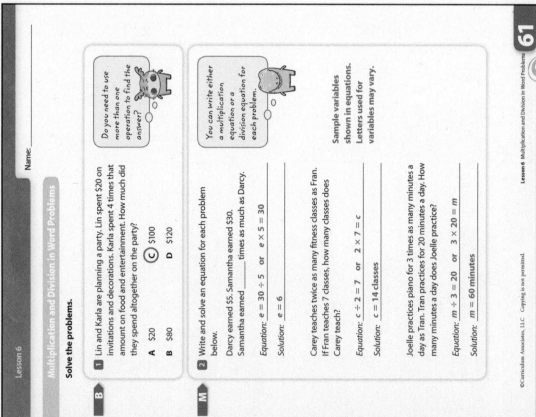

Lesson 6

Multiplication and Division in Word Problems

Solve the problems.

B 1. Lin and Karla are planning a party. Lin spent $20 on invitations and decorations. Karla spent 4 times that amount on food and entertainment. How much did they spend altogether on the party?

A $20

B $80

C $100 (circled)

D $120

Do you need to use more than one operation to find the answer?

M 2. Write and solve an equation for each problem below.

Darcy earned $5. Samantha earned $30. Samantha earned _____ times as much as Darcy.

Equation: $e = 30 \div 5$ or $e \times 5 = 30$

Solution: $e = 6$

You can write either a multiplication equation or a division equation for each problem.

Carey teaches twice as many fitness classes as Fran. If Fran teaches 7 classes, how many classes does Carey teach?

Equation: $c \div 2 = 7$ or $2 \times 7 = c$

Solution: $c = 14$ classes

Joelle practices piano for 3 times as many minutes a day as Tran. Tran practices for 20 minutes a day. How many minutes a day does Joelle practice?

Equation: $m \div 3 = 20$ or $3 \times 20 = m$

Solution: $m = 60$ minutes

Sample variables shown in equations. Letters used for variables may vary.

Name: _____

Lesson 6 Multiplication and Division in Word Problems

61

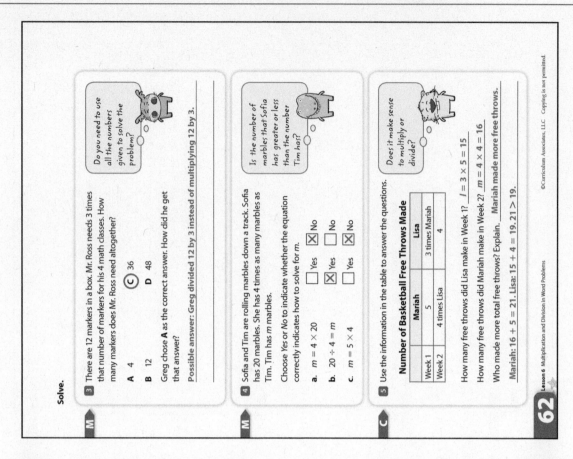

Solve.

M 3. There are 12 markers in a box. Mr. Ross needs 3 times that number of markers for his 4 math classes. How many markers does Mr. Ross need altogether?

A 4

B 12

C 36 (circled)

D 48

Greg chose **A** as the correct answer. How did he get that answer?

Possible answer: Greg divided 12 by 3 instead of multiplying 12 by 3.

Do you need to use all the numbers given to solve the problem?

M 4. Sofia and Tim are rolling marbles down a track. Sofia has 20 marbles. She has 4 times as many marbles as Tim. Tim has m marbles.

Choose *Yes* or *No* to indicate whether the equation correctly indicates how to solve for m.

a. $m = 4 \times 20$ ☐ Yes ☒ No

b. $20 \div 4 = m$ ☒ Yes ☐ No

c. $m = 5 \times 4$ ☐ Yes ☒ No

Is the number of marbles that Sofia has greater or less than the number Tim has?

C 5. Use the information in the table to answer the questions.

Number of Basketball Free Throws Made

	Mariah	Lisa
Week 1	5	3 times Mariah
Week 2	4 times Lisa	4

How many free throws did Lisa make in Week 1? $l = 3 \times 5 = 15$

How many free throws did Mariah make in Week 2? $m = 4 \times 4 = 16$

Who made more total free throws? Explain. Mariah made more free throws.

Mariah: $16 + 5 = 21$. Lisa: $15 + 4 = 19$. $21 > 19$.

Does it make sense to multiply or divide?

62 Lesson 6 Multiplication and Division in Word Problems

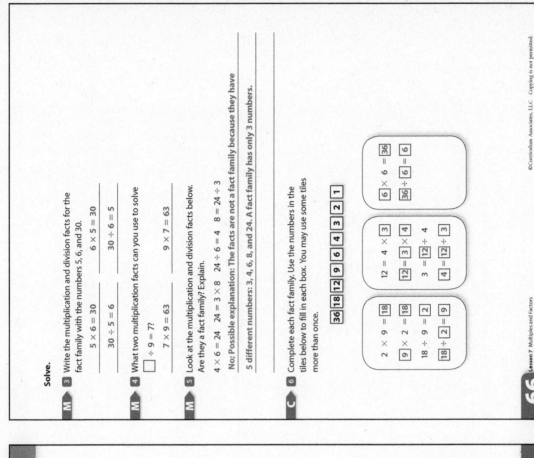

Lesson 7

Multiples and Factors

Use Fact Families

Study the example showing multiplication and division facts in a fact family. Then solve problems 1–6.

Example

Write the missing number in the multiplication fact.

$5 \times \boxed{7} = 35$ 7 jumps of 5

Write the multiplication and division facts in the fact family.

$5 \times \boxed{7} = 35$ $\boxed{7} \times 5 = 35$ $35 \div \boxed{7} = 5$ $35 \div 5 = \boxed{7}$

B 1 $6 \times \boxed{} = 48$.

a. Draw and label jumps on the number line.

b. Write the multiplication fact. $6 \times 8 = 48$

c. Write the fact family.

$6 \times 8 = 48$ $8 \times 6 = 48$ $48 \div 6 = 8$ $48 \div 8 = 6$

B 2 Look at the array at the right.

a. Write the missing number.

$4 \times 3 = \boxed{12}$

b. Write the fact family.

$4 \times 3 = \boxed{12}$ $3 \times 4 = 12$ $12 \div 4 = 3$ $12 \div 3 = 4$

Vocabulary

multiplication an operation used to find the total number of items in equal-sized groups.
$5 \times 7 = 35$

Lesson 7 Multiples and Factors **65**

Solve.

M 3 Write the multiplication and division facts for the fact family with the numbers 5, 6, and 30.

$5 \times 6 = 30$ $6 \times 5 = 30$
$30 \div 5 = 6$ $30 \div 6 = 5$

M 4 What two multiplication facts can you use to solve
$\boxed{} \div 9 = 7$?

$7 \times 9 = 63$ $9 \times 7 = 63$

M 5 Look at the multiplication and division facts below. Are they a fact family? Explain.

$4 \times 6 = 24$ $24 = 3 \times 8$ $24 \div 6 = 4$ $8 = 24 \div 3$

No; Possible explanation: The facts are not a fact family because they have 5 different numbers: 3, 4, 6, 8, and 24. A fact family has only 3 numbers.

C 6 Complete each fact family. Use the numbers in the tiles below to fill in each box. You may use some tiles more than once.

$\boxed{36}$ $\boxed{18}$ $\boxed{12}$ $\boxed{9}$ $\boxed{6}$ $\boxed{4}$ $\boxed{3}$ $\boxed{2}$ $\boxed{1}$

$2 \times 9 = \boxed{18}$
$\boxed{9} \times 2 = \boxed{18}$
$18 \div 9 = \boxed{2}$
$\boxed{18} \div \boxed{2} = \boxed{9}$

$12 = 4 \times \boxed{3}$
$\boxed{12} = \boxed{3} \times \boxed{4}$
$3 = \boxed{12} \div 4$
$\boxed{4} = \boxed{12} \div \boxed{3}$

$6 \times 6 = \boxed{36}$
$36 \div \boxed{6} = \boxed{6}$

66 Lesson 7 Multiples and Factors

Key

B Basic   **M** Medium   **C** Challenge

Lesson 7

Use Multiples

Study the example showing how to use multiples to solve a word problem. Then solve problems 1–6.

Example

Markers come in boxes of 5. Paul needs 40 markers for students in the art club. Can Paul buy exactly 40 markers in boxes of 5? How many boxes does he need to buy?

Find multiples of 5.

$5 \times 1 = 5$ $5 \times 4 = 20$ $5 \times 7 = 35$
$5 \times 2 = 10$ $5 \times 5 = 25$ $5 \times 8 = 40$
$5 \times 3 = 15$ $5 \times 6 = 30$ $5 \times 9 = 45$

40 is a multiple of 5.
Paul can buy exactly 40 markers in boxes of 5.
Paul needs to buy 8 boxes.

B **1** Skip count by 4s to find multiples of 4. Circle the multiples on the number line.

0   2   ④   6   ⑧   10   ⑫   14   ⑯   18   ⑳

B **2** Complete the multiplication facts to find more multiples of 4.

$4 \times 6 = 24$ $4 \times 9 = 36$
$4 \times 7 = 28$ $4 \times 10 = 40$
$4 \times 8 = 32$ $4 \times 11 = 44$

M **3** Look at problems 1 and 2. Are these the only multiples of 4? Use words and numbers to explain.
No. Possible explanation: A multiple of 4 is any whole number times 4. $4 \times 12 = 48$. 48 is also a multiple of 4.

Vocabulary
multiple the product of a number and any other whole number, for example, 3, 6, 9, 12, and 15 are multiples of 3.

Solve.

M **4** Max ordered 72 mugs. Mugs are packed 8 to a box. How many boxes of mugs did Max order?

Choose *Yes* or *No* to indicate whether the equation or statement could be used to solve the problem above.

a. $72 = 8 \times b$ ☒ Yes   ☐ No
b. $72 \div 8 = b$ ☒ Yes   ☐ No
c. List multiples of 8: 8, 16, 24, 32, 40, ...   ☒ Yes   ☐ No
d. $b = 72 + 8$ ☐ Yes   ☒ No

M **5** Cupcakes are packed 6 to a box. If Abby only buys full boxes of cupcakes, give two possible numbers of cupcakes that she could buy.
Show your work.

Possible answer: $6 \times 2 = 12$; $6 \times 3 = 18$

Solution: Abby could buy __12__ cupcakes or __18__ cupcakes.

C **6** Strawberries are sold in 1-pound, 2-pound, and 5-pound boxes. Stacy wants to buy exactly 10 pounds of strawberries. What are two ways that Stacy could buy exactly 10 pounds of strawberries? Tell which sizes of boxes she could buy and how many of each size box.
Show your work.

Solution: __Answers will vary. Possible answer: Stacy could buy 10 1-pound boxes or 2 5-pound boxes. $1 \times 10 = 10$; $2 \times 5 = 10$.__

Name: _____

Lesson 7

Find Factors and Factor Pairs

Study the example problem about factors and factor pairs. Then solve problems 1–6.

Example

Mr. Kennedy is arranging the 16 chairs in his classroom for a presentation. He wants to put the chairs in rows with an equal number of chairs in each row. Find all the ways he can arrange the chairs.

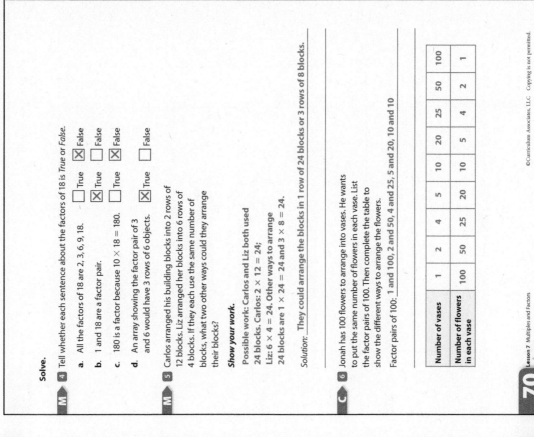

1 row of 16 chairs
$1 \times 16 = 16$

2 rows of 8 chairs
$2 \times 8 = 16$

4 rows of 4 chairs
$4 \times 4 = 16$

8 rows of 2 chairs
$8 \times 2 = 16$

16 rows of 1 chair
$16 \times 1 = 16$

Factors of 16: 1, 2, 4, 8, 16.

Factor pairs: 1 and 16, 2 and 8, 4 and 4.

Mr. Kennedy can arrange the chairs in 5 ways.

B **1** Complete the list to show the factors of 12.

1, _2_, _3_, _4_, _6_, _12_

B **2** Write the factor pairs of 12.

1 and _12_, _2_ and _6_, _3_ and _4_

M **3** The 20 students in Amanda's class each carved a wooden plate to display on the wall. They want each row to have the same number of plates. Find all the ways to display the plates.

Show your work.

Possible work: 1 × 20, 20 × 1, 2 × 10,
10 × 2, 4 × 5, 5 × 4.

Solution: _1 row of 20, 2 rows of 10, 4 rows of 5,_
5 rows of 4, 10 rows of 2, and 20 rows of 1

Vocabulary

factor pair two numbers that are multiplied together to give a product.

$2 \times 4 = 8$, so 2 and 4 are a factor pair of 8.

Solve.

M **4** Tell whether each sentence about the factors of 18 is *True* or *False*.

a. All the factors of 18 are 2, 3, 6, 9, 18. ☐ True ☒ False

b. 1 and 18 are a factor pair. ☒ True ☐ False

c. 180 is a factor because $10 \times 18 = 180$. ☐ True ☒ False

d. An array showing the factor pair of 3 and 6 would have 3 rows of 6 objects. ☒ True ☐ False

M **5** Carlos arranged his building blocks into 2 rows of 12 blocks. Liz arranged her blocks into 6 rows of 4 blocks. If they each use the same number of blocks, what two other ways could they arrange their blocks?

Show your work.

Possible work: Carlos and Liz both used
24 blocks. Carlos: $2 \times 12 = 24$;
Liz: $6 \times 4 = 24$. Other ways to arrange
24 blocks are $1 \times 24 = 24$ and $3 \times 8 = 24$.

Solution: _They could arrange the blocks in 1 row of 24 blocks or 3 rows of 8 blocks._

C **6** Jonah has 100 flowers to arrange into vases. He wants to put the same number of flowers in each vase. List the factor pairs of 100. Then complete the table to show the different ways to arrange the flowers.

Factor pairs of 100: 1 and 100, 2 and 50, 4 and 25, 5 and 20, 10 and 10

Number of vases	1	2	4	5	10	20	25	50	100
Number of flowers in each vase	100	50	25	20	10	5	4	2	1

Lesson 7

Name: _____

Identify Prime and Composite Numbers

Study the example showing how to identify prime and composite numbers. Then solve problems 1–6.

Example

Ms. Morris teaches a morning class with 13 students and an afternoon class with 14 students. Which class has a prime number of students?

13 has one factor pair: 1 and 13
13 is a prime number.
The morning class has a prime number of students.

14 has more than one factor pair: 2 and 7, 1 and 14
14 is a composite number.

B **1** Is the number 2 prime or composite? Explain.
Prime. Possible explanation: 2 is prime because it has only one factor pair, 1 and 2.

B **2** Kevin ran 23 laps around the track. Is the number 23 prime or composite? Explain.
Prime. Possible explanation: The only factors of 23 are 1 and 23.

M **3** Mae has more than 3 bracelets. She has an even number of bracelets. Is the number of bracelets a prime number or a composite number? Explain.
It is a composite number. Possible explanation: An even number greater than 2 has at least two pairs of factors: itself and 1; 2 and another number. Because the number has more than one pair of factors, it is composite.

Vocabulary

prime number a number that has only one pair of factors: itself and 1.

5 is a prime number; its factors are 5 and 1.

composite number a number that has more than one pair of factors.

8 is a composite number; it has the factors 1, 2, 4, and 8.

Lesson 7 Multiples and Factors **71**

Solve.

M **4** Tell whether each sentence is *True* or *False*.
a. The number 9 is prime. ☐ True ☒ False
b. 2 is the only even prime number. ☒ True ☐ False
c. All the odd numbers between 1 and 10 are prime. ☐ True ☒ False
d. Some composite numbers have only two factors. ☐ True ☒ False

M **5** The area of a garden is 5 square feet. The dimensions of the garden are 1 foot and 5 feet. 1 and 5 are factors of the number 5.
a. Is the number 5 a prime number? yes
b. If the area of a garden is 11 square feet, what could be the dimensions of the garden?
The dimensions could be 1 foot and 11 feet.

5 feet
1 foot

C **6** Jordan and Mitchell are planning a graduation party with 45 guests. They want to seat an equal number of guests at each table. Each table should have more than one guest. Answer the questions below.
a. List the different ways the guests and tables could be arranged. Tell how many tables are needed for each group of guests.
1 table of 45 guests; 3 tables of 15 guests; 15 tables of 3 guests; 5 tables of 9 guests; 9 tables of 5 guests
b. Jordan and Mitchell forgot to include themselves in the seating. They still want to have an equal number of guests at each table. List the ways the guests and tables could be arranged now.
1 table of 47 guests is the only way because 47 is prime; it only has the factors 1 and 47.

72 Lesson 7 Multiples and Factors

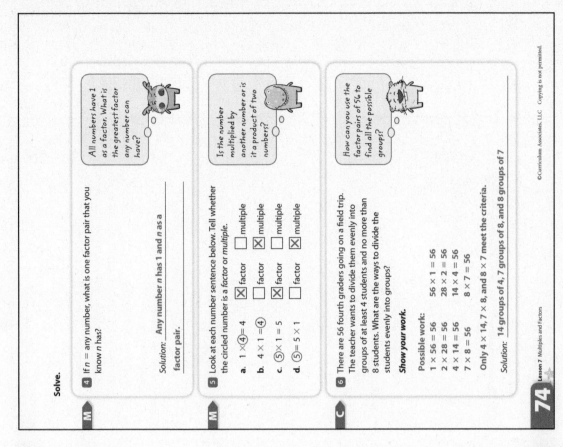

4 If *n* = any number, what is one factor pair that you know *n* has?

Solution: Any number *n* has 1 and *n* as a factor pair.

5 Look at each number sentence below. Tell whether the circled number is a *factor* or *multiple*.

a. 1 × ④ = 4   ☒ factor   ☐ multiple

b. 4 × 1 = ④   ☐ factor   ☒ multiple

c. ⑤ × 1 = 5   ☒ factor   ☐ multiple

d. ⑤ = 5 × 1   ☐ factor   ☒ multiple

6 There are 56 fourth graders going on a field trip. The teacher wants to divide them evenly into groups of at least 4 students and no more than 8 students. What are the ways to divide the students evenly into groups?

Show your work.

Possible work:

1 × 56 = 56   56 × 1 = 56
2 × 28 = 56   28 × 2 = 56
4 × 14 = 56   14 × 4 = 56
7 × 8 = 56   8 × 7 = 56

Only 4 × 14, 7 × 8, and 8 × 7 meet the criteria.

Solution: 14 groups of 4, 7 groups of 8, and 8 groups of 7

74

Solve.

Name:

Lesson 7

Multiples and Factors

Solve the problems.

1 Raffle tickets at a fundraiser are $5 per ticket. Fiona spent $40 on tickets. How many tickets did she buy?

Show your work.

5 × 8 = 40

Solution: 8 tickets

2 Which sentence(s) below are true about the numbers 1, 3, and 9? Circle the letter for all that apply.

A Adding 1 to any of the numbers will make a composite number.

B Adding 2 to any of the numbers will make a prime number.

C 3 and 9 are prime numbers.

D All the numbers are factors of 9.

E All the numbers are factors of any multiple of 3.

3 The factors of 6 are also the factors of which number?

A 5   C 20
B 10   D 30

Mike chose **D** as the correct answer. How did he get that answer?

Answers will vary. Possible answer: Factors of 6: 1, 2, 3, 6. Factors of 30: 1, 2, 3, 5, 6, 10, 15, 30. Both 6 and 30 have factors of 1, 2, 3, and 6.

73

Lesson 8

Number and Shape Patterns

Name: _____

Identify Number Patterns

**Study the example showing a number pattern.
Then solve problems 1–5.**

Example
Leo noticed a pattern in the addition table.
What pattern did Leo notice?
What is the rule for the pattern?
What is the next number in the pattern?

Pattern: 0, 2, 4, 6, 8
Rule: add 2

Use the rule to find the next number in the pattern:
$8 + 2 = 10$

10 is the next number in the pattern.

	0	1	2	3	4	5
0	0	1	2	3	4	5
1	1	2	3	4	5	6
2	2	3	4	5	6	7
3	3	4	5	6	7	8
4	4	5	6	7	8	9
5	5	6	7	8	9	?

B 1 Use the number line below to answer the questions.

+10 +10 +10 +10
0   10   20   30   40

a. What pattern of numbers do you see on the number line?
0, 10, 20, 30, 40

b. What is the rule for the pattern? add 10

B 2 Use the number line below to answer the questions.

+5 +5 +5 +5
0   5   10 15 20

a. What pattern of numbers do you see on the number line?
0, 5, 10, 15, 20

b. Label the number line to show the rule for the pattern.

Vocabulary
number pattern a series of numbers that follow a rule to repeat or change.
rule a procedure to follow to go from one number or shape to the next in a pattern.

©Curriculum Associates, LLC Copying is not permitted.

Lesson 8 Number and Shape Patterns **77**

Solve.

M 3 Fill in the missing numbers to show patterns with addends and sums.

Addend	Addend	Sum
100	10	110
90	20	110
80	30	110
70	40	110
60	50	110

M 4 Look at problem 3.

a. What pattern do you see in the first Addend column?

Possible answer: As you go down the column, each number is 10 less than the number above it.

b. What pattern do you see in the second Addend column?

Possible answer: As you go down the column, each number is 10 more than the number above it.

c. When the sum remains the same, what do you notice about the two addends?

Possible answer: When the first addend goes up by 10, the second addend goes down by 10.

C 5 What is the same and what is different about the two patterns below?

Pattern A: 5, 10, 15, 20, 25, 30

Pattern B: 30, 25, 20, 15, 10, 5   Possible answers are shown.

Same: The numbers are the same in both patterns, but in a different order.

Different: The rule for pattern A is add 5. The rule for pattern B is subtract 5.

78 Lesson 8 Number and Shape Patterns

©Curriculum Associates, LLC Copying is not permitted.

Key

B Basic   **M** Medium   **C** Challenge

Lesson 8

Name: _____

Use Number Patterns

Study the example showing how to use a pattern on a number line to solve a word problem. Then solve problems 1–8.

Example

Riley wants to save $10 from her weekly babysitting job for the next 4 weeks. She has $50 in savings now. How much will Riley have in savings at the end of 4 weeks?

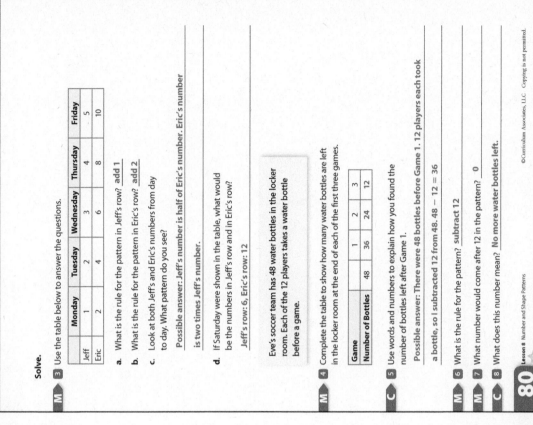

+10 +10 +10 +10

| 50 | 60 | 70 | 80 | 90 |
| Now | Week 1 | Week 2 | Week 3 | Week 4 |

Rule: add 10
Pattern: 50, 60, 70, 80, 90

Riley will have $90 in savings at the end of 4 weeks.

Eduardo practices the flute each weekday. His music teacher wants him to practice 5 minutes longer each day this week. Eduardo practices for 20 minutes on Monday. How many minutes will Eduardo practice on Friday?

B 1 Complete the table to show how many minutes Eduardo will practice each day this week.

Day	Monday	Tuesday	Wednesday	Thursday	Friday
Number of Minutes	20	25	30	35	40

+5 +5 +5 +5

B 2 Complete the sentence.
Eduardo will practice for ___40 minutes___ on Friday.

©Curriculum Associates, LLC   Copying is not permitted.
Lesson 8 Number and Shape Patterns **79**

Solve.

M 3 Use the table below to answer the questions.

	Monday	Tuesday	Wednesday	Thursday	Friday
Jeff	1	2	3	4	5
Eric	2	4	6	8	10

a. What is the rule for the pattern in Jeff's row? __add 1__
b. What is the rule for the pattern in Eric's row? __add 2__
c. Look at both Jeff's and Eric's numbers from day to day. What pattern do you see?
Possible answer: Jeff's number is half of Eric's number. Eric's number is two times Jeff's number.

d. If Saturday were shown in the table, what would be the numbers in Jeff's row and in Eric's row?
Jeff's row: 6, Eric's row: 12

Eve's soccer team has 48 water bottles in the locker room. Each of the 12 players takes a water bottle before a game.

M 4 Complete the table to show how many water bottles are left in the locker room at the end of each of the first three games.

Game	1	2	3
Number of Bottles	48	36	24	12

C 5 Use words and numbers to explain how you found the number of bottles left after Game 1.
Possible answer: There were 48 bottles before Game 1. 12 players each took a bottle, so I subtracted 12 from 48. $48 - 12 = 36$.

M 6 What is the rule for the pattern? __subtract 12__
M 7 What number would come after 12 in the pattern? __0__
C 8 What does this number mean? __No more water bottles left.__

Lesson 8 Number and Shape Patterns   ©Curriculum Associates, LLC   Copying is not permitted.
80

Lesson 8

Identify Shape Patterns

Study the example showing ways to describe a shape pattern. Then solve problems 1–7.

Example

A banner along a classroom wall has the shape pattern below.

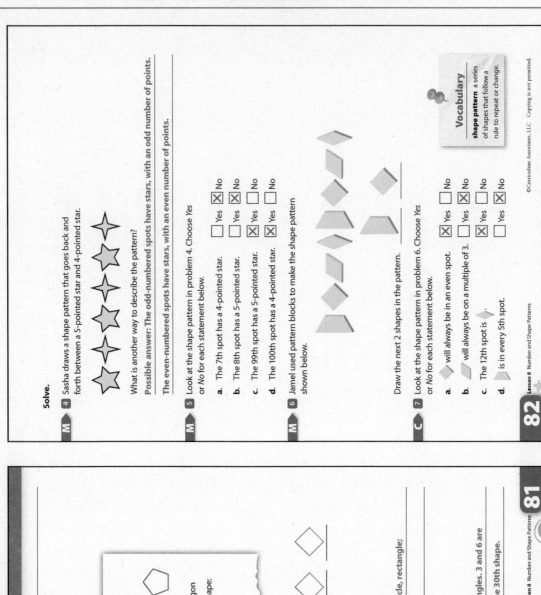

You can describe the pattern in words: circle, triangle, square, pentagon, circle, triangle, square, pentagon

You can describe the pattern by the number of sides in each shape: 0, 3, 4, 5, 0, 3, 4, 5

What will the next shape in the pattern be? A circle follows a pentagon in the shape pattern.

B **1** Draw the next two shapes in the shape pattern shown below.

M **2** What two ways could you describe the shape pattern below?

Possible answer: 1) Triangle, circle, rectangle, triangle, circle, rectangle;

2) 3 sides, 0 sides, 4 sides, 3 sides, 0 sides, 4 sides

M **3** Look at problem 2. The 3rd shape and the 6th shape are the same. Explain how to figure out what the 30th shape will be without drawing all 30 shapes.

Possible explanation: The 3rd and the 6th shape are rectangles. 3 and 6 are multiples of 3. 30 is a multiple of 3 so a rectangle will be the 30th shape.

Lesson 8 Number and Shape Patterns **81**

Solve.

M **4** Sasha draws a shape pattern that goes back and forth between a 5-pointed star and 4-pointed star.

What is another way to describe the pattern?

Possible answer: The odd-numbered spots have stars, with an odd number of points.

The even-numbered spots have stars, with an even number of points.

M **5** Look at the shape pattern in problem 4. Choose *Yes* or *No* for each statement below.

a. The 7th spot has a 4-pointed star. ☐ Yes ☒ No

b. The 8th spot has a 5-pointed star. ☐ Yes ☒ No

c. The 99th spot has a 5-pointed star. ☒ Yes ☐ No

d. The 100th spot has a 4-pointed star. ☒ Yes ☐ No

M **6** Jamel used pattern blocks to make the shape pattern shown below.

Draw the next 2 shapes in the pattern.

C **7** Look at the shape pattern in problem 6. Choose *Yes* or *No* for each statement below.

a. [trapezoid] will always be in an even spot. ☒ Yes ☐ No

b. [square] will always be on a multiple of 3. ☐ Yes ☒ No

c. The 12th spot is [triangle]. ☒ Yes ☐ No

d. [trapezoid] is in every 5th spot. ☐ Yes ☒ No

Vocabulary

shape pattern a series of shapes that follow a rule to repeat or change.

82 Lesson 8 Number and Shape Patterns

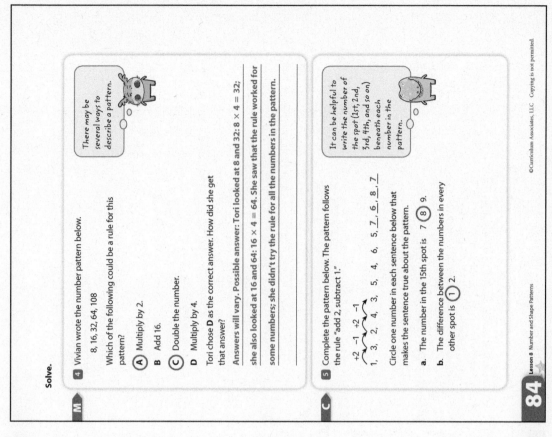

Solve.

4 Vivian wrote the number pattern below.

8, 16, 32, 64, 108

Which of the following could be a rule for this pattern?

Ⓐ Multiply by 2.

B Add 16.

Ⓒ Double the number.

D Multiply by 4.

Tori chose **D** as the correct answer. How did she get that answer?

Answers will vary. Possible answer: Tori looked at 8 and 32: $8 \times 4 = 32$; she also looked at 16 and 64: $16 \times 4 = 64$. She saw that the rule worked for some numbers; she didn't try the rule for all the numbers in the pattern.

There may be several ways to describe a pattern.

5 Complete the pattern below. The pattern follows the rule "add 2, subtract 1."

+2 −1 +2 −1
1, 3, 2, 4, 3, 5, 4, 6, 5, 7, 6, 8, 7

Circle one number in each sentence below that makes the sentence true about the pattern.

a. The number in the 15th spot is 7 ⑧ 9.

b. The difference between the numbers in every other spot is ① 2.

It can be helpful to write the number of the spot (1st, 2nd, 3rd, 4th, and so on) beneath each number in the pattern.

Lesson 8

Name: _____

Number and Shape Patterns

Solve the problems.

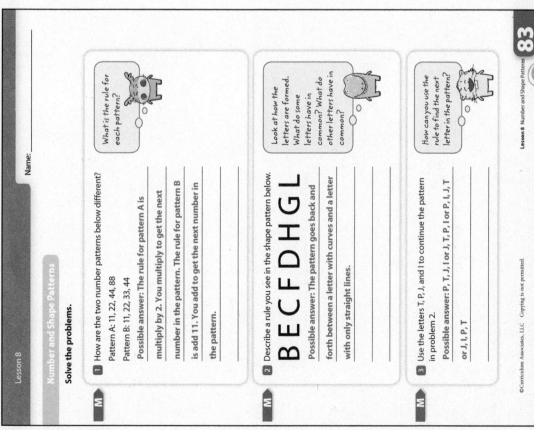

1 How are the two number patterns below different?

Pattern A: 11, 22, 44, 88

Pattern B: 11, 22, 33, 44

Possible answer: The rule for pattern A is multiply by 2. You multiply to get the next number in the pattern. The rule for pattern B is add 11. You add to get the next number in the pattern.

What is the rule for each pattern?

2 Describe a rule you see in the shape pattern below.

B E C F D H G L

Possible answer: The pattern goes back and forth between a letter with curves and a letter with only straight lines.

Look at how the letters are formed. What do some letters have in common? What do other letters have in common?

3 Use the letters T, P, J, and I to continue the pattern in problem 2.

Possible answer: P, T, J, I or J, T, P, I or P, I, J, T or J, I, P, T

How can you use the rule to find the next letter in the pattern?

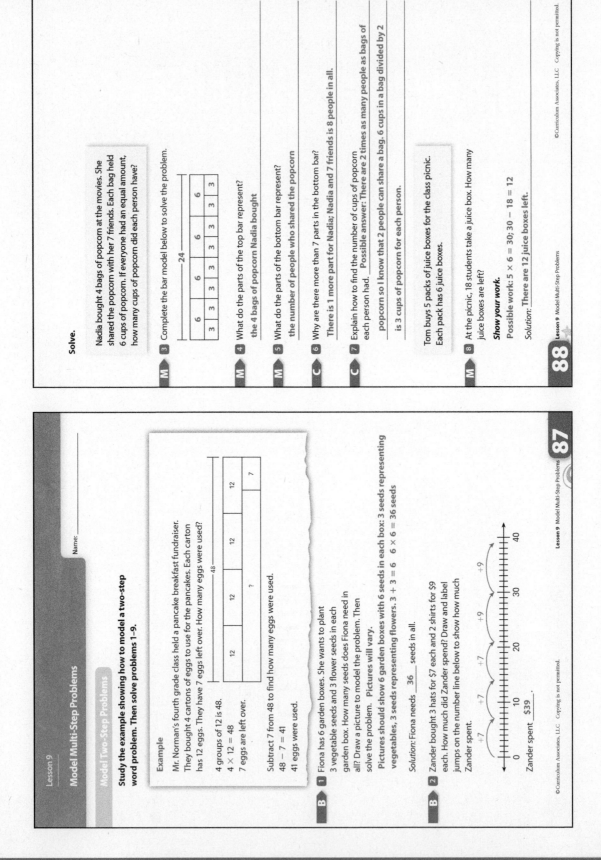

Lesson 9

Model Multi-Step Problems

Model Two-Step Problems

Study the example showing how to model a two-step word problem. Then solve problems 1–9.

Example
Mr. Norman's fourth grade class held a pancake breakfast fundraiser. They bought 4 cartons of eggs to use for the pancakes. Each carton has 12 eggs. They have 7 eggs left over. How many eggs were used?

4 groups of 12 is 48.
$4 \times 12 = 48$
7 eggs are left over.

48			
12	12	12	12
?			7

Subtract 7 from 48 to find how many eggs were used.
$48 - 7 = 41$
41 eggs were used.

B 1 Fiona has 6 garden boxes. She wants to plant 3 vegetable seeds and 3 flower seeds in each garden box. How many seeds does Fiona need in all? Draw a picture to model the problem. Then solve the problem. **Pictures will vary.**
Pictures should show 6 garden boxes with 6 seeds in each box: 3 seeds representing vegetables, 3 seeds representing flowers. $3 + 3 = 6$ $6 \times 6 = 36$ seeds

Solution: Fiona needs ___36___ seeds in all.

B 2 Zander bought 3 hats for $7 each and 2 shirts for $9 each. How much did Zander spend? Draw and label jumps on the number line below to show how much Zander spent.

+7 +7 +7 +9 +9
0   10   20   30   40

Zander spent ___$39___.

Solve.

Nadia bought 4 bags of popcorn at the movies. She shared the popcorn with her 7 friends. Each bag held 6 cups of popcorn. If everyone had an equal amount, how many cups of popcorn did each person have?

M 3 Complete the bar model below to solve the problem.

24			
6	6	6	6
3 3	3 3	3 3	3 3

M 4 What do the parts of the top bar represent? the 4 bags of popcorn Nadia bought

M 5 What do the parts of the bottom bar represent? the number of people who shared the popcorn

C 6 Why are there more than 7 parts in the bottom bar? There is 1 more part for Nadia; Nadia and 7 friends is 8 people in all.

C 7 Explain how to find the number of cups of popcorn each person had. Possible answer: There are 2 times as many people as bags of popcorn so I know that 2 people can share a bag. 6 cups in a bag divided by 2 is 3 cups of popcorn for each person.

Tom buys 5 packs of juice boxes for the class picnic. Each pack has 6 juice boxes.

M 8 At the picnic, 18 students take a juice box. How many juice boxes are left?
Show your work.
Possible work: $5 \times 6 = 30$; $30 - 18 = 12$
Solution: There are 12 juice boxes left.

Key

B Basic   **M** Medium   **C** Challenge

Lesson 9

Name: _____

Write Equations

Study the example showing how to model a multi-step problem and write an equation. Then solve problems 1–4.

Example
The table shows Eli's after-school activities. Write an equation to show how many hours a week Eli spends doing activities.

Activity	How long?	How often?
Volunteer at the library	2 hours	2 times a week
Work at the skate shop	2 hours	4 times a week
Swim practice	1 hour	5 times a week

Library
| 2 | 2 |

(2 × 2)

Skate shop
| 2 | 2 | 2 | 2 |

(4 × 2)

Swim
| 1 | 1 | 1 | 1 | 1 |

(5 × 1)

$A = (2 \times 2) + (4 \times 2) + (5 \times 1)$

Mia volunteered at the animal shelter on 7 weekends. On Saturdays, she volunteered for 3 hours. On Sundays, she volunteered for 2 hours.

B 1 Write an equation to find how many hours Mia volunteered.

a. Complete the bar model.

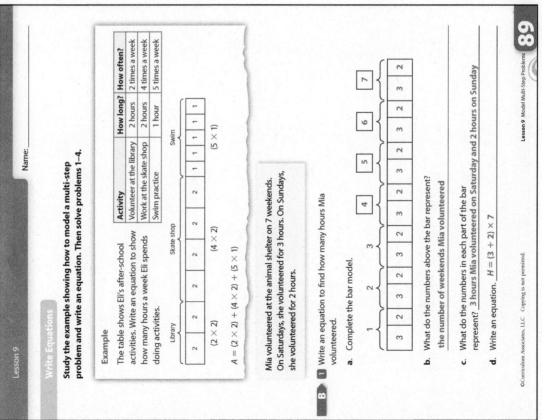

| 3 | 2 | 3 | 2 | 3 | 2 | 3 | 2 | 3 | 2 | 3 | 2 | 3 | 2 |

b. What do the numbers above the bar represent? the number of weekends Mia volunteered

c. What do the numbers in each part of the bar represent? 3 hours Mia volunteered on Saturday and 2 hours on Sunday

d. Write an equation. $H = (3 + 2) \times 7$

Solve.

M 2 A bike rental is $20 for a day and $3 for an hour. Caroline rented a bike for 2 days and 2 hours. Which equation could you use to find how much money, *M*, Caroline spent? Circle the letter for all that apply.

(A) $M = (2 \times 20) + (2 \times 3)$

B $M = (3 \times 20) + (2 \times 2)$

C $M = (20 \times 2) \times (3 \times 2)$

(D) $M = (20 \times 2) + (3 \times 2)$

M 3 Zara went to the book fair and bought 3 comic books for $5 each, 2 chapter books for $9 each, 4 posters for $2 each, and 1 picture book for $7. Write an equation that can be used to find how much Zara spent at the book fair.

Show your work.

Possible work: comic books: 3 × 5
chapter books: 2 × 9
posters: 4 × 2
picture book: 1 × 7

Students might use a bar model, a picture, or other model to show the cost of each type of item.
Possible equation:

Solution: $Z = (3 \times 5) + (2 \times 9) + (4 \times 2) + 7$

M 4 The table below shows clothing sales at a school fair. Use the information in the table to write an expression that equals *T*, the total amount of money spent on clothing.

Item	Price	Number sold
T-shirts	$12	100
Sweatshirts	$20	50

Solution: $T = (12 \times 100) + (20 \times 50)$

Vocabulary

equation a mathematical sentence that uses an equal sign (=) to show that two expressions have the same value.
$R = (6 \times 3) + 4$

expression a group of one or more numbers, unknowns and operations that represents a quantity.
$5 \times h$

Name: _____

Lesson 9

Model Multi-Step Problems

Solve the problems.

1 Phillip earns $15 an hour at his tutoring job and $10 an hour babysitting. Last week, he worked 10 hours tutoring and 4 hours babysitting. Which equation shows how much Phillip earned, E?

- **A** E = (15 × 10) + (10 × 4)
- **B** E = (15 + 10) × (10 + 4)
- **C** E = (15 × 10) × (10 × 4)
- **D** E = (15 × 4) + (10 × 10)

Remember that parentheses tell what to do first.

2 The table below shows a cell phone plan.

Phone	Cost per month
Phone	$22 each
Unlimited texting	$30 for a family
Unlimited data	$80 for a family
Insurance	$3 for each phone

Lola's family has 4 cell phones. They want to have insurance on each phone. They also want to have texting and data on each phone. Write an equation to show the monthly cost for Lola's family.

What expressions can you write to show the cost of 4 phones and the cost of insurance for 4 phones?

Show your work.

Student work will vary. Possible work:
Cost of 4 phones: 22 × 4
Cost of insurance on 4 phones: 3 × 4
Texting and data: 30 + 80
Total cost: (22 × 4) + (3 × 4) + 80 + 30

Solution: Equations will vary. Possible equation:
C = (22 × 4) + (3 × 4) + 80 + 30

©Curriculum Associates, LLC Copying is not permitted.

Solve.

3 There are 6 friends sharing 3 pizzas. Each pizza is cut into 8 slices. Which equation could be used to find the total number of slices, P, each friend will get?

- **A** (6 × 3) ÷ 8 = P
- **B** (3 × 8) ÷ 6 = P
- **C** 8 × (6 ÷ 3) = P
- **D** (8 × 6) ÷ 3 = P

First, how do you find how many slices there are in all?

Sadie chose **B** as the correct answer. How did she get that answer?

Answers will vary. Possible answer: Sadie saw that the total number of pizza slices could be represented by 3 × 8. Then she divided (3 × 8) by 6 to show that the slices will be shared by 6 friends.

4 Margaret received $20 each from 3 relatives and $50 from her parents at graduation. She spent $30. She saved half of the remaining money and donated the other half. Which equation(s) could you use to find how much money, S, she saved? Circle the letter of all that apply.

- **A** S = (3 × 20 − 50) − 30 ÷ 2
- **B** S = (3 × 20 + 50) − 30 ÷ 2
- **C** S = (20 + 20 + 20 + 50 − 30) ÷ 2
- **D** S = (3 × 20 − 50 + 30) ÷ 2
- **E** S = (3 × 20 + 50 − 30) ÷ 2

Another way to think of "half" is to think of dividing by 2.

©Curriculum Associates, LLC Copying is not permitted.

©Curriculum Associates, LLC Copying is not permitted.

Lesson 10

Solve Multi-Step Problems

Name: _____

Solve Two-Step Problems

Study the example showing how to use a model to solve a two-step word problem. Then solve problems 1–5.

Example

Brian and his friends are doing a 200-piece jigsaw puzzle. Each of the 6 friends has placed 12 puzzle pieces. How many pieces have not been placed?

200
6 × 12	p

(6 × 12)	+	p	=	200
72	+	p	=	200
		p	=	200 − 72
		p	=	128

128 pieces have not been placed.

B 1 Use estimation to check whether 128 is a reasonable answer in the example above.

p = 200 − 72

Round to the nearest ten.   p = 200 − 70

Subtract the rounded numbers. 130 = 200 − 70

130 is close to 128 so 128 is a reasonable answer.

B 2 There are 8 students at each of 4 round tables in the cafeteria. There are 64 students at long tables. Use the bar model to write and solve an equation to find how many students there are in the cafeteria.

V
4 × 8	64

Show your work.

(4 × 8) + 64 = V
32 + 64 = V
96 = V

Solution: There are 96 students in the cafeteria.

Lesson 10 Solve Multi-Step Problems **95**

Solve.

M 3 The table below shows the cost of admission tickets at a museum. Write and solve an equation to find the cost of tickets for 1 child and 2 adults.

Cost of ticket	Child	Adult
	$6	$11

Show your work.

Possible work: A = 6 + (2 × 11)
A = 6 + 22
A = 28

Solution: Tickets for 1 child and 2 adults cost $28.

M 4 Liz is training for a swim meet. Her goal is to swim 100 laps. She swam 12 laps in the pool on each of 3 days. Write and solve an equation to find how many more laps Liz needs to swim to reach her goal.

Show your work.

Possible work: (3 × 12) + L = 100
36 + L = 100
L = 100 − 36
L = 64

Solution: Liz needs to swim 64 more laps.

C 5 Paperbacks sell for $2 and hardcover books sell for $4 at the library book sale. The library made $98 at the sale. There were 25 paperback books sold. Write and solve an equation to find how many hardcover books were sold.

Show your work.

Possible work: 98 = (2 × 25) + (4 × H)
98 = 50 + (4 × H)
98 − 50 = 4 × H
48 = 4 × H
12 = H

Solution: There were 12 hardcover books sold.

96 Lesson 10 Solve Multi-Step Problems

Key

B Basic   **M** Medium   **C** Challenge

Solve.

M 3 Meghan found 15 pieces of sea glass on the beach. The next day she found 4 more pieces than she found the day before. Write and solve an equation to find how many pieces of sea glass she found altogether.

Show your work.

Possible equation: $G = 15 + (15 + 4)$
$= 15 + 19$
$= 34$

Solution: __Meghan found 34 pieces of sea glass.__

M 4 The table shows ticket prices at a movie theater. Ticket sales to an afternoon show were $146. There were 10 child tickets sold. Write and solve an equation to find how many adult tickets were sold.

	Child	Adult
Ticket price	$5	$12

Show your work.

Possible equation: $146 = (10 × 5) + (a × 12)$
$146 = 50 + (a × 12)$
$146 − 50 = a × 12$
$96 = a × 12$
$8 = a$

Solution: __8 adult tickets were sold.__

C 5 Ticket prices for 3-D movies are $10 for a child and $15 for an adult. One adult spent $55 to take a group of children to the movies. Write and solve an equation to find how many children went to the movies.

Show your work.

Possible equation: $C = (55 − 15) ÷ 10$
$C = 40 ÷ 10$
$C = 4$

Solution: __4 children went to the movies.__

Lesson 10

Name: _____

Solve Multi-Step Problems

Study the example showing how to model a multi-step problem with a remainder. Then solve problems 1–5.

Example

Mrs. Murray has 12 students in one science class and 14 students in another. She wants to combine both classes to do group work. Each table in the science room can seat 4 students. How many tables does Mrs. Murray need?

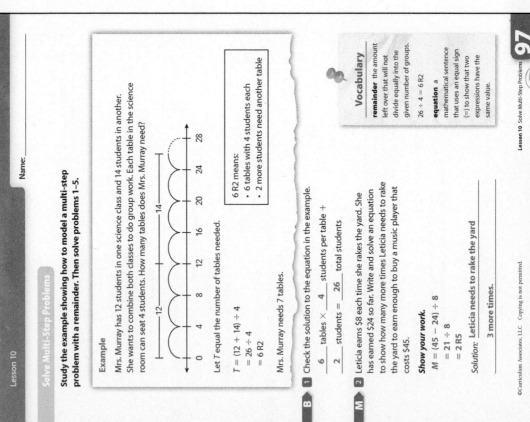

Let T equal the number of tables needed.

$T = (12 + 14) ÷ 4$
$= 26 ÷ 4$
$= 6 R2$

Mrs. Murray needs 7 tables.

6 R2 means:
• 6 tables with 4 students each
• 2 more students need another table

B 1 Check the solution to the equation in the example.

__6__ tables × __4__ students per table +
__2__ students = __26__ total students

M 2 Leticia earns $8 each time she rakes the yard. She has earned $24 so far. Write and solve an equation to show how many more times Leticia needs to rake the yard to earn enough to buy a music player that costs $45.

Show your work.

$M = (45 − 24) ÷ 8$
$= 21 ÷ 8$
$= 2 R5$

Solution: __Leticia needs to rake the yard 3 more times.__

Vocabulary

remainder the amount left over that will not divide equally into the given number of groups.
$26 ÷ 4 = 6 R2$

equation a mathematical sentence that uses an equal sign (=) to show that two expressions have the same value.

Lesson 10

Solve Multi-Step Problems

Solve the problems.

B 1 Jensen bought 10 boxes of granola bars. Each box has 8 bars. He wants to share the bars with 6 soccer teams. Which equation can be used to find how many bars each team gets?

A $b = (8 \times 10) - 6$ C $b = (6 + 8) \div 10$

B $b = (10 + 6) \div 8$ **D** $b = (10 \times 8) \div 6$

What operation can you use to put the bars into equal-sized groups?

M 2 Solve the equation in problem 1 to find how many granola bars each team gets. Are bars left over?

Show your work.

$b = (10 \times 8) \div 6$
$b = 80 \div 6 = 13 \text{ R}2$

Solution: Each team gets 13 bars. 2 bars are left over.

What does the remainder mean?

M 3 The community center used 4 recycling bins one week, twice as many the next week, 7 bins the third week, and 5 bins the last week of the month. Which equation shows how many bins were used for the month?

A $4 + (2 \times 7) + 7 + 5 = 30$

B $4 + (2 \times 4) + 7 + 5 = 24$

C $(1 \times 4) + (2 \times 4) + (3 \times 7) + 5 = 34$

D $4 + (4 \div 2) + 7 + 5 = 18$

Mia chose **A** as the correct answer. How did she get that answer?

Possible answer: Mia multiplied 2×7 for the second week instead of multiplying 2×4.

Which numbers do you place in parentheses?

Solve.

M 4 The table shows the results of a bake sale. The cost of renting tables for the bake sale was $100.

Write and solve an equation to show how much money the bake sale made.

Baked item	Number sold	Price
Cookies	90	$1 each
Brownies	75	$1 each
Crispy treats	60	$2 each
Cupcakes	50	$3 each

Show your work.

Possible work:
Cookies: $90 \times 1 = 90$
Brownies: $75 \times 1 = 75$
Crispy treats: $60 \times 2 = 120$
Cupcakes: $50 \times 3 = 150$
$M = (90 + 75 + 120 + 150) - 100$
$M = 435 - 100 = 335$

Solution: The bake sale made $335.

How do you show the cost of renting the tables in the equation?

C 5 Look at the table in problem 4. If 10 fewer cookies and 10 more cupcakes were sold, how much would the bake sale have made?

Show your work.

Possible work:
Cookies: $80 \times 1 = 80$
Brownies: $75 \times 1 = 75$
Crispy treats: $60 \times 2 = 120$
Cupcakes: $60 \times 3 = 180$
$(80 + 75 + 120 + 180) - 100 = 355$

Solution: The bake sale would have made $355.

Which numbers in the equation you wrote in problem 4 do you need to change?

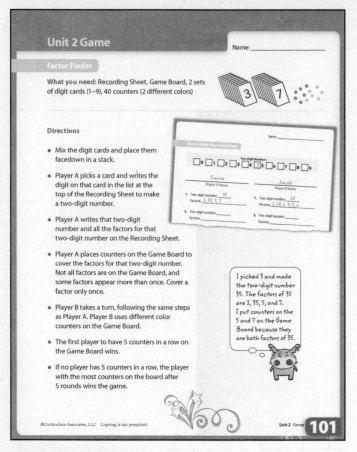

STEP BY STEP

CCSS Focus - 4.OA.B.4 *Embedded SMPs* - 6, 7, 8 **Objective:** Identify factors of 2-digit numbers.	**Materials** For each pair: Recording Sheet (TR 3), Game Board (TR 4), 2 sets of 1-9 Digit Cards (TR 5), 40 counters (20 each in 2 different colors)

- Read through the directions with students. Model one turn for students by reading aloud the Study Buddy text.

- Tell students that only one counter can be placed on each space on the game board. Not every factor for each two-digit number students make appears on the game board. Students should put their counters on the factors that do appear on the game board. If a factor appears more than once on the game board, cover the factor only once.

- Have players take turns. In each round, players choose a digit card, make a two-digit number, write the number and its factors, and cover the factors on the game board.

- The winner is the player with 5 counters in a horizontal, vertical, or diagonal row. If neither player makes a row, the player with the most counters on the board is the winner.

- After students have completed the game, discuss strategies they used when making their two-digit numbers. Did they try to make a two-digit number with more factors so that they could cover more spaces on the game board? Did they look at the factors remaining uncovered on the game board and then try to make a two-digit number that had those factors?

Vary the Game Have students cover the least amount of spaces on the Game Board. Students choose a digit card and make a two-digit number with as few factors as possible. The student with the fewest spaces covered wins the game.

Challenge Have students create their own game boards. Try a 6 × 6 board. Try different factors on the board. Which numbers are more useful as factors? Which are less useful?

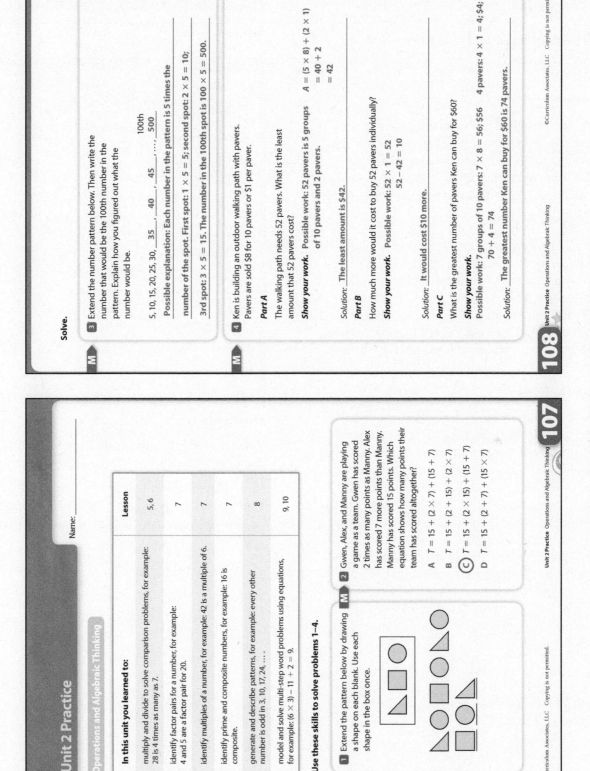

Unit 2 Practice

Operations and Algebraic Thinking

In this unit you learned to:

	Lesson
multiply and divide to solve comparison problems, for example: 28 is 4 times as many as 7.	5, 6
identify factor pairs for a number, for example: 4 and 5 are a factor pair for 20.	7
identify multiples of a number, for example: 42 is a multiple of 6.	7
identify prime and composite numbers, for example: 16 is composite.	7
generate and describe patterns, for example: every other number is odd in 3, 10, 17, 24, … .	8
model and solve multi-step word problems using equations, for example: $(6 \times 3) - 11 + 2 = 9$.	9, 10

Use these skills to solve problems 1–4.

B   **1** Extend the pattern below by drawing a shape on each blank. Use each shape in the box once.

M   **2** Gwen, Alex, and Manny are playing a game as a team. Gwen has scored 2 times as many points as Manny. Alex has scored 7 more points than Manny. Manny has scored 15 points. Which equation shows how many points their team has scored altogether?

A $T = 15 + (2 \times 7) + (15 + 7)$

B $T = 15 + (2 + 15) + (2 \times 7)$

Ⓒ $T = 15 + (2 \times 15) + (15 + 7)$

D $T = 15 + (2 + 7) + (15 \times 7)$

Solve.

M   **3** Extend the number pattern below. Then write the number that would be the 100th number in the pattern. Explain how you figured out what the number would be.

                                                                        100th

5, 10, 15, 20, 25, 30, __35__, __40__, __45__, …, __500__

Possible explanation: Each number in the pattern is 5 times the number of the spot. First spot: $1 \times 5 = 5$; second spot: $2 \times 5 = 10$; 3rd spot: $3 \times 5 = 15$. The number in the 100th spot is $100 \times 5 = 500$.

M   **4** Ken is building an outdoor walking path with pavers. Pavers are sold $8 for 10 pavers or $1 per paver.

Part A

The walking path needs 52 pavers. What is the least amount that 52 pavers cost?

Show your work.   Possible work: 52 pavers is 5 groups of 10 pavers and 2 pavers.

$$A = (5 \times 8) + (2 \times 1)$$
$$= 40 + 2$$
$$= 42$$

Solution: __The least amount is $42.__

Part B

How much more would it cost to buy 52 pavers individually?

Show your work.   Possible work: $52 \times 1 = 52$
$$52 - 42 = 10$$

Solution: __It would cost $10 more.__

Part C

What is the greatest number of pavers Ken can buy for $60?

Show your work.   Possible work: 7 groups of 10 pavers: $7 \times 8 = 56$; $56   4 pavers: $4 \times 1 = 4$; $4;
$$70 + 4 = 74$$

Solution: __The greatest number Ken can buy for $60 is 74 pavers.__

Key

B Basic   **M** Medium   **C** Challenge

TEACHER NOTES

Common Core Standards: 4.OA.A.3, 4.OA.B.4, 4.NBT.B.5
Standards for Mathematical Practice: 1, 2, 6, 7, 8
DOK: 3
Materials: none

About the Task

In this task, students use their knowledge of factors and multiples to determine a total amount. They use information in a table to write expressions that represent the cost of caring for each kind of animal and write and solve equations to find three different totals.

Getting Students Started

Read aloud the problem and go over the checklist with students. Guide them to write an expression with a variable to represent the cost of caring for each type of animal for one day. For example, $3 \times C$ represents the cost for C cats. Brainstorm possible donation amounts with students. Encourage them to try large donations, such as $100, to care for a greater number of animals. **(SMP 1)**

Completing the Task

Students may use different strategies to begin the problem. Some students may try different numbers of animals to find a donation amount. Others may be more systematic in their approach and may start by writing multiples of 3, 4, and 5. Some students may choose a donation amount and work backwards to find the number of each animal multiplied by the cost of care for the animal that equals the donation amount. Others may start with the cost of care and adjust the donation amounts. If students are having difficulty, suggest using the total cost of caring for one of each kind of animal for one day. Then they can look for multiples of that cost to find different donation amounts. **(SMP 1, 7)**

Encourage students to express their reasoning with equations and expressions. This will help them understand the relationships between quantities in the problem. **(SMP 2, 4)**

Extension

If some students have more time to spend on this problem, you can have them solve this extension:

How many different ways can you use one donation amount to feed some cats, small dogs, and large dogs for one day? Make a chart to show the combinations.

SAMPLE RESPONSES AND RUBRIC

Sample 4-Point Solution

I started with $50 and tried to find the most number of each kind of animal that amount would help for one day. I wrote expressions for the cost of caring for each animal: C cats is $3 \times C$; S small dogs is $4 \times S$; L large dogs is $5 \times L$. I wrote the multiples of 3, 4, and 5 to show different costs of caring for the animals. I looked at the list of multiples to find numbers that give a sum of 50. $24 + 16 + 10 = 50$. I solved the equation $24 = 3 \times C$; $C = 8$ to find that $24 cares for 8 cats. I solved the equation $16 = 4 \times S$; $S = 4$, to find that $16 cares for 4 small dogs. I solved the equation $10 = 5 \times L$; $L = 2$ to find that $10 cares for 2 large dogs. I write the statement: A donation of $50 helps 8 cats, 4 small dogs, and 2 large dogs for one day.

> Cats: 3, 6, 9, 12, 15, 18, 21, <u>24</u>, 27, 30
> Small dogs: 4, 8, 12, <u>16</u>, 20, 24, 28, 32, 36, 40
> Large dogs: 5, <u>10</u>, 15, 20, 25, 30, 35, 40, 45, 50

I followed the same process to write statements for $100 and $250 donations. A $100 donation cares for 8 cats, 9 small dogs, and 8 large dogs. $(3 \times 8) + (4 \times 9) + (5 \times 8) = 24 + 36 + 40 = 100$. A $250 donation cares for 40 cats, 10 small dogs, and 18 large dogs. $(3 \times 40) + (4 \times 10) + (5 \times 18) = 120 + 40 + 90 = 250$

REFLECT ON MATHEMATICAL PRACTICES

1. Look for an understanding that students can use the information in the table to write expressions representing the cost of caring for different numbers of each kind of animal. **(SMP 2)**

2. Look for explanations that show understanding of how to use the relationship between factors and multiples to find donation amounts. **(SMP 4)**

SCORING RUBRIC

4 points The student has correctly completed all parts of the problem with understanding. The student may use one or more equations to show the work. The student correctly relates the number of animals to each donation amount and explains the relationship between the cost of care and the number of animals for a given donation amount.

3 points The student has completed all parts of the problem, with one or two errors. The student may or may not show expressions or equations. The relationship between number of animals, cost of care, and donation amount(s) is not clearly expressed.

2 points The student has attempted all parts of the problem. The explanation of the calculations may be incomplete or may show only partial understanding of the relationships between number of animals, cost of care, and donation amount(s).

1 point The student has not completed all parts of the problem. There may not be calculations for three donation amounts. The explanation of the relationship between cost of care and number of animals may lack clarity or may be missing.

SOLUTION TO THE EXTENSION

Possible Solution

For a $100 donation, write multiples of 3, 4, and 5 up to 100. Then find combinations that come within $2 of $100 without going over. (If more than $2 is left, you can feed another animal.)

	Example 1 number	Example 1 cost	Example 2 number	Example 2 cost	Example 3 number	Example 3 cost	Example 4 number	Example 4 cost
Cats	8	$ 24	21	$ 63	2	$ 6	2	$ 6
Small Dogs	9	$ 36	3	$ 12	11	$ 44	1	$ 4
Large Dogs	8	$ 40	5	$ 25	10	$ 50	18	$ 90
TOTAL		$100		$100		$100		$100

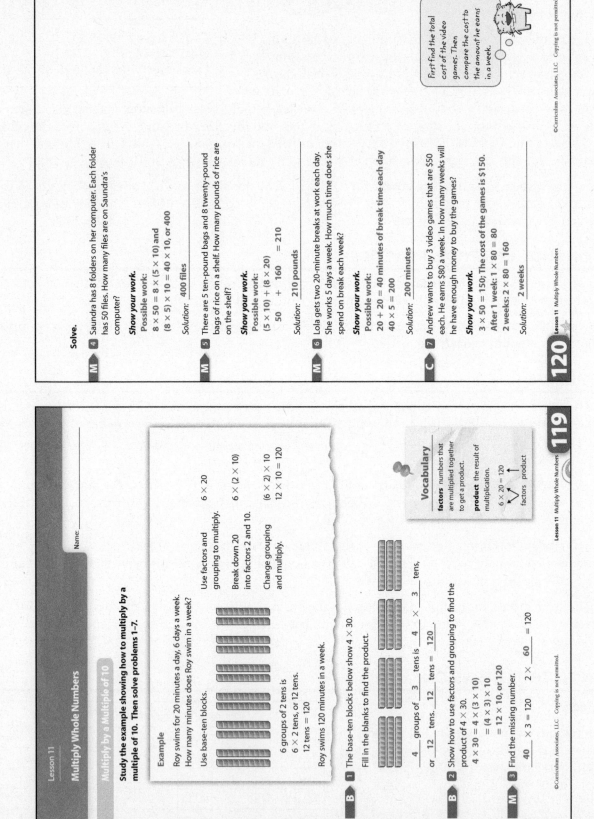

Lesson 11

Multiply Whole Numbers

Multiply by a Multiple of 10

Study the example showing how to multiply by a multiple of 10. Then solve problems 1–7.

Example

Roy swims for 20 minutes a day, 6 days a week. How many minutes does Roy swim in a week?

Use base-ten blocks.

6 groups of 2 tens is
6 × 2 tens, or 12 tens.
12 tens = 120

Roy swims 120 minutes in a week.

Use factors and grouping to multiply.	6 × 20
Break down 20 into factors 2 and 10.	6 × (2 × 10)
Change grouping and multiply.	(6 × 2) × 10
	12 × 10 = 120

Vocabulary

factors numbers that are multiplied together to get a product.

product the result of multiplication.

6 × 20 = 120 ← product

6 × 20 = 120
factors   product

B **1** The base-ten blocks below show 4 × 30. Fill in the blanks to find the product.

4 groups of __3__ tens is __4__ × __3__ tens,
or __12__ tens. __12__ tens = __120__.

B **2** Show how to use factors and grouping to find the product of 4 × 30.

4 × 30 = 4 × (3 × 10)
       = (4 × 3) × 10
       = 12 × 10, or 120

M **3** Find the missing number.

__40__ × 3 = 120   2 × __60__ = 120

Lesson 11 Multiply Whole Numbers **119**

Solve.

M **4** Saundra has 8 folders on her computer. Each folder has 50 files. How many files are on Saundra's computer?

Show your work.
Possible work:
8 × 50 = 8 × (5 × 10) and
(8 × 5) × 10 = 40 × 10, or 400

Solution: __400 files__

M **5** There are 5 ten-pound bags and 8 twenty-pound bags of rice on a shelf. How many pounds of rice are on the shelf?

Show your work.
Possible work:
(5 × 10) + (8 × 20)
  50 + 160 = 210

Solution: __210 pounds__

M **6** Lola gets two 20-minute breaks at work each day. She works 5 days a week. How much time does she spend on break each week?

Show your work.
Possible work:
20 + 20 = 40 minutes of break time each day
40 × 5 = 200

Solution: __200 minutes__

C **7** Andrew wants to buy 3 video games that are $50 each. He earns $80 a week. In how many weeks will he have enough money to buy the games?

Show your work.
3 × 50 = 150; The cost of the games is $150.
After 1 week: 1 × 80 = 80
2 weeks: 2 × 80 = 160

Solution: __2 weeks__

First find the total cost of the video games. Then compare the cost to the amount he earns in a week.

120 Lesson 11 Multiply Whole Numbers

Key

B Basic   **M** Medium   **C** Challenge

Lesson 11

Name: _____

Multiply by a One-Digit Number

Study the example showing one way to multiply by a one-digit number. Then solve problems 1–5.

Example

Jesse's family has 4 music players. Each music player can hold 8,352 songs. What is the total number of songs all 4 music players can hold?
Use an area model.

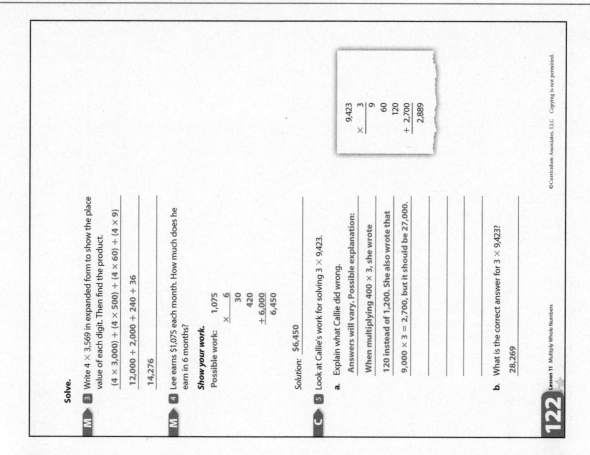

4	8,000 +	300 +	50 +	2
	4 × 8,000	4 × 300	4 × 50	4 × 2

$4 \times 8{,}352 = (4 \times 8{,}000) + (4 \times 300) + (4 \times 50) + (4 \times 2)$
$= 32{,}000 + 1{,}200 + 200 + 8$
$= 33{,}408$

All 4 music players can hold 33,408 songs.

B 1 Look at the multiplication above. Use partial products to multiply 4 × 8,352. Fill in the blanks.

```
     8 , 3 5 2
   ×       4
   -----------
           8      ← 4 × 2 ones
     2 0 0        ← 4 × 5 tens
   1,2 0 0        ← 4 × 3 hundreds
 + 3 2,0 0 0      ← 4 × 8 thousands
   -----------
   3 3,4 0 8
```

M 2 Show how to use partial products to multiply 5 × 1,643.

```
     1,643
   ×     5
   --------
       15   → 5 × 3 ones
      200   → 5 × 4 tens
    3,000   → 5 × 6 hundreds
  + 5,000   → 5 × 1 thousand
   --------
    8,215
```

Vocabulary
multiplication an operation used to find the total number of items in equal-sized groups.
product the result of multiplication.

Lesson 11 Multiply Whole Numbers   **121**

Solve.

M 3 Write 4 × 3,569 in expanded form to show the place value of each digit. Then find the product.

$(4 \times 3{,}000) + (4 \times 500) + (4 \times 60) + (4 \times 9)$

$12{,}000 + 2{,}000 + 240 + 36$

$14{,}276$

M 4 Lee earns $1,075 each month. How much does he earn in 6 months?
Show your work.

Possible work:
```
    1,075
  ×     6
  -------
       30
      420
  + 6,000
  -------
    6,450
```

Solution: **$6,450**

C 5 Look at Callie's work for solving 3 × 9,423.

```
    9,423
  ×     3
  -------
        9
       60
      120
  + 2,700
  -------
    2,889
```

a. Explain what Callie did wrong.

Answers will vary. Possible explanation:
When multiplying 400 × 3, she wrote
120 instead of 1,200. She also wrote that
9,000 × 3 = 2,700, but it should be 27,000.

b. What is the correct answer for 3 × 9,423?

28,269

122 Lesson 11 Multiply Whole Numbers

Lesson 11

Name: _____

Multiply Two-Digit Numbers by Two-Digit Numbers

Study the example showing how to multiply a two-digit number by a two-digit number to solve a word problem. Then solve problems 1–6.

Example

Aaron's guitar lesson is 35 minutes a week.
He has been taking lessons for 12 weeks.
How many minutes has Aaron spent at lessons?

Use an area model
to multiply 35 × 12.

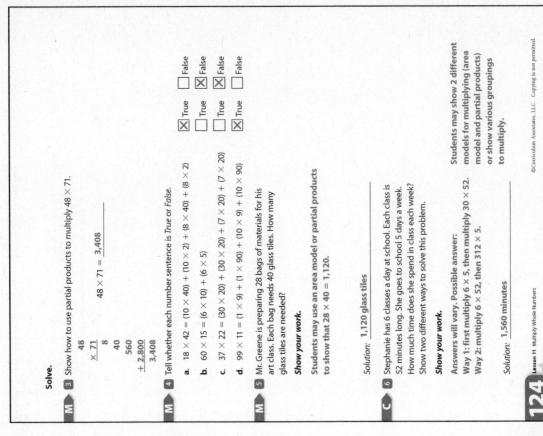

	30	+	5
10	10 × 30 1 ten × 3 tens = 3 hundreds **300**		10 × 5 1 ten × 5 = 5 tens **50**
+ 2	2 × 30 2 × 3 tens = 6 tens **60**		2 × 5 = **10**

300 + 60 + 50 + 10 = 420 minutes
Aaron has spent 420 minutes at lessons.

B 1 Look at the example above. Use partial products to multiply 35 × 12. Fill in the blanks.

```
    3 5
  × 1 2
    1 0      2 ones × 5 ones
    6 0      2 ones × 3 tens
    5 0      1 ten × 5 ones
+ 3 0 0      1 ten × 3 tens
  4 2 0
```

M 2 Show how to use an area model to multiply 71 × 48.

	70	+	1
40	40 × 70 = **2,800**		40 × 1 = **40**
+ 8	8 × 70 = **560**		8 × 1 = **8**

71 × 48 = **2,800** + **560** + **40** + **8** = **3,408**

Students can add partial products in any order.

Lesson 11 Multiply Whole Numbers   **123**

Solve.

M 3 Show how to use partial products to multiply 48 × 71.

```
    4 8
  × 7 1
      8
     40
    560
+ 2,800
  3,408
```

48 × 71 = **3,408**

M 4 Tell whether each number sentence is *True* or *False*.

a. 18 × 42 = (10 × 40) + (10 × 2) + (8 × 40) + (8 × 2)   ☒ True ☐ False

b. 60 × 15 = (6 × 10) + (6 × 5)   ☐ True ☒ False

c. 37 × 22 = (30 × 20) + (30 × 20) + (7 × 20) + (7 × 20)   ☐ True ☒ False

d. 99 × 11 = (1 × 9) + (1 × 90) + (10 × 9) + (10 × 90)   ☒ True ☐ False

M 5 Mr. Greene is preparing 28 bags of materials for his art class. Each bag needs 40 glass tiles. How many glass tiles are needed?

Show your work.

Students may use an area model or partial products to show that 28 × 40 = 1,120.

Solution: 1,120 glass tiles

C 6 Stephanie has 6 classes a day at school. Each class is 52 minutes long. She goes to school 5 days a week. How much time does she spend in class each week? Show two different ways to solve this problem.

Show your work.

Answers will vary. Possible answer:
Way 1: first multiply 6 × 5, then multiply 30 × 52.
Way 2: multiply 6 × 52, then 312 × 5.

Solution: 1,560 minutes

Students may show 2 different models for multiplying (area model and partial products) or show various groupings to multiply.

124   Lesson 11 Multiply Whole Numbers

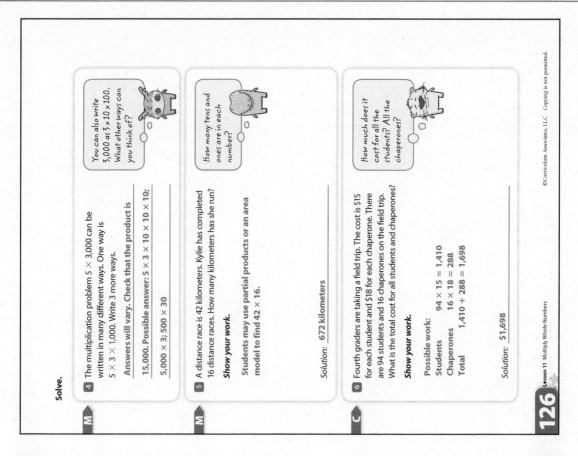

Solve.

4 The multiplication problem 5 × 3,000 can be written in many different ways. One way is 5 × 3 × 1,000. Write 3 more ways.

You can also write 3,000 as 3 × 10 × 100. What other ways can you think of?

Answers will vary. Check that the product is 15,000. Possible answer: 5 × 3 × 10 × 10 × 10;

5,000 × 3; 500 × 30

5 A distance race is 42 kilometers. Kylie has completed 16 distance races. How many kilometers has she run?

Show your work.

How many tens and ones are in each number?

Students may use partial products or an area model to find 42 × 16.

Solution: ___672 kilometers___

6 Fourth graders are taking a field trip. The cost is $15 for each student and $18 for each chaperone. There are 94 students and 16 chaperones on the field trip. What is the total cost for all students and chaperones?

How much does it cost for all the students? All the chaperones?

Show your work.

Possible work:
Students   94 × 15 = 1,410
Chaperones   16 × 18 = 288
Total   1,410 + 288 = 1,698

Solution: ___$1,698___

126

Name: _____

Multiply Whole Numbers

Solve the problems.

1 One mile is 5,280 feet. How many feet are in 6 miles?

What would an area model for 6 × 5,280 look like?

A 30,068   C 31,248

B 30,168   **D 31,680**

2 Which of the following are equal to 420 × 3? Circle the letter for all that apply.

How many hundreds, tens, and ones are in 420?

(A) (3 × 400) + (3 × 20)

(B) 420 + 420 + 420

C (3 × 400) + (3 × 2)

(D) 1,260

3 The bell on a clock tower rings every 15 minutes. If the bell has rung 24 times, how many minutes have passed?

What are the partial products of 15 × 24?

A 220 minutes

B 342 minutes

(C) 360 minutes

D 380 minutes

Amber chose **A** as the correct answer. How did she get that answer?

Answers will vary. Possible answer: She did not find all the partial products. She multiplied 20 × 10 and 4 × 5 to get 200 + 20 = 220.

125

Name: _____

Lesson 12

Divide Whole Numbers

Relate Multiplication and Division

Study the example showing how to use multiplication to solve a division problem. Then solve problems 1–7.

Example

The Lin family spent $800 on 4 airplane tickets. Each ticket was the same price. How much did each ticket cost?

Divide 800 by 4. $800 \div 4 = ?$

Use the related multiplication equation.

$4 \times 200 = 800$

So, $800 \div 4 = 200$.

Each ticket cost $200.

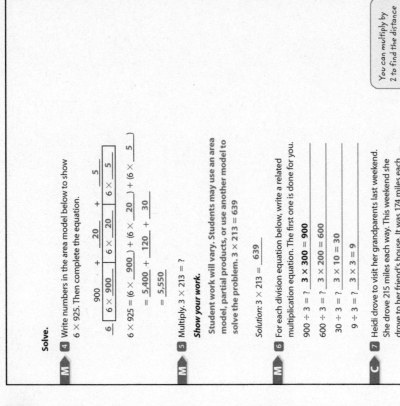

800			
200	200	200	200

B **1** Look at the model below. Write a division equation and a related multiplication equation.

3,000				
600	600	600	600	600

Division equation: $3{,}000 \div 5 = 600$

Multiplication equation: $\underline{5} \times \underline{600} = \underline{3{,}000}$

B **2** Multiply.

$4 \times 700 = \underline{2{,}800}$

$6 \times 300 = \underline{1{,}800}$

$3 \times 900 = \underline{2{,}700}$

M **3** Write the missing numbers in the equation.

$5 \times 743 = (\underline{5} \times 700) + (\underline{5} \times 40) + (\underline{5} \times 3)$

$= \underline{3{,}500} + \underline{200} + \underline{15}$

$= \underline{3{,}715}$

©Curriculum Associates, LLC   Copying is not permitted.

129 Lesson 12 Divide Whole Numbers

You can multiply by 2 to find the distance Heidi drove each weekend.

Solve.

M **4** Write numbers in the area model below to show 6×925. Then complete the equation.

	900	+	20	+	5
6	6×900		6×20		6×5

$6 \times 925 = (6 \times \underline{900}) + (6 \times \underline{20}) + (6 \times \underline{5})$

$= \underline{5{,}400} + \underline{120} + \underline{30}$

$= \underline{5{,}550}$

M **5** Multiply. $3 \times 213 = ?$

Show your work.

Student work will vary. Students may use an area model, partial products, or use another model to solve the problem. $3 \times 213 = 639$

Solution: $3 \times 213 = \underline{639}$

M **6** For each division equation below, write a related multiplication equation. The first one is done for you.

$900 \div 3 = ?$ $\mathbf{3 \times 300 = 900}$

$600 \div 3 = ?$ $3 \times 200 = 600$

$30 \div 3 = ?$ $3 \times 10 = 30$

$9 \div 3 = ?$ $3 \times 3 = 9$

C **7** Heidi drove to visit her grandparents last weekend. She drove 215 miles each way. This weekend she drove to her friend's house. It was 174 miles each way. How many miles did she drive altogether on both weekends?

Show your work.

Possible work:

$215 \times 2 = 430$

$174 \times 2 = 348$

$430 + 348 = 778$

Solution: Heidi drove $\underline{778}$ miles.

130 Lesson 12 Divide Whole Numbers

©Curriculum Associates, LLC   Copying is not permitted.

Key

B Basic	**M** Medium	**C** Challenge

Lesson 12

Name: _____

Divide Three-Digit Numbers by One-Digit Numbers

Study the example problem showing how to divide a three-digit number by a one-digit number. Then solve problems 1–6.

Example

Muffins are packed and sold in boxes of 4.
How many boxes are needed to pack 260 muffins?

$260 \div 4 = ?$

Use an area model.
$260 \div 4 = 65$

	50	$+$	10	$+$	5	$= 65$
4	$(4 \times 50 = 200)$		$(4 \times 10 = 40)$		$(4 \times 5 = 20)$	

$$
\begin{array}{r} 260 \\ -200 \\ \hline 60 \end{array}
\qquad
\begin{array}{r} 60 \\ -40 \\ \hline 20 \end{array}
\qquad
\begin{array}{r} 20 \\ -20 \\ \hline 0 \end{array}
$$

65 boxes are needed.

Use multiplication to check:
$4 \times 65 = (4 \times 60) + (4 \times 5)$
$= 240 + 20$
$= 260$

M 1 Use the example above. Show how to subtract partial products to divide 260 by 4.

Possible answer:

$$
\begin{array}{r} 260 \\ -200 \\ \hline 60 \\ -40 \\ \hline 20 \\ -20 \\ \hline 0 \end{array}
\begin{array}{l} \rightarrow 4 \times 50 \\ \\ \rightarrow 4 \times 10 \\ \\ \rightarrow 4 \times 5 \end{array}
$$

B 2 Identify the dividend, divisor, and quotient.

a. $900 \div 3 = 300$

dividend: __900__   divisor: __3__   quotient: __300__

b. $120 = 600 \div 5$

dividend: __600__   divisor: __5__   quotient: __120__

Vocabulary

dividend the number you divide in a division problem.

divisor the number you divide by in a division problem.

quotient the answer to a division problem.

dividend ÷ divisor = quotient

$260 \div 4 = 65$

$$\overset{\text{quotient}}{\underset{\text{divisor}}{} \overline{|\underset{\text{dividend}}{260}}}$$ $\dfrac{65}{4\overline{)260}}$

Solve.

C 3 A health center raised $476. The money was divided equally among 7 programs. How much did each program get? Use an area model to solve the problem.

Show your work. Possible model:

	60	$+$	8	$= 68$
7	$(7 \times 60 = 420)$		$(7 \times 8 = 56)$	

$$
\begin{array}{r} 476 \\ -420 \\ \hline 56 \end{array}
\qquad
\begin{array}{r} 56 \\ -56 \\ \hline 0 \end{array}
$$

Solution: __$68__

M 4 Mike has 876 building pieces to share among himself and 2 friends. He wants each person to have an equal number of pieces. How many pieces does each person get?

Show your work.

Student work will vary. Students may use an area model or subtract partial products to solve the problem.
$876 \div 3 = 292$

Solution: __292 pieces__

M 5 Look at how you solved problem 4. Explain how you could have used estimation before you divided so that you would know whether your answer was reasonable.

Answers will vary. Possible answer: I know that $3 \times 200 = 600$ and $3 \times 300 = 900$.

So I know the quotient will be between 200 and 300. Because 876 is closer to 900,

the answer will be closer to 300 than to 200.

M 6 Explain how to use multiplication to check your answer in problem 4.

Answers will vary. Possible answer: Multiply the divisor by the quotient. It should

equal the dividend. $3 \times 292 = 876$

Lesson 12

Divide Four-Digit Numbers by One-Digit Numbers

Name: _____

Study the example problem showing how to divide a four-digit number by a one-digit number. Then solve problems 1–5.

Example

A group of hikers plan to take 8 hours to hike a mountain trail 5,380 meters long. If they hike the same distance each hour, how many meters should they hike in an hour?

```
        2
       70
      600
8)5,380        → The sum of the partial quotients
 −4,800          is 600 + 70 + 2, or 672. The
   580           remainder is 4.
 − 560   → There are 600 groups of 8 in 5,000.
    20   → Subtract 600 groups of 8; 8 × 600.
  − 16   → There are 70 groups of 8 in 580.
     4   → Subtract 70 groups of 8; 8 × 70.
         → There are 2 groups of 8 in 20.
         → Subtract 2 groups of 8; 8 × 2.
```

5,380 ÷ 8 = 672 R4

The hikers should hike 672 meters each hour. Then they will need to hike 4 more meters to reach the end of the trail.

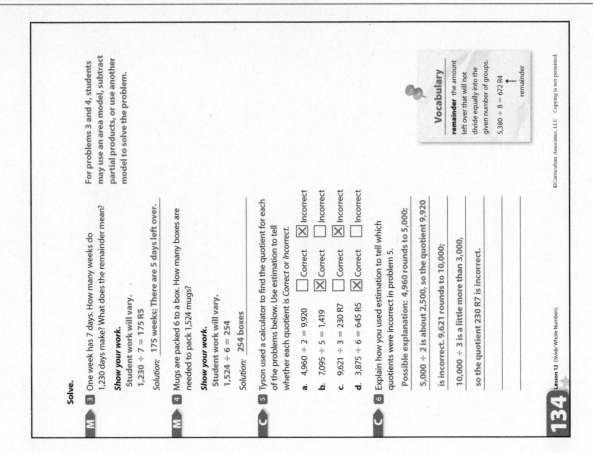

M **1** Complete the division problem.

8,236 ÷ 5 = ____ 1,647 R1

```
        7
       40
      600
     1000
5)8,236
 −5000
  3,236
 −3000
    236
  −200
     36
   −35
      1
```

M **2** Complete the division problem.

4,507 ÷ 4 = ____ 1,126 R3

```
        6
       20
      100
     1000
4)4,507
 −4,000
    507
  −400
    107
   −80
     27
   −24
      3
```

For problems 3 and 4, students may use an area model, subtract partial products, or use another model to solve the problem.

Vocabulary

remainder the amount left over that will not divide equally into the given number of groups.

5,380 ÷ 8 = 672 R4
     ↑
    remainder

©Curriculum Associates, LLC   Copying is not permitted.

Solve.

M **3** One week has 7 days. How many weeks do 1,230 days make? What does the remainder mean?

Show your work.

Student work will vary.

1,230 ÷ 7 = 175 R5

Solution: 175 weeks; There are 5 days left over.

M **4** Mugs are packed 6 to a box. How many boxes are needed to pack 1,524 mugs?

Show your work.

Student work will vary.

1,524 ÷ 6 = 254

Solution: 254 boxes

C **5** Tyson used a calculator to find the quotient for each of the problems below. Use estimation to tell whether each quotient is *Correct* or *Incorrect*.

a. 4,960 ÷ 2 = 9,920   ☐ Correct   ☒ Incorrect

b. 7,095 ÷ 5 = 1,419   ☒ Correct   ☐ Incorrect

c. 9,621 ÷ 3 = 230 R7   ☐ Correct   ☒ Incorrect

d. 3,875 ÷ 6 = 645 R5   ☒ Correct   ☐ Incorrect

C **6** Explain how you used estimation to tell which quotients were incorrect in problem 5.

Possible explanation: 4,960 rounds to 5,000;

5,000 ÷ 2 is about 2,500, so the quotient 9,920

is incorrect. 9,621 rounds to 10,000;

10,000 ÷ 3 is a little more than 3,000,

so the quotient 230 R7 is incorrect.

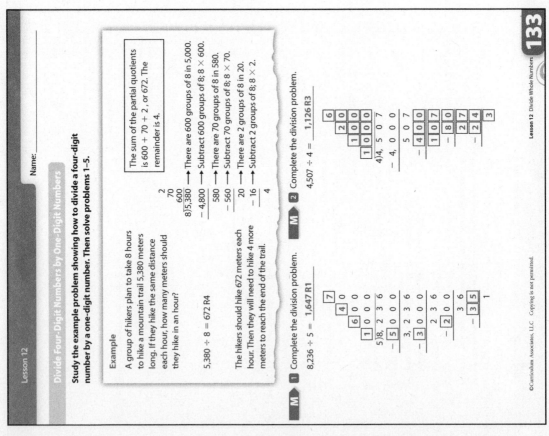

Lesson 12

Divide Whole Numbers

Solve the problems.

B ① Find the quotient.

   3,752 ÷ 6

   A 652   **C** 625

   B 652 R2   **(D)** 625 R2

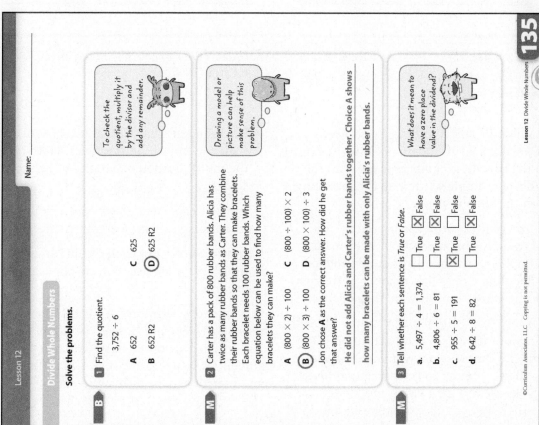

To check the quotient, multiply it by the divisor and add any remainder.

M ② Carter has a pack of 800 rubber bands. Alicia has twice as many rubber bands as Carter. They combine their rubber bands so that they can make bracelets. Each bracelet needs 100 rubber bands. Which equation below can be used to find how many bracelets they can make?

   A (800 × 2) ÷ 100   **C** (800 ÷ 100) × 2

   (B) (800 × 3) ÷ 100   **D** (800 × 100) ÷ 3

   Jon chose **A** as the correct answer. How did he get that answer?

   He did not add Alicia and Carter's rubber bands together. Choice A shows

   how many bracelets can be made with only Alicia's rubber bands.

Drawing a model or picture can help make sense of this problem.

M ③ Tell whether each sentence is *True or False*.

   a. 5,497 ÷ 4 = 1,374   ☐ True ☒ False

   b. 4,806 ÷ 6 = 81   ☐ True ☒ False

   c. 955 ÷ 5 = 191   ☒ True ☐ False

   d. 642 ÷ 8 = 82   ☐ True ☒ False

What does it mean to have a zero place value in the dividend?

Solve.

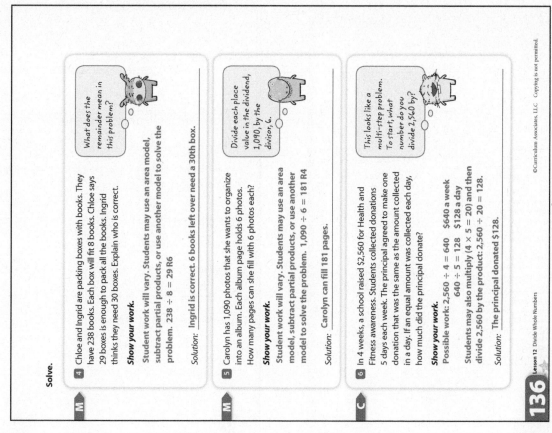

M ④ Chloe and Ingrid are packing boxes with books. They have 238 books. Each box will fit 8 books. Chloe says 29 boxes is enough to pack all the books. Ingrid thinks they need 30 boxes. Explain who is correct.

What does the remainder mean in this problem?

Show your work.

Student work will vary. Students may use an area model, subtract partial products, or use another model to solve the problem. 238 ÷ 8 = 29 R6

Solution: Ingrid is correct. 6 books left over need a 30th box.

M ⑤ Carolyn has 1,090 photos that she wants to organize into an album. Each album page holds 6 photos. How many pages can she fill with 6 photos each?

Divide each place value in the dividend, 1,090, by the divisor, 6.

Show your work.

Student work will vary. Students may use an area model, subtract partial products, or use another model to solve the problem. 1,090 ÷ 6 = 181 R4

Solution: Carolyn can fill 181 pages.

C ⑥ In 4 weeks, a school raised $2,560 for Health and Fitness awareness. Students collected donations 5 days each week. The principal agreed to make one donation that was the same as the amount collected in a day. If an equal amount was collected each day, how much did the principal donate?

This looks like a multi-step problem. To start, what number do you divide 2,560 by?

Show your work.

Possible work: 2,560 ÷ 4 = 640 $640 a week

   640 ÷ 5 = 128 $128 a day

Students may also multiply (4 × 5 = 20) and then divide 2,560 by the product: 2,560 ÷ 20 = 128.

Solution: The principal donated $128.

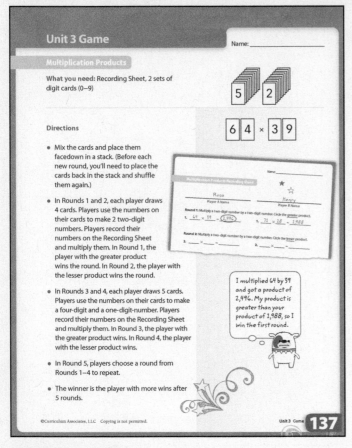

STEP BY STEP

CCSS Focus - 4.NBT.B.5, 4.NBT.A.1 *Embedded SMPs* - 6, 7, 8 **Objective:** Multiply two 2-digit numbers. Multiply a 4-digit number by a 1-digit number.	**Materials** For each pair: Recording Sheet (TR 6), 2 sets of Digit Cards (TR 2)

- Display the digit cards and recording sheet. Read through the directions with students. Relate the Study Buddy text to the two-digit numbers made with the digit cards and the example written on the recording sheet shown on the student page.

- Point out that the goal varies in each round of the game. Be sure students understand that they make 2 two-digit numbers in the first two rounds and a four-digit number and a one-digit number in the next two rounds of the game. Tell students they choose which round to repeat for Round 5.

- Model choosing four digit cards and making 2 two-digit numbers. Discuss how you might decide to arrange the digits in order to get a greater or lesser product. Then choose five digit cards and model making a four-digit and one-digit number to multiply.

- Have students use a separate sheet of paper to solve their multiplication problems. Have them write the multiplication equation on the recording sheet.

- After students finish the game, ask them to share strategies they used. How could they change the place value of digits to get a greater product? a lesser product?

Vary the Game For each round, draw two cards that both players must use. Players choose the rest of their own cards.

ELL Support Reinforce student's understanding of the terms "greater" and "lesser" before playing the game. Use counters or other classroom objects to show students a visual example of two different-sized groups, and how to use the terms to compare.

Unit 3 Practice

Numbers and Operations in Base Ten, Part 2

Name: _____

In this unit you learned to:

	Lesson
multiply a 4-digit number by a 1-digit number, for example: 2,810 × 3 = 8,430.	11
multiply a 2-digit number by a 2-digit number, for example: 62 × 33 = 2,046.	11
divide a 4-digit number by a 1-digit number, for example: 6,328 ÷ 4 = 1,582.	12
use area models and equations to explain calculations, for example: 7 × 240 = (7 × 200) + (7 × 40).	11, 12

Use these skills to solve problems 1–5.

M 1   Write numbers in each section of the area model to complete the model. Then write the product to complete the equation. Use numbers from the gray number bank at the right to complete the model and the equation.

Number bank:

4	8	10	32
20	30	50	68
40	272	160	432

Area model:

	20 +	4
10 +	200	40
8	160	32

18 × 24 = **432**

M 2   Use numbers from the gray number bank in problem 1. Write numbers in each section of the area model to complete the model. Then write the quotient to complete the equation.

	50 +	10 +	8
4	200	40	32

272

272 ÷ 4 = **68**

©Curriculum Associates, LLC   Copying is not permitted.   Unit 3 Practice Numbers and Operations in Base Ten, Part 2

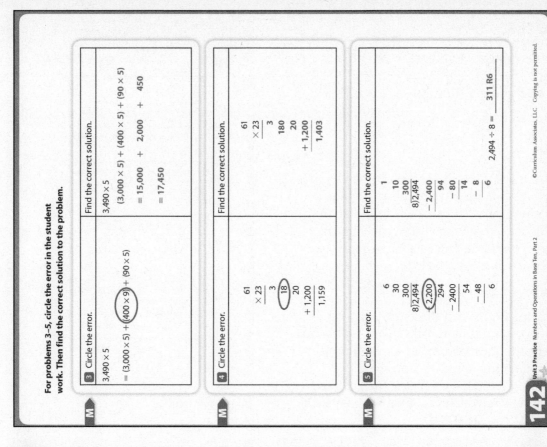

For problems 3–5, circle the error in the student work. Then find the correct solution to the problem.

M 3   Circle the error.

3,490 × 5
= (3,000 × 5) + (⟨400 × 9⟩) + (90 × 5)

Find the correct solution.

3,490 × 5
(3,000 × 5) + (400 × 5) + (90 × 5)
= 15,000   +   2,000   +   450
= 17,450

M 4   Circle the error.

```
    61
  × 23
  ----
     3
   ⟨18⟩
    20
+1,200
 -----
 1,159
```

Find the correct solution.

```
    61
  × 23
  ----
     3
   180
    20
+1,200
 -----
 1,403
```

M 5   Circle the error.

```
        6
       30
      300
   8)2,494
    ⟨-2,200⟩
       294
     -2400
        54
      -48
        6
```

Find the correct solution.

```
         1
        10
       300
    8)2,494
      -2,400
         94
        -80
         14
         -8
          6
```

2,494 ÷ 8 = _**311 R6**_

Unit 3 Practice Numbers and Operations in Base Ten, Part 2   ©Curriculum Associates, LLC   Copying is not permitted.

Key

B Basic	M Medium	C Challenge

TEACHER NOTES

Common Core Standards: 4.NBT.B.5, 4.NBT.B.6, 4.OA.A.3

Standards for Mathematical Practice: 1, 2, 3, 4, 5, 6, 8

DOK: 3

Materials: none

About the Task

To complete this task, students solve a multi-step word problem that involves multiplying, dividing, adding, and comparing whole numbers. Students use information in a table to make choices about quantities, compare their choices to a given constraint, make a plan to solve the problem, and explain how they made their choices.

Getting Students Started

Read through the problem with students. Begin by helping them understand the problem: there are two art projects, different supplies are needed for each project, supplies are packaged in quantities, and there is a budget for the cost of supplies. Point out the goal: to create a plan that tells how many campers can do each project and the total cost. **(SMP 3)**

Completing the Task

Some students may choose to find the total cost of supplies for all campers to do both projects. Others may choose a number of campers to do each project and then find the cost of supplies. **(SMP 1)**

Students may want to use a table to help them organize the information. Once they have chosen the number of campers, students will need to calculate how many supplies are needed and how many packages of each are needed in order to find the total cost. Students multiply and divide to find these quantities. Point out that they need to account for any remainders in division. For example, 500 balls of yarn are needed for 250 campers; $500 \div 9 = 55$ R5, so 56 packages of yarn are needed. **(SMP 2, 4, 5)**

Students' calculations should satisfy the total cost constraint of $4,000. Students' solutions may have all 250 campers do the less expensive paper project and fewer campers do the more expensive yarn project. Students' explanations should include a comparison of their total cost to the given budget of $4,000 to explain how they know Dan can use the plan. **(SMP 6, 8)**

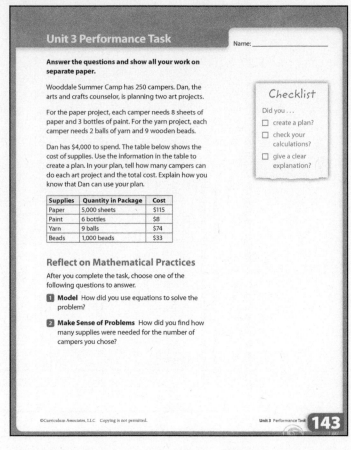

Extension

If some students have more time to spend on this problem, you can have them solve this extension:

Suppose Dan has $6,000 to spend. Can all 250 campers do both art projects? Explain how you know.

SAMPLE RESPONSES AND RUBRIC

4-Point Solution

In my plan, 250 campers do the art project and 125 campers do the yarn project. The total cost is $3,253. $3,253 < $4,000, so Dan can use the plan.

For each project, I multiplied the number of campers by the number of supplies needed for each camper to find the total supplies needed.

Supplies	Number for each camper	Number of campers	Packages needed	Cost
Paper	8 sheets	250	1	$115
Paints	3 bottles	250	125	$1,000
Yarn	2 balls	125	28	$2,072
Beads	9 beads	125	2	$66

Then I divided the total by the quantity in a package to find how many packages are needed.

Next, I multiplied the number of packages by the cost of each package to find the cost of each supply. Finally, I added the costs to find the total cost.

$250 \times 8 = 2,000$ sheets of paper   5,000 sheets of paper in a package; 1 package needed.
$250 \times 3 = 750$ bottles of paint   750 bottles ÷ 6 bottles in a package = 125 packages needed.
$125 \times 2 = 250$ balls of yarn   250 balls ÷ 9 balls in a package = 27 R7; 28 packages needed.
$125 \times 9 = 1,125$ beads   1,000 beads in a package; 2 packages needed.

The last column in the table shows the cost of each supply. I added to find the total cost:
$115 + $1,000 + $2,072 + $66 = $3,253

REFLECT ON MATHEMATICAL PRACTICES

1. Look for an understanding that equations are used to find the number of supplies for each camper, the number of packages needed, the cost of each, and the total cost. (**SMP 4**)

2. Students should recognize that they multiply the number of campers by the number of supplies needed for each camper. (**SMP 1**)

SCORING RUBRIC

4 points   The student has completed all parts of the problem and shows understanding of the problem. A plan is described for the number of campers that do each project and the total cost. The total cost is $4,000 or less. Student clearly explains how he or she knows Dan can use the plan. All calculations are shown and are accurate. Student uses equations and/or a table for calculations.

3 points   The student has completed all parts of the problem. A plan is described that tells the number of campers that do each project and the total cost. The total cost is $4,000 or less. The explanation of how Dan can use the plan may be incomplete or unclear. All calculations are shown, but one or two errors are made. Student does not describe the reasoning behind the calculations.

2 points   The student has attempted all parts of the problem. A plan is incomplete, the total cost is not given, or it exceeds $4,000. An explanation is not provided. Calculations or information in a table are incomplete or contain errors. Student's reasoning is unclear.

1 point   The student has not completed all parts of the problem. There are a number of errors. Equations or charts are incomplete and/or contain errors. Explanation is incomplete or includes an error.

SOLUTION TO THE EXTENSION

Possible Solution

Students should complete the table for 250 campers: 56 packages of yarn are needed for a cost of $4,144; 3 packages of beads are needed for a cost of $99. Total cost: $115 + $1,000 + $4,144 + $99 = $5,358. Since $5,358 < $6,000, all 250 campers can do both art projects.

Lesson 13
Understand
Equivalent Fractions

Name: _____

How do you know when fractions are equivalent?

Study the example showing one way to find equivalent fractions. Then solve problems 1–6.

Example

Find a fraction equivalent to $\frac{4}{6}$.

The number line shows both thirds and sixths.

$\frac{4}{6}$ and $\frac{2}{3}$ are at the same point on the number line.

$\frac{4}{6} = \frac{2}{3}$

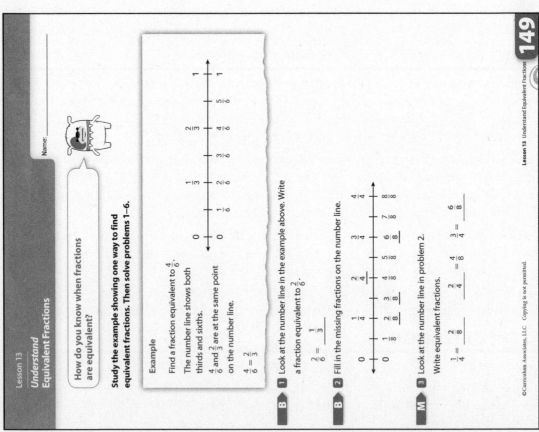

1 (B) Look at the number line in the example above. Write a fraction equivalent to $\frac{2}{6}$.

$\frac{2}{6} = \frac{1}{\rule{1cm}{0.4pt}}$

2 (B) Fill in the missing fractions on the number line.

3 (M) Look at the number line in problem 2. Write equivalent fractions.

$\frac{1}{4} = \frac{2}{8}$ $\frac{2}{4} = \frac{4}{8}$ $\frac{3}{4} = \frac{6}{8}$

Solve.

4 (M) Look at the models below. Shade the models to show two fractions equivalent to $\frac{3}{4}$. Then write the fractions.

$\frac{3}{4}$

$\frac{6}{8}$

$\frac{9}{12}$

5 (M) Use the models below to complete the sentences. The models show wholes and parts. There are 3 wholes, each divided into fourths.

Each part is $\frac{1}{4}$ of a whole.

There are 12 fourths in all. $\frac{12}{4} = 3$

6 (C) Look at the models below. Write the fractions they represent. Are the fractions equivalent? Explain.

$\frac{1}{2}$ and $\frac{2}{4}$. Possible explanation: The fractions are equivalent. The amount that is shaded in the models is the same. It is shaded in a different way, but it is the same amount.

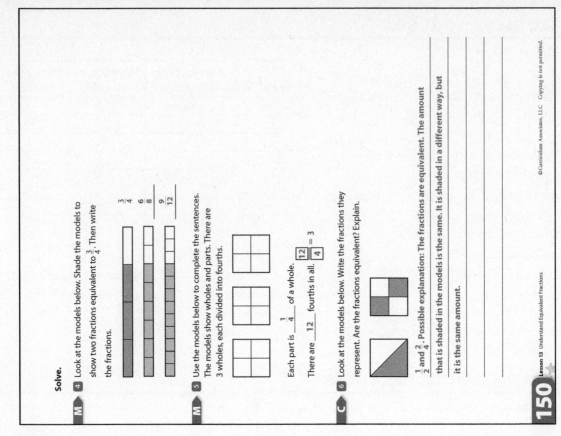

Key

B Basic   **M** Medium   **C** Challenge

Lesson 13

Name: _____

Show Equivalent Fractions

Study the example showing one way to model equivalent fractions. Then solve problems 1–8.

Example

A model can show equivalent fractions.

The model has 5 equal parts. It shows $\frac{3}{5}$.

Divide the model into 10 equal parts to show an equivalent fraction.

The model shows $\frac{6}{10}$.

$$\frac{3}{5} = \frac{6}{10}$$

B 1 Divide the model below to show $\frac{1}{2} = \frac{5}{10}$.

M 2 Draw a model to show $\frac{1}{6}$. Then divide the model into twice as many parts to find an equivalent fraction.

Drawings will vary. Possible drawing: Students might draw a circle or other model to solve the problem.

$$\frac{1}{6} = \frac{2}{12}$$

M 3 Multiply the numerator and denominator of $\frac{1}{6}$ by 2.

$$\frac{1 \times 2}{6 \times 2} = \frac{2}{12}$$

M 4 Why does it make sense that the fraction you wrote in problems 2 and 3 is the same?

Answers will vary. Possible answer: Multiplying by 2 is the same as making twice as many equal parts and twice as many shaded parts.

Solve.

M 5 Fill in the missing numbers to find two equivalent fractions to $\frac{4}{5}$.

$$\frac{4 \times \boxed{2}}{5 \times 2} = \frac{\boxed{8}}{10} \qquad \frac{4 \times 20}{5 \times 20} = \frac{\boxed{80}}{100}$$

C 6 Look at problem 5. Explain how $\frac{8}{10} = \frac{80}{100}$.
Explanations will vary.

Possible explanation: You can multiply both the numerator and the denominator in $\frac{8}{10}$ by 10 to find an equivalent fraction: $8 \times 10 = 80$ and $10 \times 10 = 100$. So $\frac{8}{10} = \frac{80}{100}$. Problem 5 also shows that $\frac{8}{10}$ and $\frac{80}{100}$ are both equivalent to $\frac{4}{5}$. So I know $\frac{8}{10}$ and $\frac{80}{100}$ are also equivalent to each other.

M 7 Shade the model below to show $\frac{1}{5}$. Then show 10 equal parts and write an equivalent fraction.

$$\frac{1}{5} = \frac{2}{10}$$

M 8 Shade the model below to show $\frac{2}{3}$. Then show 12 equal parts and write an equivalent fraction.

$$\frac{2}{3} = \frac{8}{12}$$

Possible dividing lines shown. Students may draw horizontal or vertical lines to divide each part into 4 equal parts.

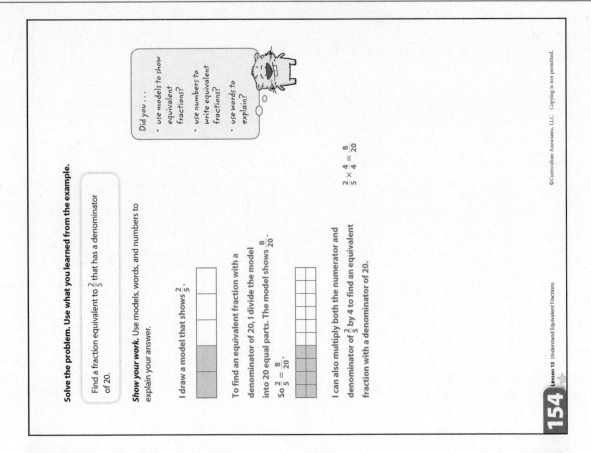

Solve the problem. Use what you learned from the example.

Find a fraction equivalent to $\frac{2}{5}$ that has a denominator of 20.

Show your work. Use models, words, and numbers to explain your answer.

I draw a model that shows $\frac{2}{5}$.

To find an equivalent fraction with a denominator of 20, I divide the model into 20 equal parts. The model shows $\frac{8}{20}$.

So $\frac{2}{5} = \frac{8}{20}$.

I can also multiply both the numerator and denominator of $\frac{2}{5}$ by 4 to find an equivalent fraction with a denominator of 20.

$$\frac{2 \times 4}{5 \times 4} = \frac{8}{20}$$

Did you . . .
- use models to show equivalent fractions?
- use numbers to write equivalent fractions?
- use words to explain?

154　Lesson 13　Understand Equivalent Fractions

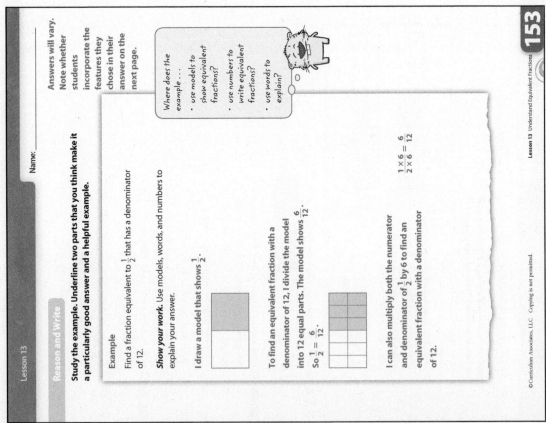

Lesson 13

Name: _____

Reason and Write

Study the example. Underline two parts that you think make it a particularly good answer and a helpful example.

Example

Find a fraction equivalent to $\frac{1}{2}$ that has a denominator of 12.

Show your work. Use models, words, and numbers to explain your answer.

I draw a model that shows $\frac{1}{2}$.

To find an equivalent fraction with a denominator of 12, I divide the model into 12 equal parts. The model shows $\frac{6}{12}$.

So $\frac{1}{2} = \frac{6}{12}$.

I can also multiply both the numerator and denominator of $\frac{1}{2}$ by 6 to find an equivalent fraction with a denominator of 12.

$$\frac{1 \times 6}{2 \times 6} = \frac{6}{12}$$

Where does the example . . .
- use models to show equivalent fractions?
- use numbers to write equivalent fractions?
- use words to explain?

Answers will vary. Note whether students incorporate the features they chose in their answer on the next page.

153

Lesson 13　Understand Equivalent Fractions

Practice Lesson 14 Compare Fractions

Unit 4

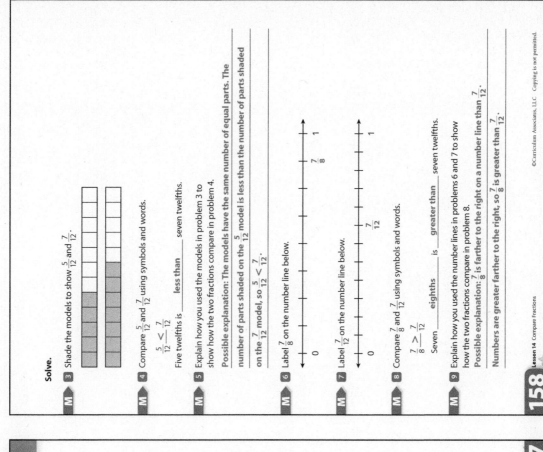

Name: _____

Lesson 14
Compare Fractions

Model Comparing Fractions

Study the example problem showing ways to compare fractions. Then solve problems 1–9.

Example

Sandy ran $\frac{3}{10}$ of a mile during gym class. Alicia ran $\frac{1}{10}$ of a mile, and Rosa ran $\frac{3}{8}$ of a mile. Compare the distance Sandy ran to the distances Alicia and Rosa ran.

Sandy

Alicia

$\frac{3}{10}$ and $\frac{1}{10}$ have the same denominator.

$$\frac{3}{10} > \frac{1}{10}$$

Sandy

Rosa

$\frac{3}{10}$ and $\frac{3}{8}$ have the same numerator.

$$\frac{3}{10} < \frac{3}{8}$$

Sandy ran a greater distance than Alicia and a lesser distance than Rosa.

B 1 Look at the example problem above. Write each comparison in words. Use *greater than* and *less than*.

$\frac{3}{10} > \frac{1}{10}$ Three tenths is ___greater than___ one tenth.

$\frac{3}{10} < \frac{3}{8}$ Three tenths is ___less than___ three eighths.

M 2 Shade the models to show $\frac{2}{8}$ and $\frac{2}{5}$. Then write <, >, or = to compare the fractions.

$$\frac{2}{5} > \frac{2}{8}$$

©Curriculum Associates, LLC   Copying is not permitted.

157 Lesson 14 Compare Fractions

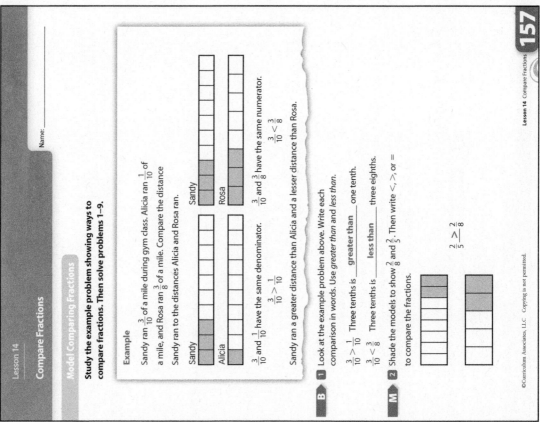

Solve.

M 3 Shade the models to show $\frac{5}{12}$ and $\frac{7}{12}$.

M 4 Compare $\frac{5}{12}$ and $\frac{7}{12}$ using symbols and words.

$$\frac{5}{12} < \frac{7}{12}$$

Five twelfths is ___less than___ seven twelfths.

M 5 Explain how you used the models in problem 3 to show how the two fractions compare in problem 4.

Possible explanation: The models have the same number of equal parts. The number of parts shaded on the $\frac{5}{12}$ model is less than the number of parts shaded on the $\frac{7}{12}$ model, so $\frac{5}{12} < \frac{7}{12}$.

M 6 Label $\frac{7}{8}$ on the number line below.

0    $\frac{7}{8}$ 1

M 7 Label $\frac{7}{12}$ on the number line below.

0    $\frac{7}{12}$ 1

M 8 Compare $\frac{7}{8}$ and $\frac{7}{12}$ using symbols and words.

$$\frac{7}{8} > \frac{7}{12}$$

Seven ___eighths___ is ___greater than___ seven twelfths.

M 9 Explain how you used the number lines in problems 6 and 7 to show how the two fractions compare in problem 8.

Possible explanation: $\frac{7}{8}$ is farther to the right on a number line than $\frac{7}{12}$. Numbers are greater farther to the right, so $\frac{7}{8}$ is greater than $\frac{7}{12}$.

158 Lesson 14 Compare Fractions

©Curriculum Associates, LLC   Copying is not permitted.

Key

B Basic **M** Medium **C** Challenge

Lesson 14

Name: _____

Find a Common Numerator or Denominator

Study the example problem showing how to compare fractions by finding a common denominator. Then solve problems 1–7.

Example

A length of ribbon is $\frac{3}{4}$ foot. Another length of ribbon is $\frac{5}{6}$ foot. Compare the lengths using a symbol.

Find a common denominator. $\frac{3\times3}{4\times3}=\frac{9}{12}$ $\frac{5\times2}{6\times2}=\frac{10}{12}$

Write the equivalent fractions. $\frac{3}{4}=\frac{9}{12}$ $\frac{5}{6}=\frac{10}{12}$

Compare the numerators. $\frac{9}{12}<\frac{10}{12}$

$9 < 10$ so $\frac{9}{12}<\frac{10}{12}$

$\frac{3}{4}<\frac{5}{6}$

Vocabulary

denominator the number below the line in a fraction. It tells how many equal parts are in the whole.

$\frac{3}{4}$ → 4 equal parts

numerator the number above the line in a fraction. It tells how many equal parts are described.

$\frac{3}{4}$ → 3 parts described

B 1 Shade the models below to show $\frac{3}{4}$ and $\frac{5}{6}$. Fill in the blank to show the comparison. $\frac{3}{4}<\frac{5}{6}$

M 2 Divide each model in problem 1 into 12 equal parts to show an equivalent fraction. Write the equivalent fractions and symbol to show the comparison.

$\frac{9}{12}<\frac{10}{12}$

M 3 Compare $\frac{2}{3}$ and $\frac{9}{12}$ by finding a common denominator.

a. Write a fraction equivalent to $\frac{2}{3}$ with a denominator of 12. $\frac{2\times4}{3\times4}=\frac{8}{12}$

b. Compare the fractions. $\frac{8}{12}<\frac{9}{12}$ So, $\frac{2}{3}<\frac{9}{12}$

Solve.

M 4 Compare $\frac{1}{5}$ and $\frac{2}{12}$ by finding a common numerator.

a. Write a fraction equivalent to $\frac{1}{5}$ with a numerator of 2. $\frac{1\times2}{5\times2}=\frac{2}{10}$

b. Compare the fractions. $\frac{2}{10}>\frac{2}{12}$ So, $\frac{1}{5}>\frac{2}{12}$

M 5 Compare the fractions. Use the symbols <, >, and =.

a. $\frac{2}{5}<\frac{8}{10}$

b. $\frac{5}{12}>\frac{1}{3}$

c. $\frac{3}{5}=\frac{60}{100}$

d. $\frac{9}{100}<\frac{9}{9}$

M 6 Tell whether each sentence is *True* or *False*.

a. $\frac{2}{3}>\frac{5}{6}$ ☐ True   ☒ False

b. $\frac{4}{10}<\frac{4}{5}$ ☒ True   ☐ False

c. $\frac{70}{100}=\frac{7}{10}$ ☒ True   ☐ False

d. $\frac{1}{3}>\frac{3}{1}$ ☐ True   ☒ False

e. $\frac{3}{4}<\frac{2}{3}$ ☐ True   ☒ False

C 7 Can two fractions with the same numerator and different denominators be equal? Use words and numbers to explain.

No. Possible explanation: Fractions with the same numerator have the same number of parts, but the size of the parts is different when the denominators are different. The fractions can't be equal, because the fraction with the smaller-size parts will be the smaller fraction. For example: $\frac{3}{4}$ is greater than $\frac{3}{5}$ because fourths are greater than fifths, $\frac{3}{4}>\frac{3}{5}$.

Lesson 14

Name: _____

Use a Benchmark to Compare Fractions

Study the example problem using 1 as a benchmark to compare fractions. Then solve problems 1–4.

Example

Carol compared $\frac{3}{4}$ and $\frac{2}{1}$. She says $\frac{3}{4} > \frac{2}{1}$ because both the numerator and the denominator in $\frac{3}{4}$ are greater than the numerator and denominator in $\frac{2}{1}$.

$3 > 2$ and $4 > 1$. Is Carol correct?

Compare each fraction to the benchmark 1.

[number line: 0, $\frac{3}{4}$, 1, $\frac{2}{1}$, 2]

$\frac{3}{4} < 1$ and $\frac{2}{1} > 1$.

$\frac{3}{4} < \frac{2}{1}$ and $\frac{2}{1} > \frac{3}{4}$. Carol is not correct.

1 Compare $\frac{9}{10}$ and $\frac{3}{2}$.

a. Label $\frac{9}{10}$ and $\frac{3}{2}$ on the number line below.

[number line: 0, $\frac{5}{10}$, $\frac{9}{10}$ 1, $\frac{15}{10}$, $\frac{3}{2}$, 2]

b. Which fraction is greater than 1? $\frac{3}{2}$

c. Which fraction is less than 1? $\frac{9}{10}$

d. Fill in the blank. Explain how you found your answer. $\frac{9}{10} < \frac{3}{2}$

Answers will vary. Possible answer: $\frac{9}{10}$ is less than $\frac{3}{2}$ because $\frac{9}{10}$ is less than 1 and $\frac{3}{2}$ is greater than 1.

Solve.

2 Compare $\frac{5}{6}$ and $\frac{1}{3}$ using the benchmark fraction $\frac{1}{2}$.

a. Label $\frac{5}{6}$ and $\frac{1}{3}$ on the number line below.

[number line: 0, $\frac{1}{3}$, $\frac{1}{2}$, $\frac{5}{6}$, 1]

b. Which fraction is greater than $\frac{1}{2}$? $\frac{5}{6}$

c. Which fraction is less than $\frac{1}{2}$? $\frac{1}{3}$

d. Fill in the blank. Explain how you found your answer.

$\frac{5}{6} > \frac{1}{3}$

Answers will vary. Possible answer: $\frac{5}{6}$ is greater than $\frac{1}{3}$ because $\frac{5}{6}$ is greater than $\frac{1}{2}$ and $\frac{1}{3}$ is less than $\frac{1}{2}$.

3 Use a benchmark fraction to compare the fractions $\frac{7}{10}$ and $\frac{5}{12}$. Explain how you found your answer.

Answers will vary. Possible answer: $\frac{1}{2}$ is equal to $\frac{5}{10}$ so $\frac{7}{10}$ is greater than $\frac{1}{2}$. $\frac{1}{2}$ is also equal to $\frac{6}{12}$ so $\frac{5}{12}$ is less than $\frac{1}{2}$. $\frac{7}{10}$ is greater than $\frac{5}{12}$.

4 Tell whether each number sentence is *True* or *False*. Then write the benchmark you could use to compare the fractions.

			Benchmark
a. $\frac{9}{8} > \frac{11}{12}$	☒ True	☐ False	1
b. $\frac{2}{5} < \frac{5}{6}$	☒ True	☐ False	$\frac{1}{2}$
c. $\frac{7}{10} < \frac{2}{4}$	☐ True	☒ False	$\frac{1}{2}$
d. $\frac{4}{5} > \frac{2}{2}$	☐ True	☒ False	1
e. $\frac{3}{2} < \frac{9}{10}$	☐ True	☒ False	1

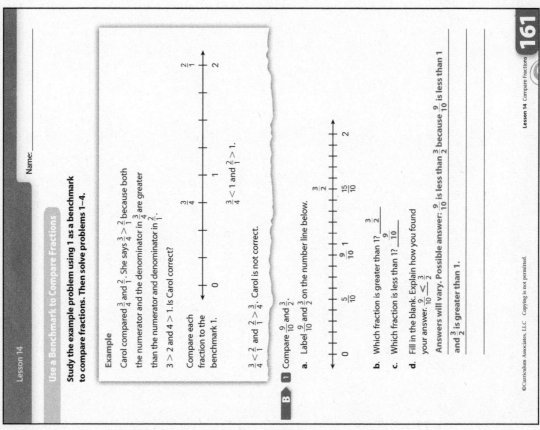
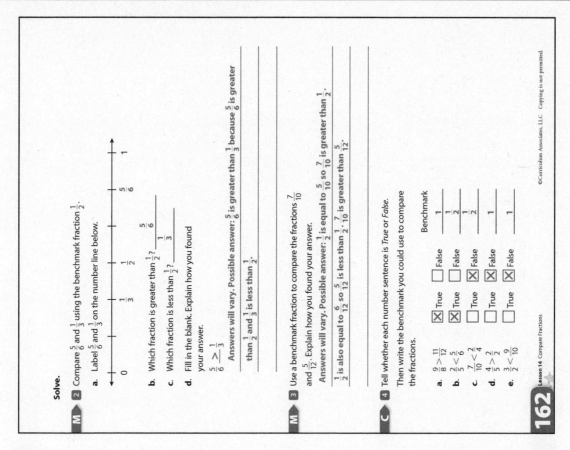

Lesson 14

Compare Fractions

Solve the problems.

B 1 Which of the following is greater than $\frac{2}{3}$?
Circle all that apply.

A $\frac{3}{4}$ **C** $\frac{8}{12}$

B $\frac{5}{6}$ **D** $\frac{3}{2}$

> Find a common denominator for each pair of fractions.

M 2 Harry ate $\frac{5}{8}$ of a sandwich. Sven ate $\frac{2}{5}$ of a sandwich. Micah ate $\frac{3}{4}$ of a sandwich. Gabe ate $\frac{6}{12}$ of a sandwich. Who ate the most of his sandwich?

A Harry   **C** Micah

B Sven   **D** Gabe

> Compare each fraction to the benchmarks $\frac{1}{2}$ and 1.

M 3 Erica and Matt earn the same amount of money each month. Erica saves $\frac{3}{10}$ of her earnings. Matt saves $\frac{3}{6}$ of his earnings. Which explanation correctly tells who saves more?

A Erica saves more because tenths are greater than sixths.

B Matt saves less because sixths are less than tenths.

C Erica saves more because $\frac{3}{10} < \frac{3}{6}$.

D Matt saves more because $\frac{3}{6} > \frac{3}{10}$.

Fran chose **C** as the correct answer. How did she get that answer?

Possible answer: Fran looked at the denominators and saw 10 > 6.

She mistakenly thought that tenths are greater than sixths.

> Can using a benchmark fraction help solve this problem?

Solve.

M 4 Melanie read 45 pages of a 100-page book. Her younger sister read $\frac{1}{2}$ of a 10-page book. Who read a greater fraction of her book, Melanie or her sister?

Show your work.

Melanie read $\frac{45}{100}$ of her book.

Her sister read $\frac{5}{10}$ of her book because $\frac{1}{2} = \frac{5}{10}$.

$\frac{5}{10} = \frac{50}{100}$

$\frac{50}{100} > \frac{45}{100}$

$\frac{5}{10} > \frac{45}{100}$

Solution: Melanie's sister read a greater fraction of her book.

> One fraction has a denominator of 100; the other fraction has a denominator of 10.

C 5 Compare $\frac{5}{4}$ and $\frac{9}{10}$. Describe two methods you could use to compare the fractions.

$\frac{5}{4} > \frac{9}{10}$

Method A   Possible explanation:

I can find a common denominator and then compare the numerators. I use 20 as a common denominator.

$\frac{5}{4} = \frac{25}{20}$ and $\frac{9}{10} = \frac{18}{20}$. $\frac{25}{20} > \frac{18}{20}$, so $\frac{5}{4} > \frac{9}{10}$.

Method B   Possible explanation:

I can compare both fractions to the benchmark 1.

$\frac{5}{4}$ is greater than 1, and $\frac{9}{10}$ is less than 1.

So $\frac{5}{4} > \frac{9}{10}$.

> Some ways to compare fractions are finding a common denominator, finding a common numerator, and using a benchmark.

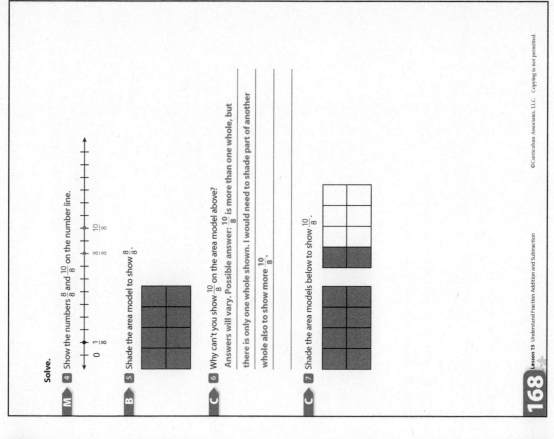

Name: _____

Lesson 15
Understand
Fraction Addition and Subtraction

How do you show fractions with number lines and area models?

Study the example problem showing fractions with number lines and area models. Then solve problems 1–7.

Example

How can you draw two different models to show $\frac{3}{4}$?

An area model for $\frac{3}{4}$ shows 4 equal parts, and 1 part shaded.

A number line model for $\frac{3}{4}$ shows each whole cut into 4 equal parts. $\frac{3}{4}$ is the mark at the end of the third part.

0   $\frac{1}{4}$ $\frac{2}{4}$ $\frac{3}{4}$ 1

M **1** Label the numbers 1 $\frac{3}{8}$, and $\frac{4}{8}$ on the number line.

0   $\frac{1}{8}$ $\frac{3}{8}$ $\frac{4}{8}$ 1

B **2** Shade the area model to show $\frac{3}{8}$.

Answers will vary.
Any 3 sections may be shaded.

B **3** Shade the area model to show $\frac{4}{8}$.

Answers will vary.
Any 4 sections may be shaded.

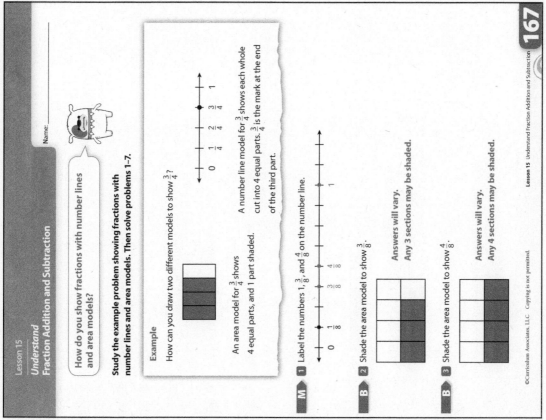

Solve.

M **4** Show the numbers $\frac{8}{8}$ and $\frac{10}{8}$ on the number line.

0   1 $\frac{1}{8}$ $\frac{8}{8}$ $\frac{10}{8}$

B **5** Shade the area model to show $\frac{8}{8}$.

C **6** Why can't you show $\frac{10}{8}$ on the area model above?

Answers will vary. Possible answer: $\frac{10}{8}$ is more than one whole, but there is only one whole shown. I would need to shade part of another whole also to show more $\frac{10}{8}$.

C **7** Shade the area models below to show $\frac{10}{8}$.

Key

B Basic   **M** Medium   **C** Challenge

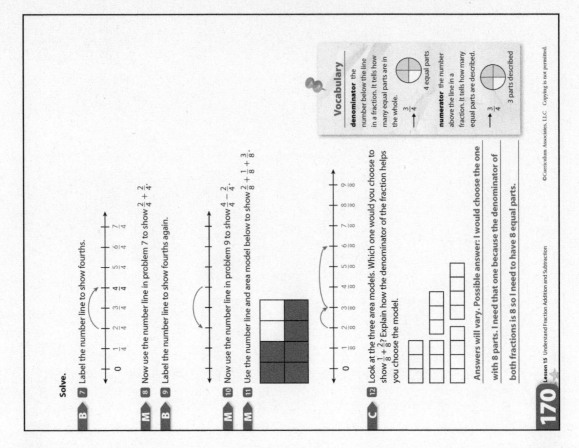

Lesson 15

Name: _____

Show Adding and Subtracting Fractions

Study how the example shows adding fractions.
Then solve problems 1–12.

Example

You can count on or count back to add or subtract whole numbers.
You can do the same to add or subtract fractions.

To add fourths, use a number line that shows fourths.

Add $\frac{3}{4} + \frac{2}{4}$.

0 $\frac{1}{4}$ $\frac{2}{4}$ $\frac{3}{4}$ $\frac{4}{4}$ $\frac{5}{4}$

Start at $\frac{3}{4}$. One more fourth is $\frac{4}{4}$ and another fourth is $\frac{5}{4}$.

$$\frac{3}{4} + \frac{2}{4} = \frac{5}{4}$$

B 1 Count by sixths to fill in the blanks:
$1\frac{2}{6}$, $\frac{3}{6}$, $\frac{4}{6}$, $\frac{5}{6}$, $\frac{6}{6}$, $\frac{7}{6}$, $\frac{8}{6}$, $\frac{9}{6}$, $\frac{10}{6}$

B 2 Now label the number line to show sixths.

0 $\frac{1}{6}$ $\frac{2}{6}$ $\frac{3}{6}$ $\frac{4}{6}$ $\frac{5}{6}$ 1 $\frac{7}{6}$ $\frac{8}{6}$ $\frac{9}{6}$ $\frac{10}{6}$

M 3 What is $\frac{1}{6}$ more than $\frac{2}{6}$? $\frac{3}{6}$

M 4 What is $\frac{1}{6}$ less than $\frac{2}{6}$? $\frac{1}{6}$

M 5 What is $\frac{1}{6}$ more than $\frac{6}{6}$? $\frac{7}{6}$

M 6 What is $\frac{1}{6}$ less than $\frac{6}{6}$? $\frac{5}{6}$

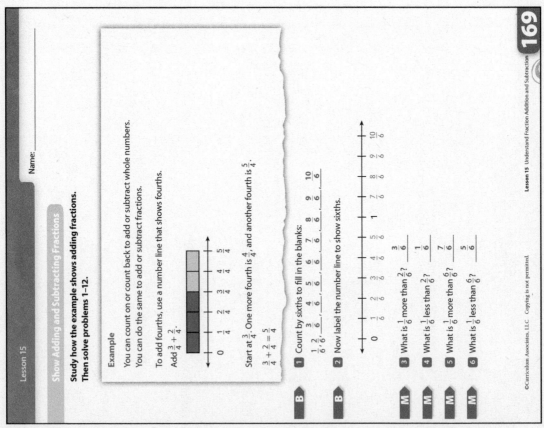

Solve.

B 7 Label the number line to show fourths.

0 $\frac{1}{4}$ $\frac{2}{4}$ $\frac{3}{4}$ $\frac{4}{4}$ $\frac{5}{4}$ $\frac{6}{4}$ $\frac{7}{4}$

M 8 Now use the number line in problem 7 to show $\frac{2}{4} + \frac{2}{4}$.

B 9 Label the number line to show fourths again.

M 10 Now use the number line in problem 9 to show $\frac{4}{4} - \frac{2}{4}$.

M 11 Use the number line and area model below to show $\frac{2}{8} + \frac{1}{8} + \frac{3}{8}$.

0 $\frac{1}{8}$ $\frac{2}{8}$ $\frac{3}{8}$ $\frac{4}{8}$ $\frac{5}{8}$ $\frac{6}{8}$ $\frac{7}{8}$ $\frac{8}{8}$ $\frac{9}{8}$

C 12 Look at the three area models. Which one would you choose to show $\frac{1}{8} + \frac{2}{8}$? Explain how the denominator of the fraction helps you choose the model.

Answers will vary. Possible answer: I would choose the one with 8 parts. I need that one because the denominator of both fractions is 8 so I need to have 8 equal parts.

Vocabulary

denominator the number below the line in a fraction. It tells how many equal parts are in the whole.

$\frac{3}{4}$ → 4 equal parts

numerator the number above the line in a fraction. It tells how many equal parts are described.

$\frac{3}{4}$ → 3 parts described

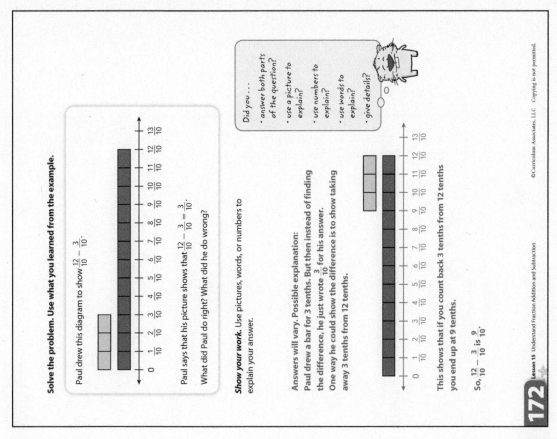

Solve the problem. Use what you learned from the example.

Paul drew this diagram to show $\frac{12}{10} - \frac{3}{10}$.

Paul says that his picture shows that $\frac{12}{10} - \frac{3}{10} = \frac{3}{10}$.

What did Paul do wrong?

Show your work. Use pictures, words, or numbers to explain your answer.

Answers will vary. Possible explanation:
Paul drew a bar for 3 tenths. But then instead of finding the difference, he just wrote $\frac{3}{10}$ for his answer. One way he could show the difference is to show taking away 3 tenths from 12 tenths.

This shows that if you count back 3 tenths from 12 tenths you end up at 9 tenths.

So, $\frac{12}{10} - \frac{3}{10}$ is $\frac{9}{10}$.

Did you . . .
• answer both parts of the question?
• use a picture to explain?
• use numbers to explain?
• use words to explain?
• give details?

172   **Lesson 15** Understand Fraction Addition and Subtraction   ©Curriculum Associates, LLC   Copying is not permitted.

Lesson 15

Name:

Reason and Write

Study the example. Underline two parts that you think make it a particularly good answer and a helpful example.

Answers will vary. Note whether students incorporate the features they chose in their answer on the next page.

Example

Rob drew this diagram to show $\frac{1}{10} + \frac{3}{10} + \frac{4}{10}$.

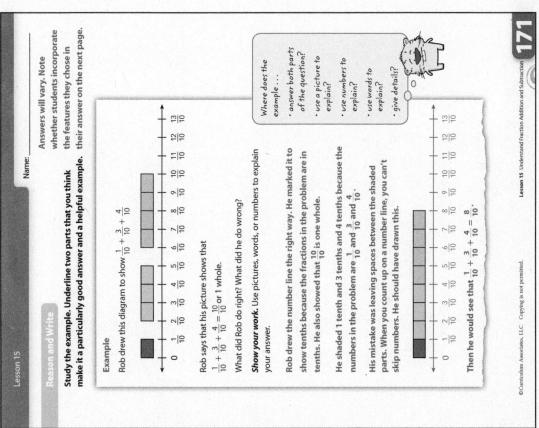

Rob says that his picture shows that
$\frac{1}{10} + \frac{3}{10} + \frac{4}{10} = \frac{10}{10}$ or 1 whole.

What did Rob do right? What did he do wrong?

Show your work. Use pictures, words, or numbers to explain your answer.

Rob drew the number line the right way. He marked it to show tenths because the fractions in the problem are in tenths. He also showed that $\frac{10}{10}$ is one whole.

He shaded 1 tenth and 3 tenths and 4 tenths because the numbers in the problem are $\frac{1}{10}$ and $\frac{3}{10}$ and $\frac{4}{10}$.

His mistake was leaving spaces between the shaded parts. When you count up on a number line, you can't skip numbers. He should have drawn this.

Then he would see that $\frac{1}{10} + \frac{3}{10} + \frac{4}{10} = \frac{8}{10}$.

Where does the example . . .
• answer both parts of the question?
• use a picture to explain?
• use numbers to explain?
• use words to explain?
• give details?

171

©Curriculum Associates, LLC   Copying is not permitted.   **Lesson 15** Understand Fraction Addition and Subtraction

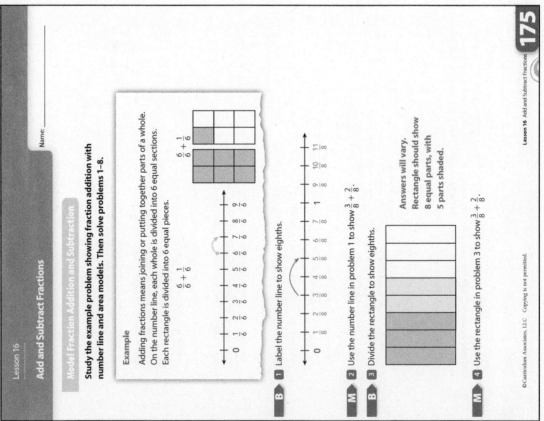

Lesson 16

Add and Subtract Fractions

Name: _____

Model Fraction Addition and Subtraction

Study the example problem showing fraction addition with number line and area models. Then solve problems 1–8.

Example

Adding fractions means joining or putting together parts of a whole. On the number line, each whole is divided into 6 equal sections. Each rectangle is divided into 6 equal pieces.

$$\frac{6}{6} + \frac{1}{6}$$

$0 \quad \frac{1}{6} \quad \frac{2}{6} \quad \frac{3}{6} \quad \frac{4}{6} \quad \frac{5}{6} \quad \frac{6}{6} \quad \frac{7}{6} \quad \frac{8}{6} \quad \frac{9}{6}$

$$\frac{6}{6} + \frac{1}{6}$$

B 1 Label the number line to show eighths.

$0 \quad \frac{1}{8} \quad \frac{2}{8} \quad \frac{3}{8} \quad \frac{4}{8} \quad \frac{5}{8} \quad \frac{6}{8} \quad \frac{7}{8} \quad 1 \quad \frac{9}{8} \quad \frac{10}{8} \quad \frac{11}{8}$

M 2 Use the number line in problem 1 to show $\frac{3}{8} + \frac{2}{8}$.

B 3 Divide the rectangle to show eighths.

Answers will vary.
Rectangle should show
8 equal parts, with
5 parts shaded.

M 4 Use the rectangle in problem 3 to show $\frac{3}{8} + \frac{2}{8}$.

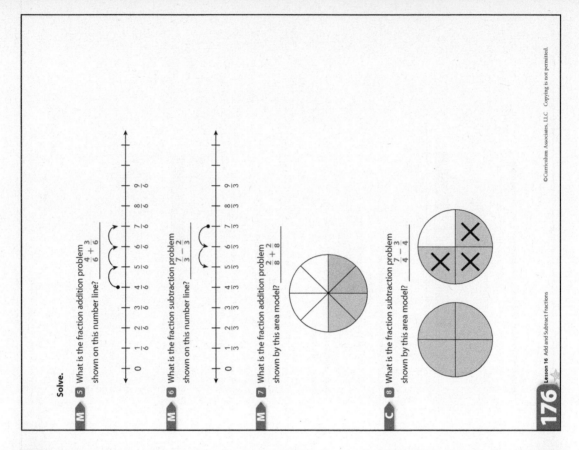

Solve.

M 5 What is the fraction addition problem shown on this number line?

$0 \quad \frac{1}{6} \quad \frac{2}{6} \quad \frac{3}{6} \quad \frac{4}{6} \quad \frac{5}{6} \quad \frac{6}{6} \quad \frac{7}{6} \quad \frac{8}{6} \quad \frac{9}{6}$

$$\frac{4}{6} + \frac{3}{6}$$

M 6 What is the fraction subtraction problem shown on this number line?

$0 \quad \frac{1}{3} \quad \frac{2}{3} \quad \frac{3}{3} \quad \frac{4}{3} \quad \frac{5}{3} \quad \frac{6}{3} \quad \frac{7}{3} \quad \frac{8}{3} \quad \frac{9}{3}$

$$\frac{7}{3} - \frac{2}{3}$$

M 7 What is the fraction addition problem shown by this area model?

$$\frac{2}{8} + \frac{2}{8}$$

C 8 What is the fraction subtraction problem shown by this area model?

$$\frac{7}{4} - \frac{3}{4}$$

Key

| **B** Basic | **M** Medium | **C** Challenge |

Lesson 16

Name: _____

Add Fractions

Study the example problem showing one way to add fractions. Then solve problems 1–13.

Example

Shrina has a muffin tray that holds 12 muffins. She fills $\frac{3}{12}$ of the tray with apple muffin batter. Then she fills $\frac{6}{12}$ with pumpkin muffin batter. What fraction of the tray is filled?

$$\frac{3}{12} + \frac{6}{12} = \frac{9}{12}$$

So, $\frac{9}{12}$ of the muffin tray is filled.

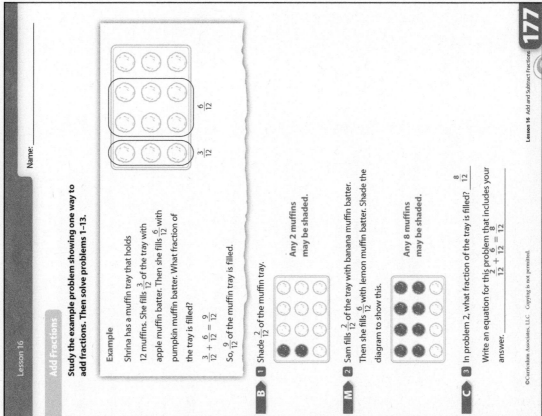

$\frac{3}{12}$ $\frac{6}{12}$

B **1** Shade $\frac{2}{12}$ of the muffin tray.

Any 2 muffins may be shaded.

M **2** Sam fills $\frac{2}{12}$ of the tray with banana muffin batter. Then she fills $\frac{6}{12}$ with lemon muffin batter. Shade the diagram to show this.

Any 8 muffins may be shaded.

C **3** In problem 2, what fraction of the tray is filled? $\frac{8}{12}$

Write an equation for this problem that includes your answer. $\frac{2}{12} + \frac{6}{12} = \frac{8}{12}$

Lesson 16 Add and Subtract Fractions   **177**

Solve.

Kay ran $\frac{6}{8}$ mile and rested. Then she ran another $\frac{6}{8}$ mile.

B **4** Divide the number line below to show eighths.

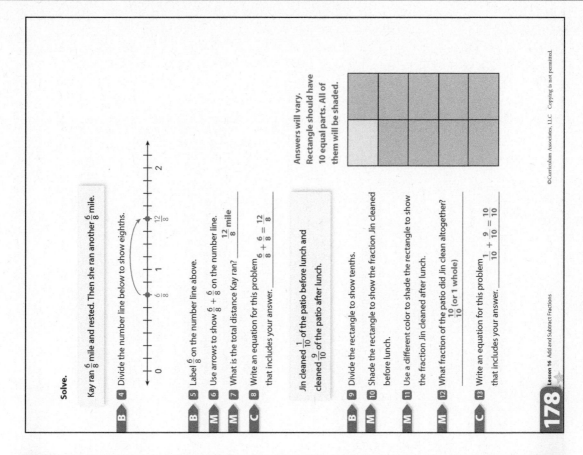

$\frac{6}{8}$ $\frac{12}{8}$

0   1   2

B **5** Label $\frac{6}{8}$ on the number line above.

M **6** Use arrows to show $\frac{6}{8} + \frac{6}{8}$ on the number line.

M **7** What is the total distance Kay ran? $\frac{12}{8}$ mile

C **8** Write an equation for this problem that includes your answer. $\frac{6}{8} + \frac{6}{8} = \frac{12}{8}$

Jin cleaned $\frac{1}{10}$ of the patio before lunch and cleaned $\frac{9}{10}$ of the patio after lunch.

B **9** Divide the rectangle to show tenths.

M **10** Shade the rectangle to show the fraction Jin cleaned before lunch.

M **11** Use a different color to shade the rectangle to show the fraction Jin cleaned after lunch.

M **12** What fraction of the patio did Jin clean altogether? $\frac{10}{10}$ (or 1 whole)

C **13** Write an equation for this problem that includes your answer. $\frac{1}{10} + \frac{9}{10} = \frac{10}{10}$

Answers will vary. Rectangle should have 10 equal parts. All of them will be shaded.

178   **Lesson 16** Add and Subtract Fractions

Lesson 16

Subtract Fractions

Study the example showing one way to subtract fractions. Then solve problems 1–7.

Example

Ali bought a carton of eggs. He used $\frac{3}{12}$ of the eggs to cook breakfast. He used another $\frac{2}{12}$ to make a dessert for dinner. What fraction of the carton is left?

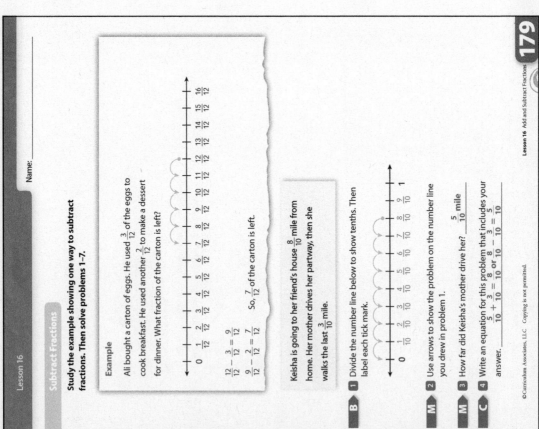

$$\frac{12}{12} - \frac{3}{12} = \frac{9}{12}$$
$$\frac{9}{12} - \frac{2}{12} = \frac{7}{12} \qquad \text{So, } \frac{7}{12} \text{ of the carton is left.}$$

Keisha is going to her friend's house $\frac{8}{10}$ mile from home. Her mother drives her partway, then she walks the last $\frac{3}{10}$ mile.

B 1 Divide the number line below to show tenths. Then label each tick mark.

M 2 Use arrows to show the problem on the number line you drew in problem 1.

M 3 How far did Keisha's mother drive her? $\frac{5}{10}$ mile

C 4 Write an equation for this problem that includes your answer. $\frac{5}{10} + \frac{3}{10} = \frac{8}{10}$ or $\frac{8}{10} - \frac{3}{10} = \frac{5}{10}$

Solve.

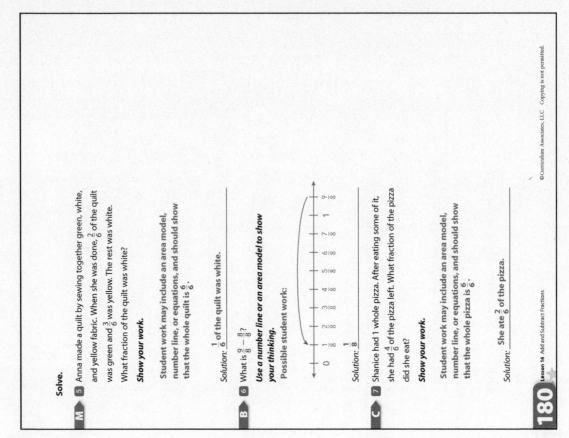

M 5 Anna made a quilt by sewing together green, white, and yellow fabric. When she was done, $\frac{2}{6}$ of the quilt was green and $\frac{3}{6}$ was yellow. The rest was white. What fraction of the quilt was white?

Show your work.

Student work may include an area model, number line, or equations, and should show that the whole quilt is $\frac{6}{6}$.

Solution: $\frac{1}{6}$ of the quilt was white.

B 6 What is $\frac{9}{8} - \frac{8}{8}$?

Use a number line or an area model to show your thinking.

Possible student work:

Solution: $\frac{1}{8}$

C 7 Shanice had 1 whole pizza. After eating some of it, she had $\frac{4}{6}$ of the pizza left. What fraction of the pizza did she eat?

Show your work.

Student work may include an area model, number line, or equations, and should show that the whole pizza is $\frac{6}{6}$.

Solution: _She ate $\frac{2}{6}$ of the pizza._

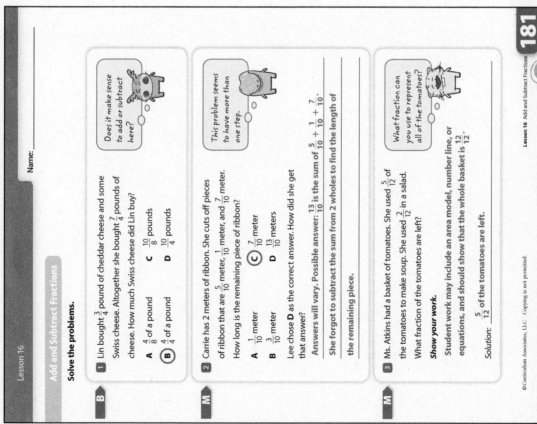

Lesson 16

Add and Subtract Fractions

Name: _____

Solve the problems.

1 Lin bought $\frac{3}{4}$ pound of cheddar cheese and some Swiss cheese. Altogether she bought $\frac{7}{4}$ pounds of cheese. How much Swiss cheese did Lin buy?

A $\frac{4}{8}$ of a pound   C $\frac{10}{8}$ pounds

(B) $\frac{4}{4}$ of a pound   D $\frac{10}{4}$ pounds

Does it make sense to add or subtract here?

2 Carrie has 2 meters of ribbon. She cuts off pieces of ribbon that are $\frac{5}{10}$ meter, $\frac{1}{10}$ meter, and $\frac{7}{10}$ meter. How long is the remaining piece of ribbon?

A $\frac{1}{10}$ meter   (C) $\frac{7}{10}$ meter

B $\frac{3}{10}$ meter   D $\frac{13}{10}$ meters

This problem seems to have more than one step.

Lee chose **D** as the correct answer. How did she get that answer?

Answers will vary. Possible answer: $\frac{13}{10}$ is the sum of $\frac{5}{10} + \frac{1}{10} + \frac{7}{10}$.

She forgot to subtract the sum from 2 wholes to find the length of the remaining piece.

3 Ms. Atkins had a basket of tomatoes. She used $\frac{5}{12}$ of the tomatoes to make soup. She used $\frac{2}{12}$ in a salad. What fraction of the tomatoes are left?

What fraction can you use to represent all of the tomatoes?

Show your work.

Student work may include an area model, number line, or equations, and should show that the whole basket is $\frac{12}{12}$.

Solution: $\frac{5}{12}$ of the tomatoes are left.

Lesson 16 Add and Subtract Fractions   **181**

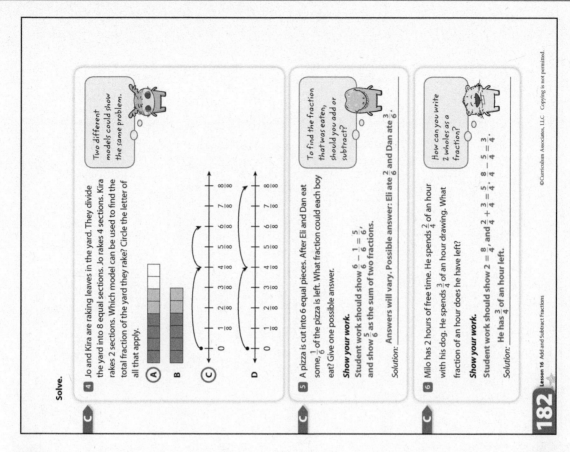

Solve.

4 Jo and Kira are raking leaves in the yard. They divide the yard into 8 equal sections. Jo rakes 4 sections. Kira rakes 2 sections. Which model can be used to find the total fraction of the yard they rake? Circle the letter of all that apply.

Two different models could show the same problem.

(A)   B   (C)   D

5 A pizza is cut into 6 equal pieces. After Eli and Dan eat some, $\frac{1}{6}$ of the pizza is left. What fraction could each boy eat? Give one possible answer.

To find the fraction that was eaten, should you add or subtract?

Show your work.

Student work should show $\frac{6}{6} - \frac{1}{6} = \frac{5}{6}$, and show $\frac{5}{6}$ as the sum of two fractions.

Solution: ___ Answers will vary. Possible answer: Eli ate $\frac{2}{6}$ and Dan ate $\frac{3}{6}$.

6 Milo has 2 hours of free time. He spends $\frac{2}{4}$ of an hour with his dog. He spends $\frac{3}{4}$ of an hour drawing. What fraction of an hour does he have left?

How can you write 2 wholes as a fraction?

Show your work.

Student work should show $2 = \frac{8}{4}$, and $\frac{2}{4} + \frac{3}{4} = \frac{5}{4}$, $\frac{8}{4} - \frac{5}{4} = \frac{3}{4}$.

Solution: ___ He has $\frac{3}{4}$ of an hour left.

182   Lesson 16 Add and Subtract Fractions

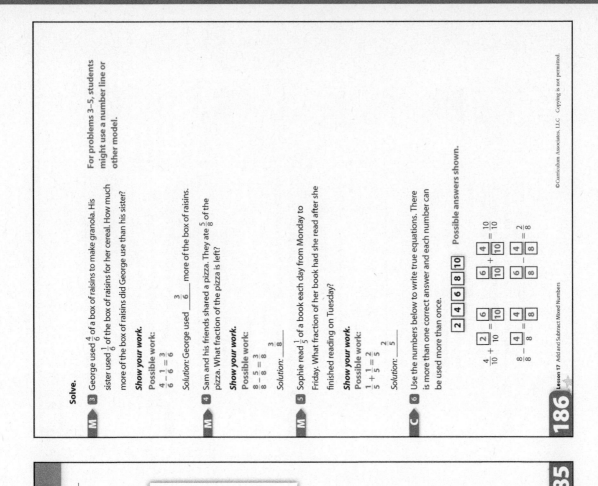

Name: _____

Lesson 17

Add and Subtract Mixed Numbers

Add and Subtract Fractions

Study the example problem showing a way to add fractions. Then solve problems 1–5.

Example
Darcy used $\frac{5}{8}$ of a carton of strawberries to make a cake. She used another $\frac{2}{8}$ of a carton of strawberries to decorate the cake. What fraction of a carton of strawberries did Darcy use in all?

$$\frac{5}{8} + \frac{2}{8} = \frac{7}{8}$$

Darcy used $\frac{7}{8}$ of a carton of strawberries.

Jeremy biked $\frac{3}{10}$ of a mile to a friend's house. Then he biked $\frac{5}{10}$ of a mile to school.

B 1 Draw jumps on the number line to show $\frac{3}{10} + \frac{5}{10}$.

B 2 Fill in the boxes to write an equation that shows how far Jeremy biked.

$$\frac{\boxed{3}}{10} + \frac{\boxed{5}}{10} = \frac{\boxed{8}}{10}$$

Solve.

For problems 3–5, students might use a number line or other model.

M 3 George used $\frac{4}{6}$ of a box of raisins to make granola. His sister used $\frac{1}{6}$ of the box of raisins for her cereal. How much more of the box of raisins did George use than his sister?

Show your work.
Possible work:
$$\frac{4}{6} - \frac{1}{6} = \frac{3}{6}$$

Solution: George used $\frac{3}{6}$ more of the box of raisins.

M 4 Sam and his friends shared a pizza. They ate $\frac{5}{8}$ of the pizza. What fraction of the pizza is left?

Show your work.
Possible work:
$$\frac{8}{8} - \frac{5}{8} = \frac{3}{8}$$

Solution: $\frac{3}{8}$

M 5 Sophie read $\frac{1}{5}$ of a book each day from Monday to Friday. What fraction of her book had she read after she finished reading on Tuesday?

Show your work.
Possible work:
$$\frac{1}{5} + \frac{1}{5} = \frac{2}{5}$$

Solution: $\frac{2}{5}$

C 6 Use the numbers below to write true equations. There is more than one correct answer and each number can be used more than once.

$\boxed{2}\ \boxed{4}\ \boxed{6}\ \boxed{8}\ \boxed{10}$ Possible answers shown.

$$\frac{4}{10} + \frac{\boxed{2}}{10} = \frac{\boxed{6}}{10} \qquad \frac{\boxed{6}}{10} + \frac{\boxed{4}}{10} = \frac{\boxed{10}}{10}$$

$$\frac{8}{8} - \frac{\boxed{4}}{8} = \frac{\boxed{4}}{8} \qquad \frac{\boxed{6}}{8} - \frac{\boxed{4}}{8} = \frac{\boxed{2}}{8}$$

Lesson 17 Add and Subtract Mixed Numbers **186**

Key
B Basic   **M** Medium   **C** Challenge

Lesson 17

Add Mixed Numbers

Study the example problem showing a way to add mixed numbers. Then solve problems 1–6.

Name: _____

Example

Aaron used $2\frac{1}{4}$ cups of flour to make muffins and another $1\frac{3}{4}$ cups of flour to make pancakes. How many cups of flour did he use altogether?

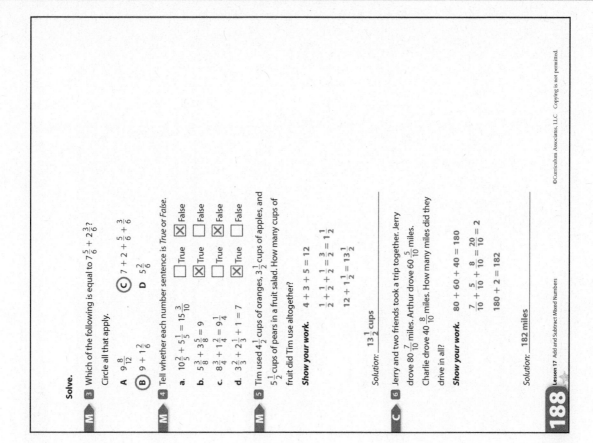

Find $2\frac{1}{4} + 1\frac{3}{4}$.

Add the whole numbers. $2 + 1 = 3$

Add the fractions. $\frac{1}{4} + \frac{3}{4} = 1$

Add both sums. $3 + 1 = 4$

Aaron used 4 cups of flour.

B **1** Marissa used $3\frac{1}{3}$ cups of oats to make oatmeal and $2\frac{1}{3}$ cups of oats to make snack bars. How many cups of oats did Marissa use in all?

   a. Add the whole numbers. $3 + 2 = 5$

   b. Add the fractions. $\frac{1}{3} + \frac{1}{3} = \frac{2}{3}$

   c. Add both sums. $5 + \frac{2}{3} = 5\frac{2}{3}$

   Marissa used $5\frac{2}{3}$ cups of oats.

M **2** Draw and label a number line to show $1\frac{1}{4} + 2\frac{2}{4}$.

Possible student work shown.

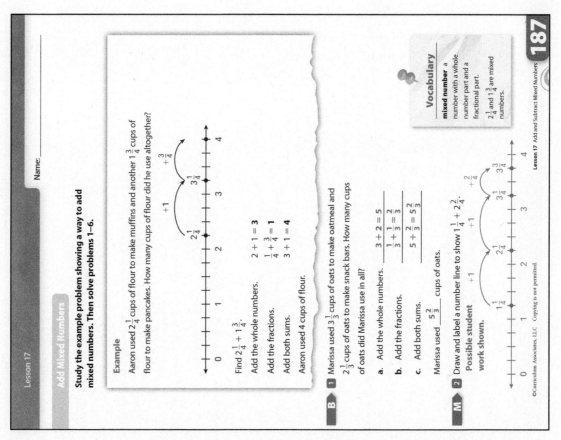

Vocabulary

mixed number a number with a whole number part and a fractional part.

$2\frac{1}{4}$ and $1\frac{3}{4}$ are mixed numbers.

Lesson 17   Add and Subtract Mixed Numbers   **187**

Solve.

M **3** Which of the following is equal to $7\frac{5}{6} + 2\frac{3}{6}$? Circle all that apply.

   A $9\frac{8}{12}$ **C** $7 + 2 + \frac{5}{6} + \frac{3}{6}$

   B $9 + 1\frac{2}{6}$ **D** $5\frac{2}{6}$

(B and C are circled)

M **4** Tell whether each number sentence is *True* or *False*.

   a. $10\frac{2}{5} + 5\frac{1}{5} = 15\frac{3}{10}$ ☐ True   ☒ False

   b. $5\frac{3}{8} + 3\frac{5}{8} = 9$ ☒ True   ☐ False

   c. $8\frac{3}{4} + 1\frac{2}{4} = 9\frac{1}{4}$ ☐ True   ☒ False

   d. $3\frac{2}{3} + 2\frac{1}{3} + 1 = 7$ ☒ True   ☐ False

M **5** Tim used $4\frac{1}{2}$ cups of oranges, $3\frac{1}{2}$ cups of apples, and $5\frac{1}{2}$ cups of pears in a fruit salad. How many cups of fruit did Tim use altogether?

Show your work. $4 + 3 + 5 = 12$

$$\frac{1}{2} + \frac{1}{2} + \frac{1}{2} = \frac{3}{2} = 1\frac{1}{2}$$

$$12 + 1\frac{1}{2} = 13\frac{1}{2}$$

Solution: $13\frac{1}{2}$ cups

C **6** Jerry and two friends took a trip together. Jerry drove $80\frac{7}{10}$ miles. Arthur drove $60\frac{5}{10}$ miles. Charlie drove $40\frac{8}{10}$ miles. How many miles did they drive in all?

Show your work. $80 + 60 + 40 = 180$

$$\frac{7}{10} + \frac{5}{10} + \frac{8}{10} = \frac{20}{10} = 2$$

$$180 + 2 = 182$$

Solution: 182 miles

Lesson 17   Add and Subtract Mixed Numbers

188

Name: _____

Lesson 17

Subtract Mixed Numbers

Study the example problem showing a way to subtract mixed numbers. Then solve problems 1–5.

Example

On a holiday, Sara's family drove $3\frac{1}{4}$ hours to her cousin's house. The drive usually takes $2\frac{2}{4}$ hours. How much longer did the drive take on the holiday?

Find $3\frac{1}{4} - 2\frac{2}{4}$.

$3\frac{1}{4} - 2\frac{2}{4} = \frac{3}{4}$

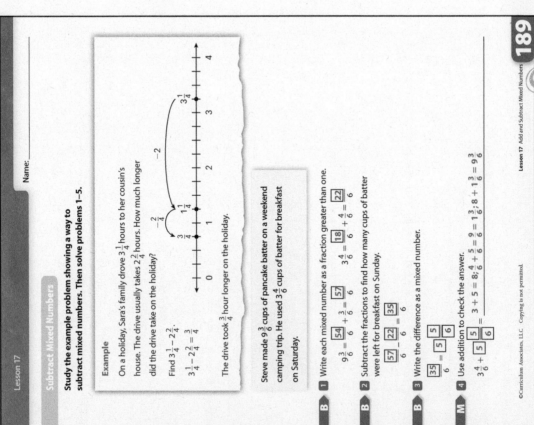

The drive took $\frac{3}{4}$ hour longer on the holiday.

Steve made $9\frac{3}{6}$ cups of pancake batter on a weekend camping trip. He used $3\frac{4}{6}$ cups of batter for breakfast on Saturday.

B **1** Write each mixed number as a fraction greater than one.

$9\frac{3}{6} = \boxed{\frac{54}{6}} + 3 = \boxed{\frac{57}{6}}$ $3\frac{4}{6} = \boxed{\frac{18}{6}} + \frac{4}{6} = \boxed{\frac{22}{6}}$

B **2** Subtract the fractions to find how many cups of batter were left for breakfast on Sunday.

$\boxed{\frac{57}{6}} - \boxed{\frac{22}{6}} = \boxed{\frac{35}{6}}$

B **3** Write the difference as a mixed number.

$\boxed{\frac{35}{6}} = \boxed{5}\dfrac{\boxed{5}}{\boxed{6}}$

M **4** Use addition to check the answer.

$3\frac{4}{6} + \boxed{5}\dfrac{\boxed{5}}{\boxed{6}} =$ ___ ; $3 + 5 = 8$; $\frac{4}{6} + \frac{5}{6} = \frac{9}{6} = 1\frac{3}{6}$; $8 + 1\frac{3}{6} = 9\frac{3}{6}$

Solve.

M **5** Which of the following has the same value as $7\frac{5}{6} - 2\frac{3}{6}$? Circle all that apply.

A $10\frac{2}{6}$

B $\frac{47}{6} - \frac{15}{6}$

C $(7-2) + \left(\frac{5}{6} - \frac{3}{6}\right)$

D $5\frac{2}{6}$

M **6** Helen bought 5 pounds of oranges. She sliced $2\frac{3}{10}$ pounds of oranges to bring to a party. How many pounds of oranges does Helen have left?

Show your work.

Possible work:

$5 - 2\frac{3}{10} = \frac{50}{10} - \frac{23}{10} = \frac{27}{10} = 2\frac{7}{10}$

Solution: $2\frac{7}{10}$ pounds

C **7** Kira reasoned that $6\frac{1}{4} - 2\frac{3}{4} = 4\frac{2}{4}$ because the difference between 6 and 2 is 4 and the difference between $\frac{1}{4}$ and $\frac{3}{4}$ is $\frac{2}{4}$. Is Kira's reasoning correct? Explain why or why not.

No. Possible explanation: Kira subtracted the fraction part of the mixed numbers incorrectly: $\frac{1}{4} - \frac{3}{4}$ does not equal $\frac{2}{4}$. To subtract mixed numbers, rewrite each mixed number as a fraction. So, $6\frac{1}{4} = \frac{25}{4}$, and $2\frac{3}{4} = \frac{11}{4}$. Then subtract the fractions. $\frac{25}{4} - \frac{11}{4} = \frac{14}{4}$. Rewrite the fraction as a mixed number: $\frac{14}{4} = 3\frac{2}{4}$.

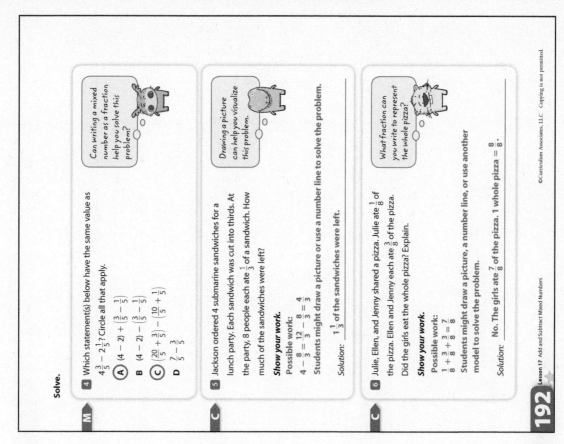

Lesson 17

Name: _____

Add and Subtract Mixed Numbers

Solve the problems.

B **1** Alexandra ran $2\frac{4}{5}$ miles last weekend. This weekend she ran $3\frac{1}{5}$ miles. How many miles did she run in all?

A $1\frac{3}{5}$ miles   C $5\frac{3}{5}$ miles

B $5\frac{5}{10}$ miles   **(D)** 6 miles

Do you move left or right on a number line to solve this problem?

M **2** Madelyn bought $12\frac{5}{8}$ yards of fabric. She used $6\frac{7}{8}$ yards of the fabric for a costume. How much fabric did Madelyn have left?

A $5\frac{2}{8}$ yards   C $6\frac{2}{8}$ yards

(B) $5\frac{6}{8}$ yards   D $19\frac{4}{8}$ yards

Cory chose **C** as the correct answer. How did he get that answer?

How can you use addition to check the answer?

Possible answer: Cory found the difference between the whole numbers

and added that to the difference between the fractions.

M **3** Look at Mina's work below.

$$10\frac{7}{12} - 9\frac{9}{12} = \left(\frac{10}{12} + \frac{7}{12}\right) - \frac{9}{12}$$
$$= \frac{17}{12} - \frac{9}{12}$$
$$= \frac{8}{12}$$

Is Mina's solution reasonable? Explain.

No. Possible explanation: I can estimate the difference. $10\frac{7}{12}$ is close to 11

and $\frac{9}{12}$ is close to 1, so $11 - 1 = 10$. A reasonable solution would be about

10. $\frac{8}{12}$ is much less than 10, so it is not a reasonable solution.

You can estimate to find out whether a solution is reasonable.

©Curriculum Associates, LLC   Copying is not permitted.   **Lesson 17** Add and Subtract Mixed Numbers   **191**

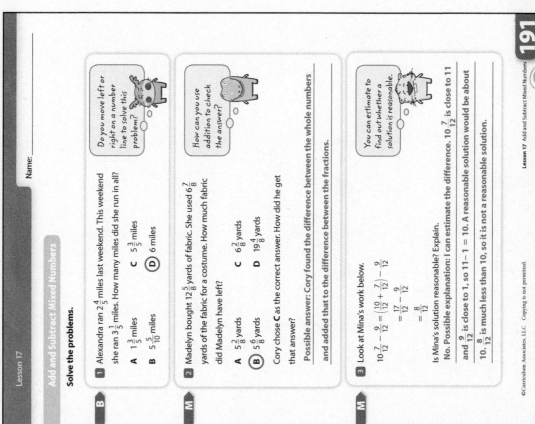

Solve.

M **4** Which statement(s) below have the same value as $4\frac{3}{5} - 2\frac{1}{5}$? Circle all that apply.

(A) $(4-2) + \left(\frac{3}{5} - \frac{1}{5}\right)$

B $(4-2) - \left(\frac{3}{5} - \frac{1}{5}\right)$

(C) $\left(\frac{20}{5} + \frac{3}{5}\right) - \left(\frac{10}{5} + \frac{1}{5}\right)$

D $\frac{7}{5} - \frac{3}{5}$

Can writing a mixed number as a fraction help you solve this problem?

C **5** Jackson ordered 4 submarine sandwiches for a lunch party. Each sandwich was cut into thirds. At the party, 8 people each ate $\frac{1}{3}$ of a sandwich. How much of the sandwiches were left?

Drawing a picture can help you visualize this problem.

Show your work.

Possible work:

$4 = \frac{8}{3} = \frac{12}{3}$ $\frac{8}{3} = \frac{4}{3}$

$4 - \frac{8}{3} = \frac{12}{3} - \frac{8}{3} = \frac{4}{3}$

Students might draw a picture or use a number line to solve the problem.

Solution: $1\frac{1}{3}$ of the sandwiches were left.

C **6** Julie, Ellen, and Jenny shared a pizza. Julie ate $\frac{1}{8}$ of the pizza. Ellen and Jenny each ate $\frac{3}{8}$ of the pizza. Did the girls eat the whole pizza? Explain.

What fraction can you write to represent the whole pizza?

Show your work.

Possible work:

$\frac{1}{8} + \frac{3}{8} + \frac{3}{8} = \frac{7}{8}$

Students might draw a picture, a number line, or use another model to solve the problem.

Solution: No. The girls ate $\frac{7}{8}$ of the pizza. 1 whole pizza $= \frac{8}{8}$.

192 **Lesson 17** Add and Subtract Mixed Numbers   ©Curriculum Associates, LLC   Copying is not permitted.

Lesson 18

Understand
Fraction Multiplication

Name: _____

> **What does it mean to multiply numbers?**

Study the example shows ways to describe multiplication. Then solve problems 1–8.

Example

Use words and models to show 5 × 3 = 15.

5 groups of 3 is 15.

3

3	3	3	3	3
15 is 5 times as many as 3.
⎵ 15

B **1** Complete the sentences to describe the multiplication that the picture shows.

Words: 6 groups of 4 is 24 .

Equation: 6 × 4 = 24

B **2** Use the bar model at the right to complete the sentences.

6

6	6	6	6
⎵ 24

Words: 24 is 4 times as many as 6 .

Equation: 4 × 6 = 24

M **3** How is 6 × 4 related to 4 × 6? They are equal. 6 × 4 = 24 and 4 × 6 = 24.

Solve.

M **4** Complete the sentences to describe the multiplication that the array shows.

 5 rows of 8 is 40 .

 5 × 8 = 40

M **5** Draw and label a bar model to show 5 × 9.

9

9	9	9	9	9
⎵ 45

M **6** Nick read 7 books last month. He read twice as many books this month. Draw a bar model that represents the number of books Nick read this month.

7

7	7
⎵ 14

M **7** Look at problem 6. Write the multiplication equation that the bar model describes.

 2 × 7 = 14

C **8** Write a word problem that could be modeled by the equation 3 × 6 = 18.

Answers will vary. Possible answer: Anna rode her bike 6 miles. Jordan rode his bike three times as far as Anna. How many miles did Jordan ride his bike?

Key

B Basic	**M** Medium	**C** Challenge

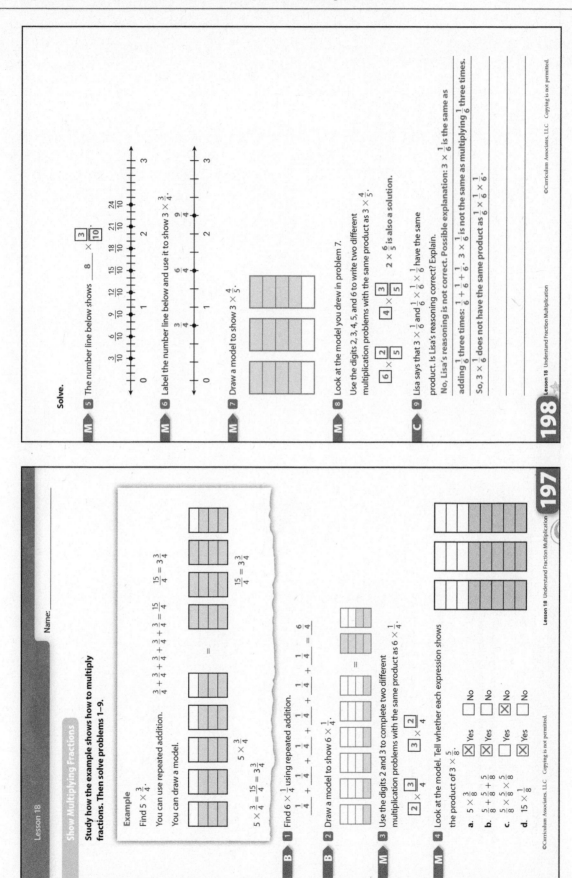

Lesson 18

Name: _____

Show Multiplying Fractions

Study how the example shows how to multiply fractions. Then solve problems 1–9.

Example

Find $5 \times \frac{3}{4}$.

You can use repeated addition. $\frac{3}{4} + \frac{3}{4} + \frac{3}{4} + \frac{3}{4} + \frac{3}{4} = \frac{15}{4} = 3\frac{3}{4}$

You can draw a model.

$5 \times \frac{3}{4}$

$5 \times \frac{3}{4} = \frac{15}{4} = 3\frac{3}{4}$

B 1 Find $6 \times \frac{1}{4}$ using repeated addition.

$\frac{1}{4} + \frac{1}{4} + \frac{1}{4} + \frac{1}{4} + \frac{1}{4} + \frac{1}{4} = \frac{6}{4}$

B 2 Draw a model to show $6 \times \frac{1}{4}$.

M 3 Use the digits 2 and 3 to complete two different multiplication problems with the same product as $6 \times \frac{1}{4}$.

$\boxed{2} \times \frac{\boxed{3}}{4}$ $\boxed{3} \times \frac{\boxed{2}}{4}$

M 4 Look at the model. Tell whether each expression shows the product of $3 \times \frac{5}{8}$.

a. 5×3 ☒ Yes ☐ No
b. $\frac{5}{8} + \frac{5}{8} + \frac{5}{8}$ ☒ Yes ☐ No
c. $\frac{5}{8} \times \frac{5}{8}$ ☐ Yes ☒ No
d. $15 \times \frac{1}{8}$ ☒ Yes ☐ No

Lesson 18 Understand Fraction Multiplication **197**

Solve.

M 5 The number line below shows $\boxed{8} \times \frac{\boxed{3}}{\boxed{10}}$.

$\frac{3}{10}$ $\frac{6}{10}$ $\frac{9}{10}$ $\frac{12}{10}$ $\frac{15}{10}$ $\frac{18}{10}$ $\frac{21}{10}$ $\frac{24}{10}$
0   1   2   3

M 6 Label the number line below and use it to show $3 \times \frac{3}{4}$.

$\frac{3}{4}$ $\frac{6}{4}$ $\frac{9}{4}$
0   1   2   3

M 7 Draw a model to show $3 \times \frac{4}{5}$.

M 8 Look at the model you drew in problem 7.
Use the digits 2, 3, 4, 5, and 6 to write two different multiplication problems with the same product as $3 \times \frac{4}{5}$.

$\boxed{6} \times \frac{\boxed{2}}{\boxed{5}}$ $\boxed{4} \times \frac{\boxed{3}}{\boxed{5}}$

$2 \times \frac{6}{5}$ is also a solution.

C 9 Lisa says that $3 \times \frac{1}{6}$ and $\frac{1}{6} \times \frac{1}{6} \times \frac{1}{6}$ have the same product. Is Lisa's reasoning correct? Explain.

No, Lisa's reasoning is not correct. Possible explanation: $3 \times \frac{1}{6}$ is the same as adding $\frac{1}{6}$ three times: $\frac{1}{6} + \frac{1}{6} + \frac{1}{6}$. $3 \times \frac{1}{6}$ is not the same as multiplying $\frac{1}{6}$ three times. So, $3 \times \frac{1}{6}$ does not have the same product as $\frac{1}{6} \times \frac{1}{6} \times \frac{1}{6}$.

198 Lesson 18 Understand Fraction Multiplication

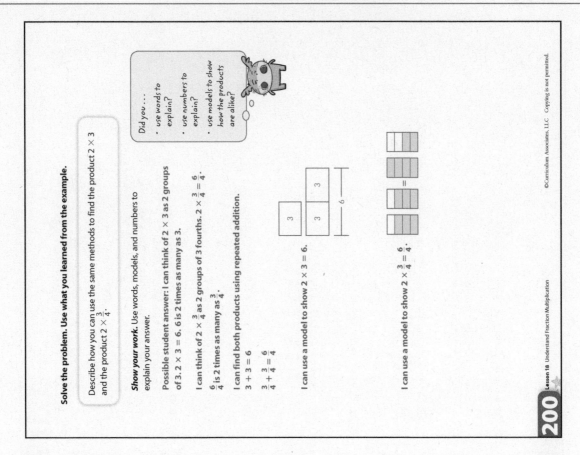

Solve the problem. *Use what you learned from the example.*

Describe how you can use the same methods to find the product 2×3 and the product $2 \times \frac{3}{4}$.

Show your work. Use words, models, and numbers to explain your answer.

Possible student answer: I can think of 2×3 as 2 groups of 3. $2 \times 3 = 6$. 6 is 2 times as many as 3.

I can think of $2 \times \frac{3}{4}$ as 2 groups of 3 fourths. $2 \times \frac{3}{4} = \frac{6}{4}$.
$\frac{6}{4}$ is 2 times as many as $\frac{3}{4}$.

I can find both products using repeated addition.

$3 + 3 = 6$

$\frac{3}{4} + \frac{3}{4} = \frac{6}{4}$

I can use a model to show $2 \times 3 = 6$.

I can use a model to show $2 \times \frac{3}{4} = \frac{6}{4}$.

Did you . . .
• use words to explain?
• use numbers to explain?
• use models to show how the products are alike?

Lesson 18 Understand Fraction Multiplication **200**

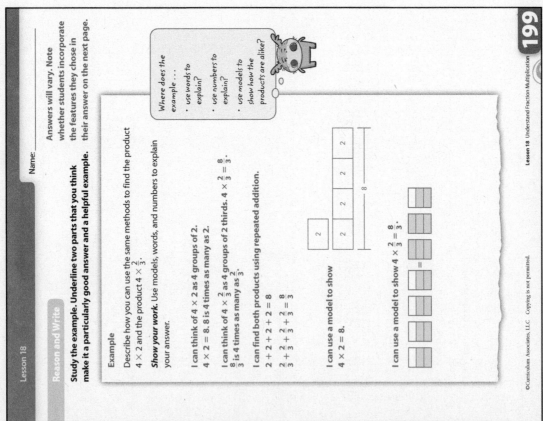

Lesson 18

Name: _____

Reason and Write

Study the example. Underline two parts that you think make it a particularly good answer and a helpful example.

Answers will vary. Note whether students incorporate the features they chose in their answer on the next page.

Example

Describe how you can use the same methods to find the product 4×2 and the product $4 \times \frac{2}{3}$.

Show your work. Use models, words, and numbers to explain your answer.

I can think of 4×2 as 4 groups of 2.
$4 \times 2 = 8$. 8 is 4 times as many as 2.

I can think of $4 \times \frac{2}{3}$ as 4 groups of 2 thirds. $4 \times \frac{2}{3} = \frac{8}{3}$.
$\frac{8}{3}$ is 4 times as many as $\frac{2}{3}$.

I can find both products using repeated addition.

$2 + 2 + 2 + 2 = 8$

$\frac{2}{3} + \frac{2}{3} + \frac{2}{3} + \frac{2}{3} = \frac{8}{3}$

I can use a model to show
$4 \times 2 = 8$.

I can use a model to show $4 \times \frac{2}{3} = \frac{8}{3}$.

Where does the example . . .
• use words to explain?
• use numbers to explain?
• use models to show how the products are alike?

Lesson 18 Understand Fraction Multiplication **199**

Lesson 19

Multiply Fractions

Model Fraction Multiplication

Study the example showing fraction multiplication with models. Then solve problems 1–10.

Example
Find $4 \times \frac{2}{5}$.

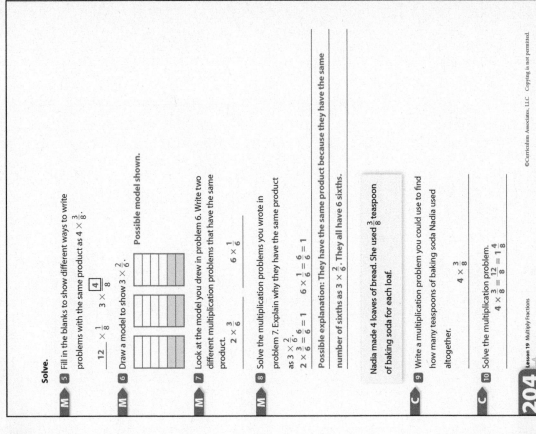

$\frac{2}{5}$ $\frac{2}{5}$ $\frac{2}{5}$ $\frac{2}{5}$
$4 \times \frac{2}{5}$

$= $

$\frac{8}{5} = 1\frac{3}{5}$

$4 \times \frac{2}{5} = \frac{8}{5} = 1\frac{3}{5}$

B **1** Write the fraction multiplication problem that the model below shows.

$\boxed{3} \times \frac{\boxed{3}}{\boxed{4}}$

M **2** Label the number line below and use it to show $7 \times \frac{1}{2}$.

$$0 \quad 1 \quad 2 \quad 3 \quad 4$$
$$\frac{1}{2} \ \frac{2}{2} \ \frac{3}{2} \ \frac{4}{2} \ \frac{5}{2} \ \frac{6}{2} \ \frac{7}{2}$$

M **3** Write $7 \times \frac{1}{2}$ as repeated addition.

$\frac{1}{2} + \frac{1}{2} + \frac{1}{2} + \frac{1}{2} + \frac{1}{2} + \frac{1}{2} + \frac{1}{2}$

M **4** Find $7 \times \frac{1}{2}$.

$7 \times \frac{1}{2} = \frac{7}{2} = 3\frac{1}{2}$

203

Solve.

M **5** Fill in the blanks to show different ways to write problems with the same product as $4 \times \frac{3}{8}$.

$12 \times \frac{1}{8} \qquad 3 \times \frac{\boxed{4}}{8}$

M **6** Draw a model to show $3 \times \frac{2}{6}$.

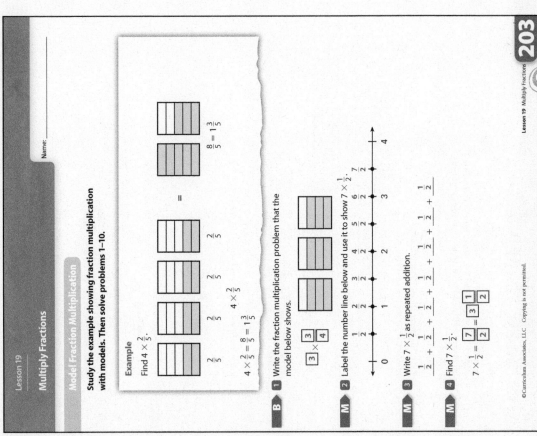

Possible model shown.

M **7** Look at the model you drew in problem 6. Write two different multiplication problems that have the same product.

$2 \times \frac{3}{6} \qquad\qquad 6 \times \frac{1}{6}$

M **8** Solve the multiplication problems you wrote in problem 7. Explain why they have the same product as $3 \times \frac{2}{6}$.

$2 \times \frac{3}{6} = \frac{6}{6} = 1 \qquad 6 \times \frac{1}{6} = \frac{6}{6} = 1$

Possible explanation: They have the same product because they have the same number of sixths as $3 \times \frac{2}{6}$. They all have 6 sixths.

C **9** Nadia made 4 loaves of bread. She used $\frac{3}{8}$ teaspoon of baking soda for each loaf. Write a multiplication problem you could use to find how many teaspoons of baking soda Nadia used altogether.

$4 \times \frac{3}{8}$

C **10** Solve the multiplication problem.

$4 \times \frac{3}{8} = \frac{12}{8} = 1\frac{4}{8}$

204

Key

B Basic   **M** Medium   **C** Challenge

Lesson 19

Name: _____

Solve Problems with Fraction Multiplication

Study the example problem that shows how to solve a word problem with fraction multiplication. Then solve problems 1–7.

Example

Henry doubled a cookie recipe to make two batches of cookies. The recipe calls for $\frac{7}{8}$ cup of flour for each batch. How much flour did Henry use for both batches of cookies?

$$2 \times \frac{7}{8} = \frac{14}{8} \text{ or } 1\frac{6}{8}$$

number of batches   cups per batch   cups used

Henry used $\frac{14}{8}$, or $1\frac{6}{8}$, cups of flour.

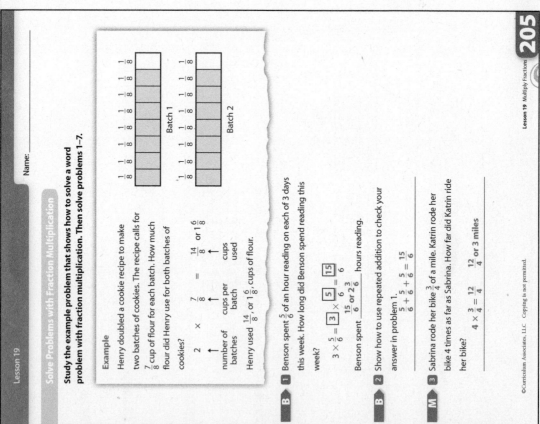

B **1** Benson spent $\frac{5}{6}$ of an hour reading on each of 3 days this week. How long did Benson spend reading this week?

$$3 \times \frac{5}{6} = \boxed{3} \times \frac{\boxed{5}}{6} = \frac{\boxed{15}}{6}$$

$\frac{15}{6}$ or $2\frac{3}{6}$ hours reading.

Benson spent _____ hours reading.

B **2** Show how to use repeated addition to check your answer in problem 1.

$$\frac{5}{6} + \frac{5}{6} + \frac{5}{6} = \frac{15}{6}$$

M **3** Sabrina rode her bike $\frac{3}{4}$ of a mile. Katrin rode her bike 4 times as far as Sabrina. How far did Katrin ride her bike?

$$4 \times \frac{3}{4} = \frac{12}{4} \qquad \frac{12}{4} \text{ or 3 miles}$$

Solve.

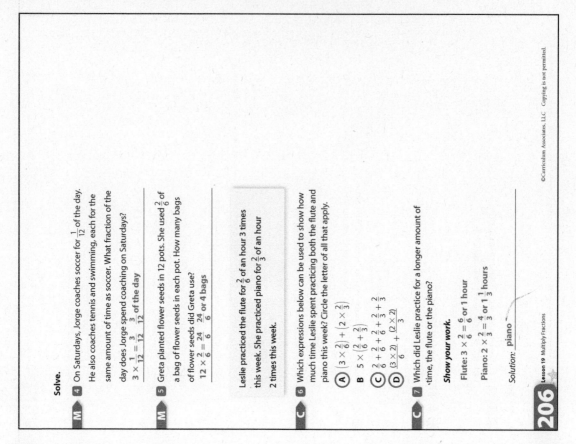

M **4** On Saturdays, Jorge coaches soccer for $\frac{1}{12}$ of the day. He also coaches tennis and swimming, each for the same amount of time as soccer. What fraction of the day does Jorge spend coaching on Saturdays?

$$3 \times \frac{1}{12} = \frac{3}{12} \qquad \frac{3}{12} \text{ of the day}$$

M **5** Greta planted flower seeds in 12 pots. She used $\frac{2}{6}$ of a bag of flower seeds in each pot. How many bags of flower seeds did Greta use?

$$12 \times \frac{2}{6} = \frac{24}{6} \qquad \frac{24}{6} \text{ or 4 bags}$$

Leslie practiced the flute for $\frac{2}{6}$ of an hour 3 times this week. She practiced piano for $\frac{2}{3}$ of an hour 2 times this week.

C **6** Which expressions below can be used to show how much time Leslie spent practicing both the flute and piano this week? Circle the letter of all that apply.

Ⓐ $\left(3 \times \frac{2}{6}\right) + \left(2 \times \frac{2}{3}\right)$

B $5 \times \left(\frac{2}{6} + \frac{2}{3}\right)$

Ⓒ $\frac{2}{6} + \frac{2}{6} + \frac{2}{6} + \frac{2}{3} + \frac{2}{3}$

Ⓓ $\frac{(3 \times 2)}{6} + \frac{(2 \times 2)}{3}$

C **7** Which did Leslie practice for a longer amount of time, the flute or the piano?
Show your work.

Flute: $3 \times \frac{2}{6} = \frac{6}{6}$ or 1 hour

Piano: $2 \times \frac{2}{3} = \frac{4}{3}$ or $1\frac{1}{3}$ hours

Solution: _piano_

Solve.

M **4** Luke and Matt went fishing. Luke caught 4 fish, each weighing $\frac{7}{8}$ of a pound. Matt caught 6 fish, each weighing $\frac{3}{4}$ of a pound. Who caught more pounds of fish?

How do you figure out how many pounds each person caught?

Show your work.

Luke: $4 \times \frac{7}{8} = \frac{28}{8}$

Matt: $6 \times \frac{3}{4} = \frac{18}{4}$

$\frac{18}{4} = \frac{36}{8}$, $\frac{36}{8} > \frac{28}{8}$

Solution: ___Matt caught more pounds of fish.___

C **5** Penny is training for a distance race. She ran $\frac{1}{10}$ of the race's distance for 4 weeks. She ran $\frac{1}{5}$ of the distance for 3 weeks. She ran $\frac{3}{10}$ of the distance for 2 weeks. How far of the race's distance has Penny run during training?

Drawing a picture can help you decide which numbers to multiply and which numbers to add.

Show your work.

$4 \times \frac{1}{10} = \frac{4}{10}$

$2 \times \frac{3}{10} = \frac{6}{10}$

$3 \times \frac{1}{5} = \frac{3}{5} = \frac{6}{10}$

$\frac{4}{10} + \frac{6}{10} + \frac{6}{10} = \frac{16}{10} = 1\frac{6}{10}$

Solution: ___Penny has run $1\frac{6}{10}$ of the race's distance.___

208 Lesson 19 Multiply Fractions

Lesson 19

Multiply Fractions

Solve the problems.

Name: _____

B **1** Rick cut a sheet of paper into 4 strips. Each strip was $\frac{3}{4}$ of an inch wide. How wide was the paper Rick cut?

Is the answer going to be greater than or less than $\frac{3}{4}$?

A $\frac{3}{16}$ inch
C $\frac{7}{4}$ inches
B $\frac{12}{16}$ inch
D $\frac{12}{4}$ inches

M **2** Diane walked her dog $\frac{4}{10}$ of a mile on 5 days this week. How far did Diane walk her dog this week?

When you multiply a whole number by a fraction, do you multiply the whole number by the numerator or denominator?

A $\frac{20}{50}$ mile
C $\frac{20}{10}$ miles
B $\frac{9}{15}$ mile
D $\frac{40}{5}$ miles

Zoe chose **A**. How did she get that answer?
Possible answer: She multiplied the whole number by both the numerator and denominator, instead of multiplying it by the numerator.

M **3** Leo feeds his cat $\frac{2}{3}$ of a can of food 2 times a day. Leo is going out of town for 3 days. How many cans of food does Leo need to give a neighbor to feed his cat?

What two numbers can you multiply to find how many times the neighbor needs to feed Leo's cat?

Show your work.
Possible work:
2 times a day for 3 days = 2 × 3 = 6
$6 \times \frac{2}{3} = \frac{12}{3} = 4$

Solution: ___4 cans of food___

Lesson 19 Multiply Fractions **207**

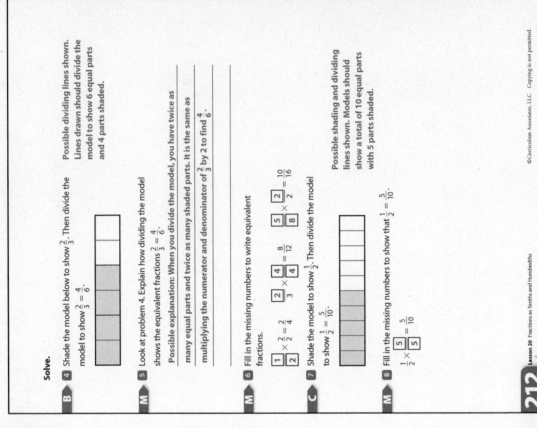

Lesson 20

Fractions as Tenths and Hundredths

Identify Equivalent Fractions

Study the example showing how to use a number line to find equivalent fractions. Then solve problems 1–8.

Example

Find a fraction equivalent to $\frac{3}{4}$ and a fraction equivalent to $\frac{5}{6}$.

The number lines show $\frac{3}{4} = \frac{9}{12}$ and $\frac{5}{6} = \frac{10}{12}$.

1 Look at the number lines in the example above. Write each equivalent fraction.

$\frac{8}{12} = \frac{4}{6}$ $\frac{2}{6} = \frac{4}{12}$ $\frac{3}{12} = \frac{1}{4}$ $\frac{1}{6} = \frac{2}{12}$

2 Write three fractions equivalent to $\frac{1}{2}$. Use the number lines above to help you.

$\frac{2}{4}, \frac{3}{6}, \frac{6}{12}$

3 Fill in the missing numbers to find fractions equivalent to $\frac{5}{4}$.

$\frac{5}{4} \times \frac{2}{2} = \frac{10}{8}$ $\frac{5}{4} \times \frac{4}{4} = \frac{20}{16}$ $\frac{5}{4} \times \frac{10}{10} = \frac{50}{40}$

Vocabulary

equivalent fractions two or more fractions that name the same part of a whole.

211

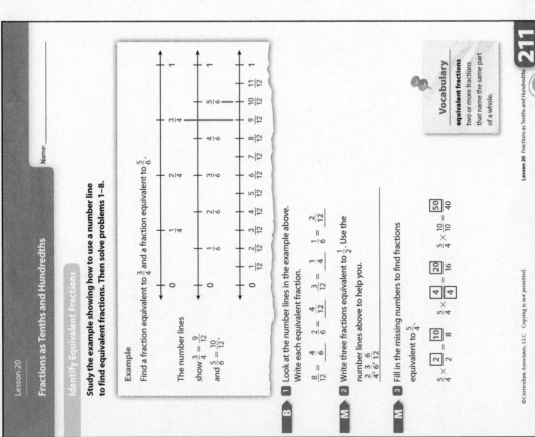

Solve.

4 Shade the model below to show $\frac{2}{3}$. Then divide the model to show $\frac{2}{3} = \frac{4}{6}$.

Possible dividing lines shown. Lines drawn should divide the model to show 6 equal parts and 4 parts shaded.

5 Look at problem 4. Explain how dividing the model shows the equivalent fractions $\frac{2}{3} = \frac{4}{6}$.

Possible explanation: When you divide the model, you have twice as many equal parts and twice as many shaded parts. It is the same as multiplying the numerator and denominator of $\frac{2}{3}$ by 2 to find $\frac{4}{6}$.

6 Fill in the missing numbers to write equivalent fractions.

$\frac{1}{2} \times \frac{2}{2} = \frac{2}{4}$ $\frac{2}{3} \times \frac{4}{4} = \frac{8}{12}$ $\frac{5}{8} \times \frac{2}{2} = \frac{10}{16}$

7 Shade the model to show $\frac{1}{2}$. Then divide the model to show $\frac{1}{2} = \frac{5}{10}$.

Possible shading and dividing lines shown. Models should show a total of 10 equal parts with 5 parts shaded.

8 Fill in the missing numbers to show that $\frac{1}{2} = \frac{5}{10}$.

$\frac{1}{2} \times \frac{5}{5} = \frac{5}{10}$

212   Lesson 20 Fractions as Tenths and Hundredths

Key

B Basic   **M** Medium   **C** Challenge

Unit 4 Number and Operations—Fractions

Name: _____

Lesson 20

Add Tenths and Hundredths Fractions

Study the example problem showing how to add tenths and hundredths fractions. Then solve problems 1–8.

Example

Jaden found $\frac{8}{10}$ of a dollar in change in his backpack.

He found $\frac{15}{100}$ of a dollar in change in his lunch bag.

What fraction of a dollar in change did he find altogether?

Multiply to find the hundredths fraction equivalent to $\frac{8}{10}$.
$$\frac{8}{10} = \left(\frac{8 \times 10}{10 \times 10}\right) = \frac{80}{100}$$

Add the hundredths fractions.
$$\frac{80}{100} + \frac{15}{100} = \frac{95}{100}$$

Jaden found $\frac{95}{100}$ of a dollar in change.

1 Write $\frac{2}{10}$ as an equivalent fraction with a denominator of 100.
$$\frac{2}{10} = \left(\frac{2 \times 10}{10 \times 10}\right) = \frac{\boxed{20}}{\boxed{100}}$$

2 Fill in the blanks to show how to find the sum of $\frac{2}{10}$ and $\frac{10}{100}$.
$$\frac{\boxed{20}}{100} + \frac{10}{100} = \frac{\boxed{30}}{\boxed{100}}$$

3 Look at problem 2. $\frac{10}{100} = \frac{1}{10}$. What is another way that you could show the sum of $\frac{2}{10}$ and $\frac{10}{100}$?
$$\frac{2}{10} + \frac{1}{10} = \frac{3}{10}$$

4 Look at problems 2 and 3. Are the sums equivalent? Explain.

Yes. Possible explanation: You can write $\frac{3}{10}$ as an equivalent fraction with a denominator of 100. $\frac{3}{10} = \frac{30}{100}$

Lesson 20 Fractions as Tenths and Hundredths **213**

Solve.

Mila has 100 math problems to finish this week.
She solved $\frac{2}{10}$ of the problems on Monday and $\frac{25}{100}$ of the problems on Tuesday.

5 Did Mila solve more problems on Monday or on Tuesday? Explain.

Show your work.
$$\frac{2}{10} = \frac{20}{100} \qquad \frac{20}{100} < \frac{25}{100}$$

Solution: Possible answer: Mila solved more problems on Tuesday because $\frac{2}{10}$ is the same as $\frac{20}{100}$ and $\frac{25}{100} > \frac{20}{100}$.

6 What fraction of the math problems for the week did Mila solve on Monday and Tuesday?

Show your work.
$$\frac{20}{100} + \frac{25}{100} = \frac{45}{100}$$

Solution: Mila solved $\frac{45}{100}$ of the math problems.

7 Look at problem 6. Is the sum you found greater or less than $\frac{1}{2}$? Explain.

Possible explanation: The sum of $\frac{45}{100}$ is less than $\frac{1}{2}$.
$$\frac{1}{2} = \frac{50}{100} \qquad \frac{45}{100} < \frac{50}{100}$$

8 Has Mila completed more than half of her math problems for the week? Explain.

Possible explanation: Mila has not completed more than half of her math problems. She has completed $\frac{45}{100}$ of her math problems. $\frac{45}{100}$ is less than $\frac{1}{2}$.

214 Lesson 20 Fractions as Tenths and Hundredths

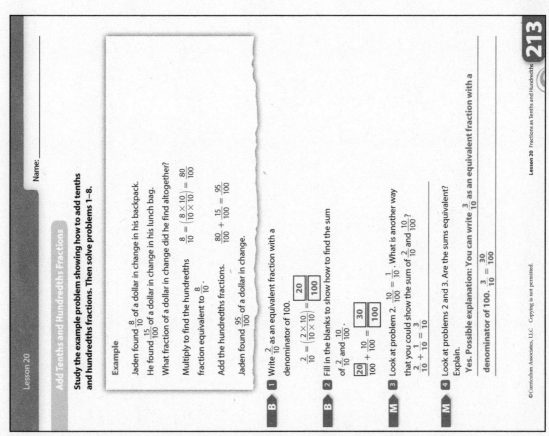

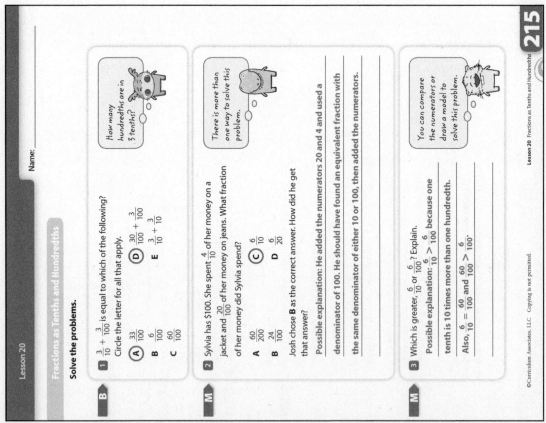

Page 215

Lesson 20

Name: _____

Fractions as Tenths and Hundredths

Solve the problems.

B 1 $\frac{3}{10} + \frac{3}{100}$ is equal to which of the following?
Circle the letter for all that apply.

(A) $\frac{33}{100}$ (D) $\frac{30}{100} + \frac{3}{100}$

B $\frac{6}{10}$ E $\frac{3}{10} + \frac{3}{10}$

C $\frac{60}{100}$

How many hundredths are in 3 tenths?

M 2 Sylvia has $100. She spent $\frac{4}{10}$ of her money on a jacket and $\frac{20}{100}$ of her money on jeans. What fraction of her money did Sylvia spend?

A $\frac{60}{200}$ C $\frac{6}{10}$

B $\frac{24}{100}$ D $\frac{6}{20}$

Josh chose **B** as the correct answer. How did he get that answer?

Possible explanation: He added the numerators 20 and 4 and used a denominator of 100. He should have found an equivalent fraction with the same denominator of either 10 or 100, then added the numerators.

There is more than one way to solve this problem.

M 3 Which is greater, $\frac{6}{10}$ or $\frac{6}{100}$? Explain.

Possible explanation: $\frac{6}{10} > \frac{6}{100}$ because one tenth is 10 times more than one hundredth.

Also, $\frac{6}{10} = \frac{60}{100}$ and $\frac{60}{100} > \frac{6}{100}$.

You can compare the numerators or draw a model to solve this problem.

Page 216

Solve.

M 4 Tell whether each addition problem has a sum greater than $\frac{1}{2}$.

		Yes	No
a.	$\frac{4}{10} + \frac{9}{100}$	☐	☒
b.	$\frac{1}{100} + \frac{5}{10}$	☒	☐
c.	$\frac{45}{100} + \frac{1}{10}$	☒	☐
d.	$\frac{25}{100} + \frac{3}{10}$	☒	☐
e.	$\frac{3}{10} + \frac{15}{100}$	☐	☒

What tenths and hundredths fractions are equivalent to $\frac{1}{2}$?

M 5 Find the sum of $\frac{2}{100} + \frac{20}{100} + \frac{2}{10}$.

Show your work.
Possible work: $\frac{2}{10} = \frac{20}{100}$

$\frac{2}{100} + \frac{20}{100} + \frac{20}{100} = \frac{42}{100}$

Solution: $\frac{42}{100}$

Estimate the sum before solving this problem. Is the sum close to 1? Is it close to $\frac{1}{2}$?

C 6 Owen received $100 for his birthday. He wants to spend $\frac{2}{10}$ of his money on a video game. He wants to spend $\frac{55}{100}$ of his money on a skateboard. He wants to spend $\frac{3}{10}$ of his money on comic books. What fraction of his birthday money does Owen want to spend? Does he have enough money? Explain.

Show your work. $\frac{2}{10} = \frac{20}{100}$ $\frac{3}{10} = \frac{30}{100}$

$\frac{20}{100} + \frac{55}{100} + \frac{30}{100} = \frac{105}{100}$

Solution: Answers will vary. Possible answer: Owen wants to spend $\frac{105}{100}$ of his birthday money. He does not have enough money. He wants to spend a fraction of his birthday money that is greater than 1.

What fraction represents all the money that Owen received?

Name: _____

Lesson 21

Relate Decimals and Fractions

Find Equivalent Fractions

Study the example showing how to identify equivalent fractions with denominators of 10 and 100. Then solve problems 1–5.

Example
Explain how $\frac{6}{10} = \frac{60}{100}$.

Use multiplication to find equivalent fractions.

$$\frac{6}{10} = \left(\frac{6 \times 10}{10 \times 10}\right) = \frac{60}{100}$$

Use models to show equivalent fractions.

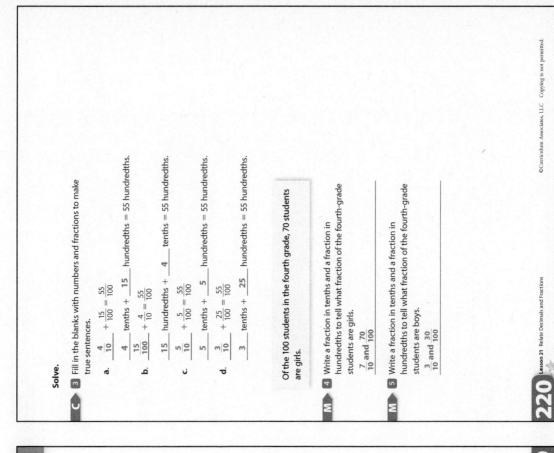

$\frac{6}{10}$ = $\frac{60}{100}$

Vocabulary
equivalent fractions two or more fractions that name the same part of a whole.

B **1** Write the fractions that the models below show.

$\frac{4}{10}$ $\frac{40}{100}$

B **2** Look at problem 1. Use multiplication to find the equivalent fractions.

$$\frac{4}{10} = \left(\frac{4 \times 10}{10 \times 10}\right) = \frac{40}{100}$$

Lesson 21 Relate Decimals and Fractions **219**

Solve.

C **3** Fill in the blanks with numbers and fractions to make true sentences.

a. $\frac{4}{10} + \frac{15}{100} = \frac{55}{100}$

   4 tenths + **15** hundredths = 55 hundredths.

b. $\frac{15}{100} + \frac{4}{10} = \frac{55}{100}$

   15 hundredths + **4** tenths = 55 hundredths.

c. $\frac{5}{10} + \frac{5}{100} = \frac{55}{100}$

   5 tenths + **5** hundredths = 55 hundredths.

d. $\frac{3}{10} + \frac{25}{100} = \frac{55}{100}$

   3 tenths + **25** hundredths = 55 hundredths.

Of the 100 students in the fourth grade, 70 students are girls.

M **4** Write a fraction in tenths and a fraction in hundredths to tell what fraction of the fourth-grade students are girls.

$\frac{7}{10}$ and $\frac{70}{100}$

M **5** Write a fraction in tenths and a fraction in hundredths to tell what fraction of the fourth-grade students are boys.

$\frac{3}{10}$ and $\frac{30}{100}$

Lesson 21 Relate Decimals and Fractions **220**

Key

B Basic   **M** Medium   **C** Challenge

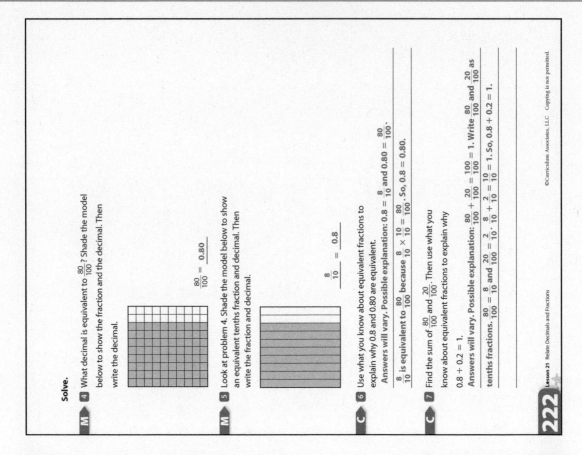

Lesson 21

Name: _____

Name the Same Amount

Study the example showing ways to name the same amount as a fraction and a decimal. Then solve problems 1–7.

Example

How do you write decimals equivalent to $\frac{7}{10}$ and $\frac{70}{100}$?

The model shows $\frac{7}{10}$.

The model shows $\frac{70}{100}$.

$\frac{7}{10} = 0.7$ $\frac{70}{100} = 0.70$

A place-value chart shows the value of $\frac{7}{10}$ and $\frac{70}{100}$.

$\frac{7}{10} = 0.7$ $\frac{70}{100} = 0.70$

Ones	.	Tenths	Hundredths
0	.	7	0

B 1 What decimal is equivalent to $\frac{3}{10}$?

Fill in the place-value chart to show the decimal.

Ones	.	Tenths
0	.	3

B 2 What decimal is equivalent to $\frac{55}{100}$?

Fill in the place-value chart to show the decimal.

Ones	.	Tenths	Hundredths
0	.	5	5

M 3 Write a decimal equivalent to $\frac{75}{100}$. 0.75

Vocabulary

decimal fraction (or decimal) a number containing a decimal point that separates a whole from fractional place values, such as tenths and hundredths. 0.7 and 0.70 are decimals.

Lesson 21 Relate Decimals and Fractions **221**

©Curriculum Associates, LLC   Copying is not permitted.

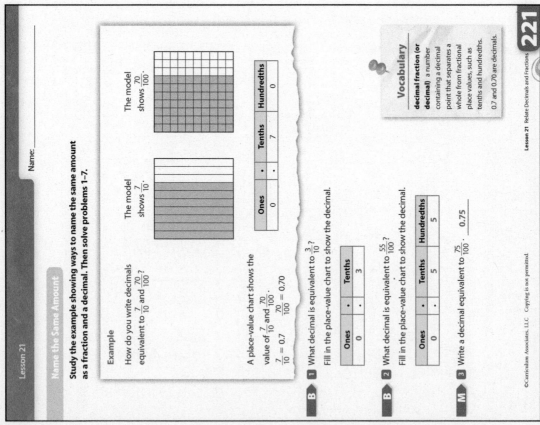

Solve.

M 4 What decimal is equivalent to $\frac{80}{100}$? Shade the model below to show the fraction and the decimal. Then write the decimal.

$\frac{80}{100} = $ __0.80__

M 5 Look at problem 4. Shade the model below to show an equivalent tenths fraction and decimal. Then write the fraction and decimal.

$\frac{8}{10} = $ __0.8__

C 6 Use what you know about equivalent fractions to explain why 0.8 and 0.80 are equivalent.

Answers will vary. Possible explanation: $0.8 = \frac{8}{10}$ and $0.80 = \frac{80}{100}$. $\frac{8}{10}$ is equivalent to $\frac{80}{100}$ because $\frac{8}{10} \times \frac{10}{10} = \frac{80}{100}$. So, $0.8 = 0.80$.

C 7 Find the sum of $\frac{80}{100}$ and $\frac{20}{100}$. Then use what you know about equivalent fractions to explain why $0.8 + 0.2 = 1$.

Answers will vary. Possible explanation: $\frac{80}{100} + \frac{20}{100} = \frac{100}{100} = 1$. Write $\frac{80}{100}$ and $\frac{20}{100}$ as tenths fractions. $\frac{80}{100} = \frac{8}{10}$ and $\frac{20}{100} = \frac{2}{10}$. $\frac{8}{10} + \frac{2}{10} = \frac{10}{10} = 1$. So, $0.8 + 0.2 = 1$.

222 Lesson 21 Relate Decimals and Fractions

©Curriculum Associates, LLC   Copying is not permitted.

Lesson 21

Name: _____

Write a Decimal as an Equivalent Fraction

Study the example problem showing how to write a decimal as an equivalent fraction. Then solve problems 1–8.

Example

Alanna has an assortment of books in her bookcase. 0.09 of her books are comic books. What fraction of the books are comic books?

Decimal: 0.09

Words: 9 hundredths

Fraction: $\frac{9}{100}$

$\frac{9}{100}$ of the books are comic books.

Ones	.	Tenths	Hundredths
0	.	0	9

B 1 Shade the model below to show 0.34.

B 2 Show 0.34 in a place-value chart.

Ones	.	Tenths	Hundredths
0	.	3	4

M 3 Write 0.34 in words. ___thirty-four hundredths___

M 4 Write 0.34 as a fraction. $\frac{34}{100}$

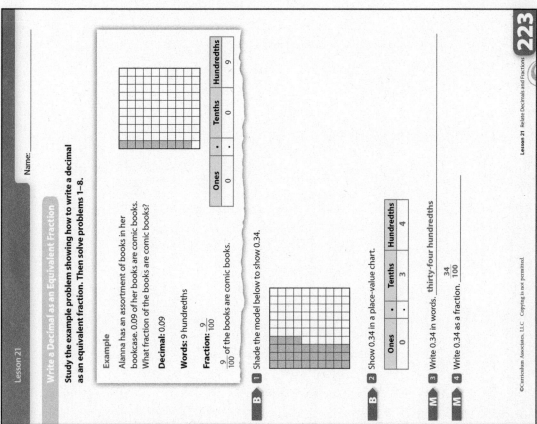

Lesson 21 Relate Decimals and Fractions

223

Solve.

M 5 Tell whether each number sentence is *True* or *False*.

a. $0.3 = \frac{3}{100}$ ☐ True   ☒ False

b. $0.03 = \frac{3}{100}$ ☒ True   ☐ False

c. $0.3 = \frac{30}{100}$ ☒ True   ☐ False

d. $0.3 = \frac{3}{10}$ ☒ True   ☐ False

M 6 Write two equivalent fractions to 0.3. $\frac{3}{10}$ and $\frac{30}{100}$

M 7 Which of the following names the same number as 0.62? Circle the letter for all that apply.

(A) sixty-two hundredths

(B) six tenths and 2 hundredths

C $\frac{62}{10}$

(D) $\frac{62}{100}$

C 8 The number line below shows 1 whole divided into tenths. Write numbers in the boxes to label the missing fractions and decimal. Explain how you know what numbers to write.

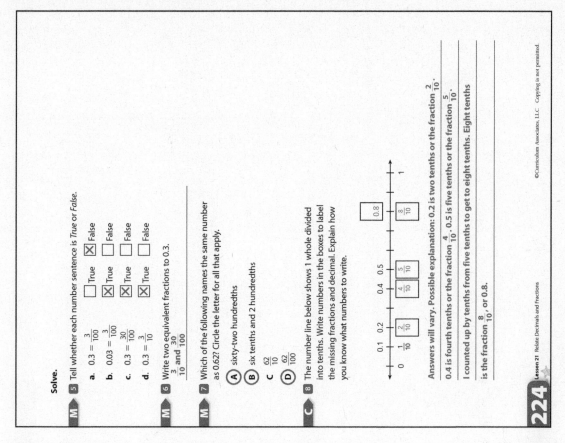

Answers will vary. Possible explanation: 0.2 is two tenths or the fraction $\frac{2}{10}$. 0.4 is fourth tenths or the fraction $\frac{4}{10}$. 0.5 is five tenths or the fraction $\frac{5}{10}$. I counted up by tenths from five tenths to get to eight tenths. Eight tenths is the fraction $\frac{8}{10}$, or 0.8.

224 Lesson 21 Relate Decimals and Fractions

Lesson 21

Relate Decimals and Fractions

Solve the problems.

B 1 What is 0.5 written as a fraction?
Circle the letter for all that apply.

How can you say the decimal in words?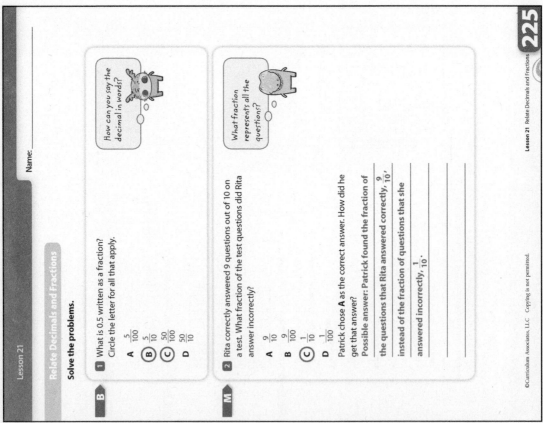

A $\frac{5}{100}$

B $\frac{5}{10}$

C $\frac{50}{100}$

D $\frac{50}{10}$

M 2 Rita correctly answered 9 questions out of 10 on a test. What fraction of the test questions did Rita answer incorrectly?

What fraction represents all the questions?

A $\frac{9}{10}$

B $\frac{9}{100}$

C $\frac{1}{10}$

D $\frac{1}{100}$

Patrick chose **A** as the correct answer. How did he get that answer?

Possible answer: Patrick found the fraction of the questions that Rita answered correctly, $\frac{9}{10}$, instead of the fraction of questions that she answered incorrectly, $\frac{1}{10}$.

Solve.

M 3 Austin bought an eraser for 65 cents and a pencil for 20 cents. What fraction of a dollar did he spend? Write the fraction as a decimal.

What fraction of a dollar is 1 cent?

Show your work.

$\frac{65}{100} + \frac{20}{100} = \frac{85}{100}$

$\frac{85}{100} = 0.85$ or 85 cents

Students might also draw a hundredths model and a tenths model to solve the problem.

Solution: Austin spent $\frac{85}{100}$ or 0.85 of a dollar.

M 4 Tell whether each number below is equivalent to $\frac{15}{100}$.

a. fifteen hundredths   ☒ Yes   ☐ No

b. 1.5   ☐ Yes   ☒ No

c. $\frac{15}{10}$ ☐ Yes   ☒ No

d. 0.15   ☒ Yes   ☐ No

How do you write this fraction in words and as a decimal?

C 5 Mackenzie has 1 dollar, 2 dimes, and 3 pennies. Jorge has only dimes and pennies but has the same amount of money as Mackenzie. How many dimes and pennies could Jorge have?

Can you represent the value of a dollar, a dime, and a penny as fractions or decimals to help you solve this problem?

Show your work.

Answers may vary. Possible work:

Mackenzie: $1 + 0.2 + 0.03$

$1 + \frac{2}{10} + \frac{3}{100} = 1\frac{23}{100}$

Solution: Any combination of dimes and pennies that equals $1.23 is acceptable. Possible answer: Jorge could have 12 dimes and 3 pennies.

Name: _____

Lesson 22

Compare Decimals

Compare Fractions

Study the example showing ways to compare fractions. Then solve problems 1–6.

Example
Compare $\frac{9}{10}$ and $\frac{5}{10}$.

Use models.

The model shows $\frac{9}{10}$.

The model shows $\frac{5}{10}$.

$\frac{9}{10} > \frac{5}{10}$

Use a number line and the fraction $\frac{1}{2}$ as a benchmark.

$\frac{9}{10} > \frac{1}{2}$ and $\frac{5}{10} = \frac{1}{2}$

$\frac{9}{10} > \frac{5}{10}$

B **1** Label $\frac{2}{10}$ and $\frac{6}{10}$ on the number line below.

Write a symbol to compare the two fractions.
$\frac{2}{10} < \frac{6}{10}$

M **2** Look at problem 1. Explain how to use the fraction $\frac{1}{2}$ as a benchmark to compare $\frac{2}{10}$ and $\frac{6}{10}$.
$\frac{1}{2} = \frac{5}{10}$. $\frac{2}{10}$ is less than $\frac{5}{10}$ and $\frac{6}{10}$ is greater than $\frac{5}{10}$, so $\frac{2}{10}$ is less than $\frac{6}{10}$.

M **3** Label $\frac{10}{10}$ and $\frac{8}{10}$ on the number line below.

Write a symbol to compare the two fractions.
$\frac{10}{10} > \frac{8}{10}$

©Curriculum Associates, LLC   Copying is not permitted.
Lesson 22 Compare Decimals
229

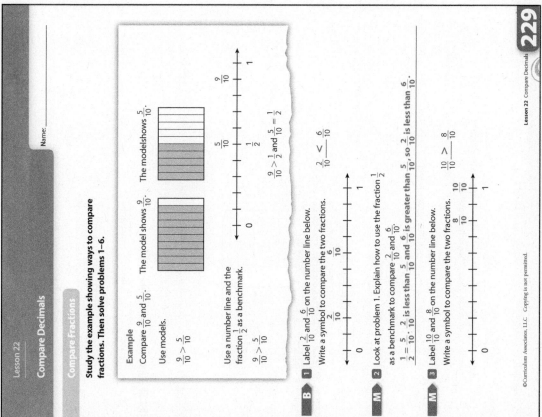

Solve.

M **4** Shade and label the models below to show $\frac{3}{10}$ and $\frac{3}{100}$.
Write a symbol to compare the fractions. $\frac{3}{10} > \frac{3}{100}$.

Possible shading shown.

$\frac{3}{10}$ $\frac{3}{100}$

M **5** Use the symbols <, >, and = to compare the fractions.

a. $\frac{5}{10} \;=\; \frac{50}{100}$

b. $\frac{4}{10} \;>\; \frac{4}{100}$

c. $\frac{11}{10} \;<\; \frac{12}{10}$

d. $\frac{62}{100} \;>\; \frac{6}{10}$

e. $\frac{9}{100} \;<\; \frac{9}{10}$

C **6** Write the fraction that each model shows. Explain which fraction is greater.

$\frac{21}{100}$ $\frac{31}{100}$

$\frac{31}{100} > \frac{21}{100}$. Possible explanation: Both fractions have the same denominator so compare the numerators, 31 > 21.

230 **Lesson 22** Compare Decimals
©Curriculum Associates, LLC   Copying is not permitted.

Key

B Basic   **M** Medium   **C** Challenge

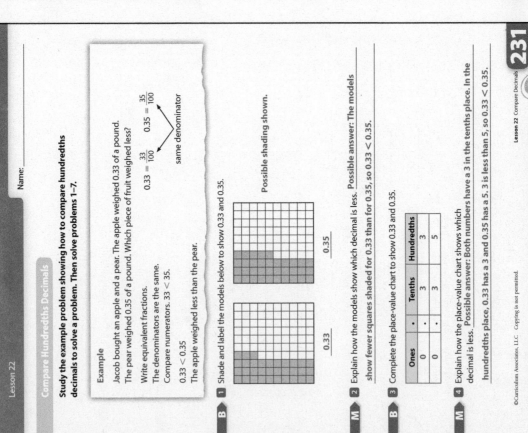

Page 231

Lesson 22

Compare Hundredths Decimals

Study the example problem showing how to compare hundredths decimals to solve a problem. Then solve problems 1–7.

Name: _____

Example

Jacob bought an apple and a pear. The apple weighed 0.33 of a pound. The pear weighed 0.35 of a pound. Which piece of fruit weighed less?

Write equivalent fractions.
The denominators are the same.
Compare numerators. 33 < 35.

$0.33 = \frac{33}{100}$ $0.35 = \frac{35}{100}$

same denominator

0.33 < 0.35
The apple weighed less than the pear.

1 Shade and label the models below to show 0.33 and 0.35.

Possible shading shown.

0.33   0.35

2 Explain how the models show which decimal is less. _Possible answer: The models show fewer squares shaded for 0.33 than for 0.35, so 0.33 < 0.35._

3 Complete the place-value chart to show 0.33 and 0.35.

Ones	.	Tenths	Hundredths
0	.	3	3
0	.	3	5

4 Explain how the place-value chart shows which decimal is less. _Possible answer: Both numbers have a 3 in the tenths place. In the hundredths place, 0.33 has a 3 and 0.35 has a 5. 3 is less than 5, so 0.33 < 0.35._

©Curriculum Associates, LLC   Copying is not permitted.

Lesson 22 Compare Decimals **231**

Page 232

Solve.

5 Use the digits in the tiles below to create decimals that make each inequality true.

| 0 | 1 | 2 | 3 | 4 | 5 |

a.   0.21 > 0.2[0]

b.   0.46 < 0.[5]6

c.   0.99 < [1].00

d.   0.7[3] > 0.7[2]

Answers may vary for c. and d. Possible answers shown. For c., digits 1, 2, 3, 4, or 5 are correct. For d., the first digit written should be greater than the second digit.

6 Write the symbol (>, <, =) that makes each statement below true.

a.   0.85 > 0.82

b.   0.09 < 0.10

c.   0.45 < 0.54

d.   1.10 > 1.01

e.   0.30 = 0.3

7 Ryder bought 0.75 pound of turkey and 0.57 pound of cheese. Did he buy more turkey or cheese?

Show your work.

Possible work:

$0.75 = \frac{75}{100}$ and $0.57 = \frac{57}{100}$

$\frac{75}{100}$ is greater than $\frac{57}{100}$, so 0.75 > 0.57.

Solution: ___ turkey: 0.75 > 0.57 ___

Students might use hundredths models, a place-value chart, or other model to solve the problem.

©Curriculum Associates, LLC   Copying is not permitted.

232 Lesson 22 Compare Decimals

Solve.

M 4 Compare 0.2 and 0.25 using $>$, $=$, or $<$. Use equivalent fractions to explain your answer. Possible explanation: $0.2 = \frac{2}{10}$ or $\frac{20}{100}$. $0.25 = \frac{25}{100}$.

Explanations will vary. Possible explanation: $\frac{20}{100} < \frac{25}{100}$ because 20 < 25. So, 0.2 < 0.25.

M 5 Compare 0.09 and 0.1 using $>$, $=$, or $<$. Use a place-value chart to explain your answer.

Ones	.	Tenths	Hundredths
0	.	0	9
0	.	1	

Explanations will vary. Possible explanation: Compare tenths. The tenths digits are different. 1 tenth is greater than 0 tenths. So, 0.1 > 0.09.

C 6 Write the decimals 1.00, 0.20, and 0.03 in the place-value chart below. Which number is the greatest? Which number is the least? Use equivalent fractions to explain.

Ones	.	Tenths	Hundredths
1	.	0	0
0	.	2	0
0	.	0	3

Explanations will vary. Possible explanation: 1.00 is the greatest because 1 equals a whole. 0.2 and 0.03 are fractions of a whole. $1 = \frac{100}{100}$; $0.2 = \frac{2}{10} = \frac{20}{100}$; and $0.03 = \frac{3}{100}$. Compare the numerators of the three fractions. 100 is greater than 20; 20 is greater than 3. $\frac{3}{100}$ is the least, so 0.03 is the least.

234 Lesson 22 Compare Decimals

Lesson 22

Name: _____

Compare Tenths and Hundredths Decimals

Study the example problem showing how to compare tenths and hundredths decimals. Then solve problems 1–6.

Example

Colin lives 0.6 mile from school and 0.65 mile from the park. Which place is closer to his home?

Write each decimal as an equivalent fraction. $0.6 = \frac{6}{10}$ $0.65 = \frac{65}{100}$

Write the tenths fraction as a hundredths fraction. $\frac{6}{10} = \frac{60}{100}$

Compare hundredths fractions. $\frac{60}{100} < \frac{65}{100}$

0.6 < 0.65

The school is closer to his home.

Lucas bought 0.6 pound of fish and 0.85 pound of shrimp to make a stew.

B 1 Shade the models below to compare 0.6 and 0.85.

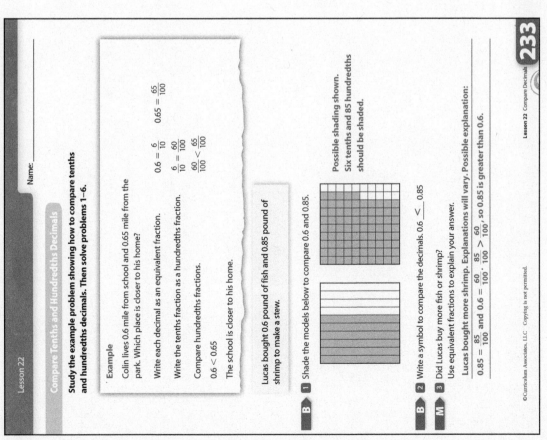

Possible shading shown. Six tenths and 85 hundredths should be shaded.

B 2 Write a symbol to compare the decimals. 0.6 $<$ 0.85

M 3 Did Lucas buy more fish or shrimp? Use equivalent fractions to explain your answer.
Lucas bought more shrimp. Explanations will vary. Possible explanation: $0.85 = \frac{85}{100}$ and $0.6 = \frac{6}{10} = \frac{60}{100}$. $\frac{85}{100} > \frac{60}{100}$, so 0.85 is greater than 0.6.

233 Lesson 22 Compare Decimals

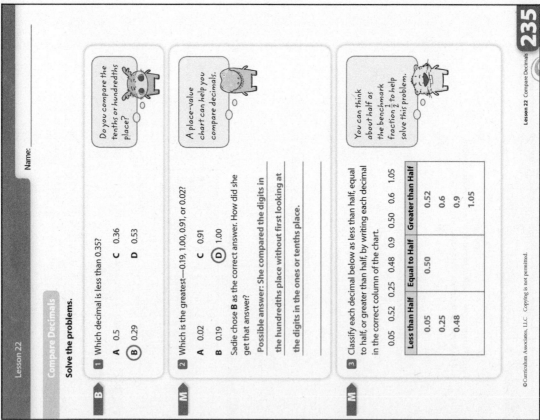

Name: _____

Lesson 22

Compare Decimals

Solve the problems.

B 1 Which decimal is less than 0.35?

A 0.5 C 0.36

(B) 0.29 D 0.53

> Do you compare the tenths or hundredths place?

M 2 Which is the greatest—0.19, 1.00, 0.91, or 0.02?

A 0.02 C 0.91

B 0.19 (D) 1.00

Sadie chose **B** as the correct answer. How did she get that answer?

Possible answer: She compared the digits in the hundredths place without first looking at the digits in the ones or tenths place.

> A place-value chart can help you compare decimals.

M 3 Classify each decimal below as less than half, equal to half, or greater than half, by writing each decimal in the correct column of the chart.

0.05 0.52 0.25 0.48 0.9 0.50 0.6 1.05

Less than Half	Equal to Half	Greater than Half
0.05	0.50	0.52
0.25		0.6
0.48		0.9
		1.05

> You can think about half as the benchmark fraction $\frac{1}{2}$ to help solve this problem.

Lesson 22 Compare Decimals **235**

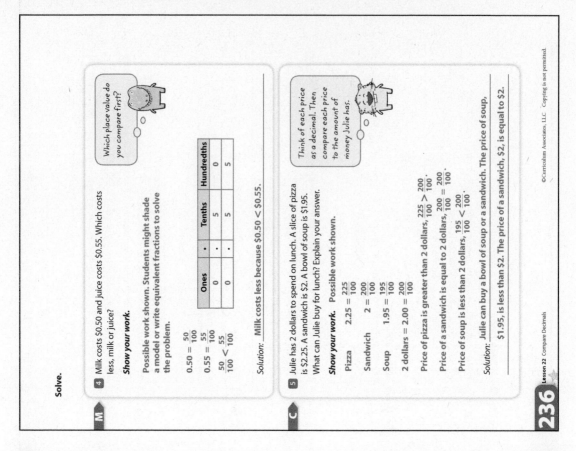

Solve.

M 4 Milk costs $0.50 and juice costs $0.55. Which costs less, milk or juice?

Show your work.

Possible work shown. Students might shade a model or write equivalent fractions to solve the problem.

$0.50 = \frac{50}{100}$

$0.55 = \frac{55}{100}$

$\frac{50}{100} < \frac{55}{100}$

Ones	.	Tenths	Hundredths
0	.	5	0
0	.	5	5

Solution: Milk costs less because $0.50 < $0.55.

> Which place value do you compare first?

C 5 Julie has 2 dollars to spend on lunch. A slice of pizza is $2.25. A sandwich is $2. A bowl of soup is $1.95. What can Julie buy for lunch? Explain your answer.

Show your work. Possible work shown.

Pizza $2.25 = \frac{225}{100}$

Sandwich $2 = \frac{200}{100}$

Soup $1.95 = \frac{195}{100}$

2 dollars = $2.00 = \frac{200}{100}$

Price of pizza is greater than 2 dollars, $\frac{225}{100} > \frac{200}{100}$.

Price of a sandwich is equal to 2 dollars, $\frac{200}{100} = \frac{200}{100}$.

Price of soup is less than 2 dollars, $\frac{195}{100} < \frac{200}{100}$.

Solution: Julie can buy a bowl of soup or a sandwich. The price of soup, $1.95, is less than $2. The price of a sandwich, $2, is equal to $2.

> Think of each price as a decimal. Then compare each price to the amount of money Julie has.

Lesson 22 Compare Decimals **236**

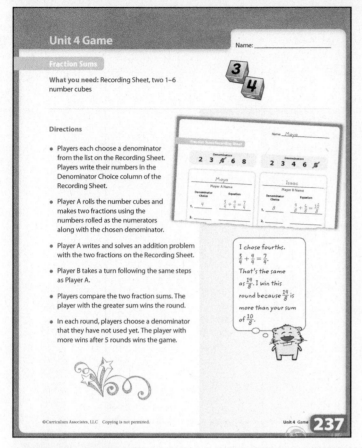

STEP BY STEP

CCSS Focus - 4.NF.A.2, 4.NF.B.3 *Embedded SMPs* - 2, 7, 8 **Objective:** Add fractions with like denominators. Compare fractions with different numerators and different denominators.	**Materials** For each pair: two 1–6 number cubes, Recording Sheet (TR 7)

- Player A chooses a denominator from the list on the Recording Sheet. The student crosses it off the list and writes the choice on the Recording Sheet. Then Player B chooses and writes a denominator.

- Both players roll the number cubes. They make two fractions using the numbers they rolled as the numerators with the denominators they selected.

- Both players write and solve an addition problem with their two fractions.

- The player with the greater sum wins the round.

- For the next round, choose another denominator. Use each denominator only once. The player with more wins after 5 rounds wins the game. To be fair, players should alternate who chooses a denominator first.

- Model one complete round for the students before they play. After they play, encourage a discussion of strategies.

Vary the Game Practice subtracting fractions by finding the difference of the two fractions.

Extra Support Have students only use the denominators 2, 4, and 8. Allow students to use the same denominator in more than one round.

Unit 4 Practice

Number and Operations—Fractions

Name: _____

In this unit you learned to:

	Lesson
find equivalent fractions, for example: $\frac{2}{3} = \frac{4}{6}$.	13
compare fractions with unlike denominators, for example: $\frac{2}{5} > \frac{3}{10}$.	14
add and subtract fractions with like denominators; add and subtract mixed numbers, for example: $\frac{2}{6} + \frac{3}{6} = \frac{5}{6}$.	15, 16, 17
multiply a fraction by a whole number, for example, $3 \times \frac{1}{2} = \frac{3}{2}$.	18, 19
write a decimal as a fraction, for example: $0.4 = \frac{4}{10}$.	20, 21
compare decimals, for example: $0.65 < 0.7$.	22

Use these skills to solve problems 1–5.

B **1** Use <, >, or = to complete each number sentence.

a. $\frac{2}{4}$ [>] $\frac{1}{3}$

b. $\frac{3}{4}$ [<] $3 \times \frac{4}{4} \times 3$

c. $\frac{2}{10}$ [=] 0.20

d. $\frac{3}{4}$ [=] $\frac{15}{20}$

e. 0.5 [>] 0.09

B **2** Write each of the following numbers in one box below to show where on the number line it belongs.

1.03

1.4

1.34

[1.03] 1.3 [1.34] 1.36 [1.4]

What is another number that could go between 1.3 and 1.36?

Solution: __Possible answer: 1.35__

239

Unit 4 Practice Number and Operations—Fractions

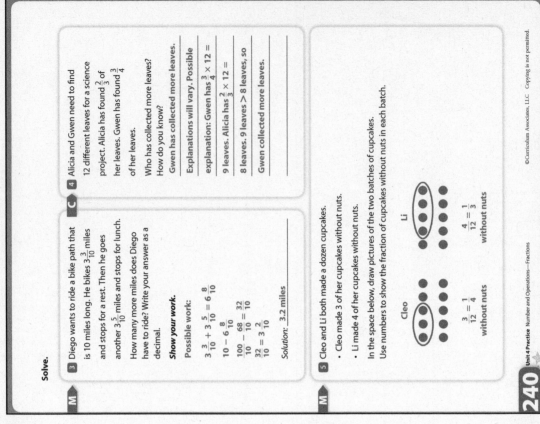

Solve.

M **3** Diego wants to ride a bike path that is 10 miles long. He bikes $3\frac{3}{10}$ miles and stops for a rest. Then he goes another $3\frac{5}{10}$ miles and stops for lunch. How many more miles does Diego have to ride? Write your answer as a decimal.

Show your work.

Possible work:

$3\frac{3}{10} + 3\frac{5}{10} = 6\frac{8}{10}$

$10 - 6\frac{8}{10}$

$\frac{100}{10} - \frac{68}{10} = \frac{32}{10}$

$\frac{32}{10} = 3\frac{2}{10}$

Solution: __3.2 miles__

C **4** Alicia and Gwen need to find 12 different leaves for a science project. Alicia has found $\frac{2}{3}$ of her leaves. Gwen has found $\frac{3}{4}$ of her leaves.

Who has collected more leaves? How do you know?

Gwen has collected more leaves.

Explanations will vary. Possible explanation: Gwen has $\frac{3}{4} \times 12 =$ 9 leaves. Alicia has $\frac{2}{3} \times 12 =$ 8 leaves. 9 leaves > 8 leaves, so Gwen collected more leaves.

M **5** Cleo and Li both made a dozen cupcakes.

- Cleo made 3 of her cupcakes without nuts.
- Li made 4 of her cupcakes without nuts.

In the space below, draw pictures of the two batches of cupcakes. Use numbers to show the fraction of cupcakes without nuts in each batch.

Cleo   Li

$\frac{3}{12} = \frac{1}{4}$ $\frac{4}{12} = \frac{1}{3}$
without nuts   without nuts

240

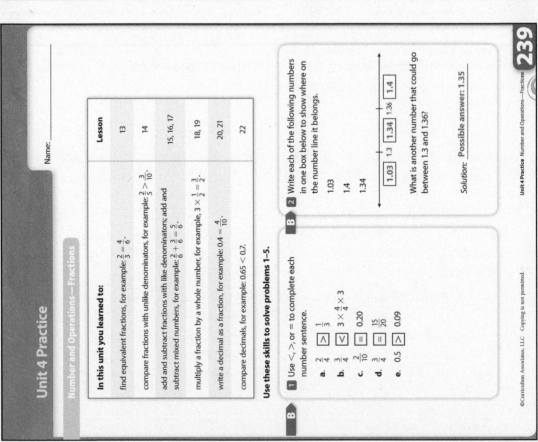

Key

B Basic   **M** Medium   **C** Challenge

TEACHER NOTES

Common Core Standards: 4.NF.A.2, 4.NF.A.3a, 4.NF.3b, 4.NF.B.3d
Standards for Mathematical Practice: 1, 2, 3, 7
DOK: 3
Materials: none

About the Task:

To complete this task, students compare fractions, finding fractions that are both greater than and less than $\frac{1}{2}$. They add fractions with like denominators. The task has more than one possible answer and it calls for students to explain or justify the answer that they give.

Getting Students Started

Read the problem out loud with students. Guide students to see that they must list the ingredients for each salad and then decide how much of each fruit should be in each recipe. They will express the amount of each kind of fruit as a fraction of the whole salad.

Ask students which fruit they should assign a fraction to first and why. Help students understand that since more than $\frac{1}{2}$ of the Hawaiian salad is made of pineapples, they need to determine this fraction first. Guide them to apply this reasoning to see that they must find a fraction for the grapes first in the Red Rose salad. Ask students how they would approach finding fractions for the fruit in the Berry Basket. **(SMP 1, SMP 2)**

Completing the Task

Students should notice that the fractions given in the problem all have denominators of 8. To find fractions that are greater than and less than $\frac{1}{2}$, they can use the equivalent fraction $\frac{4}{8}$. Guide students to understand that they get to choose the fractions that are greater than or less than $\frac{1}{2}$ $\left(\text{or } \frac{4}{8}\right)$ and also the fractions for each fruit in the salad. **(SMP 2)**

Unit 4 Performance Task   Name: _____

Answer the questions and show all your work on separate paper.

A grocery store sells fruit salad made with pineapples, strawberries, raspberries, blueberries, blackberries, and grapes. The store sells three different kinds of salad:

The Hawaiian: More than $\frac{1}{2}$ of the salad is made of pineapple. The rest is made of grapes and blueberries.

The Red Rose: Less than $\frac{1}{2}$ of the salad is made of red grapes. The rest is made of strawberries and raspberries.

The Berry Basket: The salad has equal parts of strawberries, blueberries, raspberries, and blackberries.

Make an ingredient list for each of the salads. Write a fraction for the fruits that are included in each salad. Explain why your lists fit the description of each salad.

Checklist

Did you . . .
☐ meet the given conditions?
☐ check your work?
☐ reread your explanation to see if it makes sense?

The Hawaiian	The Red Rose	The Berry Basket
$\frac{}{8}$ _____	$\frac{}{8}$ _____	$\frac{}{8}$ _____
$\frac{}{8}$ _____	$\frac{}{8}$ _____	$\frac{}{8}$ _____
$\frac{}{8}$ _____	$\frac{}{8}$ _____	$\frac{}{8}$ _____
		$\frac{}{8}$ _____

Reflect on Mathematical Practices

After you complete the task, choose one of the following questions to answer.

1 **Make Sense of Problems** How did you know which fraction to find first for The Hawaiian and The Red Rose salads?

2 **Use Structure** How did you decide which fractions to use after you found the first fraction?

©Curriculum Associates, LLC Copying is not permitted.   Unit 4 Performance Task **241**

Ask students what the sum of the fractions in each list should be and why. Students should understand that there are 8 eighths $\left(\frac{8}{8}\right)$ in the whole salad. Discuss how knowing this can help them decide what fractions to use for each of the fruits. Remind students that there is more than one possible answer for the The Hawaiian and Red Rose salads. Ask students why this is not true for the Berry Basket salad. **(SMP 7)**

Finally, students must justify their answer and explain why it meets all the criteria given in the problem. You may want to pair students so they can evaluate one another's explanations. **(SMP 3)**

Extension

If some students have more time to spend on this problem, you can have them solve this extension:

What are possible combinations of fractions for the fruits in the Hawaiian and the Red Rose salads if the denominator is 10?

SAMPLE RESPONSES AND RUBRIC

4-Point Solution

The Hawaiian:	**The Red Rose:**	**The Berry Basket:**
$\frac{5}{8}$ pineapples	$\frac{3}{8}$ grapes	$\frac{2}{8}$ strawberries
$\frac{1}{8}$ grapes	$\frac{3}{8}$ strawberries	$\frac{2}{8}$ blueberries
$\frac{2}{8}$ blueberries	$\frac{2}{8}$ raspberries	$\frac{2}{8}$ raspberries
		$\frac{2}{8}$ blackberries

I used the equivalent fraction $\frac{4}{8}$ to find eighths fractions greater than and less than $\frac{1}{2}$. The fractions for all salads must add to 1, which is the whole salad. Since $\frac{5}{8}$ is greater than $\frac{4}{8}$, pineapples make up more than $\frac{1}{2}$ of The Hawaiian salad. Add $\frac{5}{8} + \frac{1}{8} + \frac{2}{8}$ to get $\frac{8}{8}$, which is equal to 1. Since $\frac{3}{8}$ is less than $\frac{4}{8}$, grapes make up less than $\frac{1}{2}$ of The Red Rose salad and $\frac{3}{8} + \frac{3}{8} + \frac{2}{8} = \frac{8}{8}$, or 1. For the Berry Basket, all four fractions are equal and they also add to $\frac{8}{8}$, or 1.

REFLECT ON MATHEMATICAL PRACTICES

1. Students should realize that the problem only gives constraints for one fruit in each of the two salads, so those are the fractions to find first. **(SMP 1)**

2. Students should recognize that the whole is 1 and that the fractions for all the parts (the different fruits) must have a sum of 1. **(SMP 7)**

SCORING RUBRIC

4 points   The student has completed all parts of the problem and correctly identifies fractions greater than and less than $\frac{1}{2}$. The response indicates an understanding that the sum of the fractions for each salad has to be 1 to represent the whole. The student writes a thorough and clear explanation of how the answer meets all of the constraints given in the problem.

3 points   The student has completed all parts of the problem, but has made one error. The student may have an error with one of the fractions in the three groups or added incorrectly. A correct explanation of how the answer meets the constraints is given.

2 points   The student has attempted all parts of the problem. There may be errors in identifying fractions greater than or less than 1 or in selecting fractions that have a sum of 1. An explanation of how the answer meets all constraints is given, but it may be unclear or incomplete.

1 point   The student has not completed all parts of the problem. The student may have been able to identify fractions that are less than or greater than one. The remaining fractions are assigned randomly, indicating a lack of understanding that there must be a sum of 1 for each group of fractions. An explanation of how the answer meets all constraints is not given.

SOLUTION TO THE EXTENSION

Possible response:

The Hawaiian: $\frac{6}{10}$ pineapple, $\frac{3}{10}$ grapes, $\frac{1}{10}$ blueberries. The Red Rose: $\frac{4}{10}$ grapes, $\frac{3}{10}$ strawberries, $\frac{3}{10}$ raspberries.

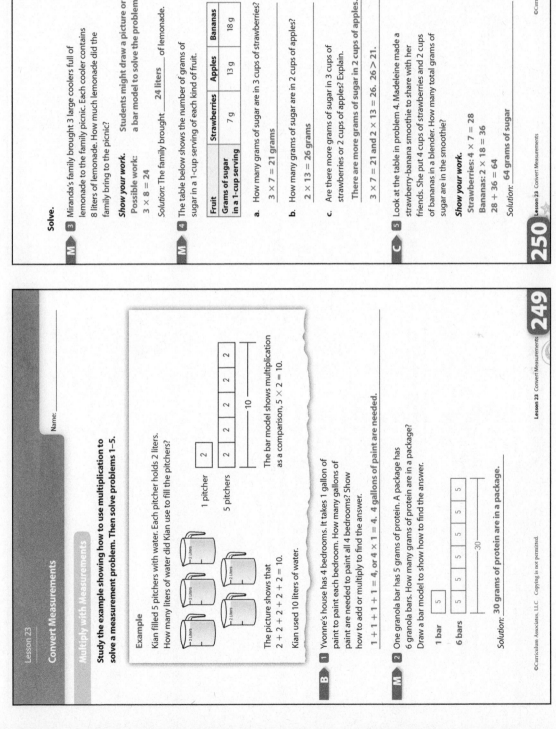

Lesson 23

Convert Measurements

Multiply with Measurements

Study the example showing how to use multiplication to solve a measurement problem. Then solve problems 1–5.

Example

Kian filled 5 pitchers with water. Each pitcher holds 2 liters. How many liters of water did Kian use to fill the pitchers?

The picture shows that
2 + 2 + 2 + 2 + 2 = 10.
Kian used 10 liters of water.

1 pitcher | 2 |

5 pitchers | 2 | 2 | 2 | 2 | 2 |
——— 10 ———

The bar model shows multiplication as a comparison, 5 × 2 = 10.

B **1** Yvonne's house has 4 bedrooms. It takes 1 gallon of paint to paint each bedroom. How many gallons of paint are needed to paint all 4 bedrooms? Show how to add or multiply to find the answer.

1 + 1 + 1 + 1 = 4, or 4 × 1 = 4. 4 gallons of paint are needed.

M **2** One granola bar has 5 grams of protein. A package has 6 granola bars. How many grams of protein are in a package? Draw a bar model to show how to find the answer.

1 bar | 5 |

6 bars | 5 | 5 | 5 | 5 | 5 | 5 |
——— 30 ———

Solution: 30 grams of protein are in a package.

Solve.

M **3** Miranda's family brought 3 large coolers full of lemonade to the family picnic. Each cooler contains 8 liters of lemonade. How much lemonade did the family bring to the picnic?

Show your work.   Students might draw a picture or a bar model to solve the problem.
Possible work:
3 × 8 = 24

Solution: The family brought ___24 liters___ of lemonade.

M **4** The table below shows the number of grams of sugar in a 1-cup serving of each kind of fruit.

Fruit	Strawberries	Apples	Bananas
Grams of sugar in a 1-cup serving	7 g	13 g	18 g

a. How many grams of sugar are in 3 cups of strawberries?

3 × 7 = 21 grams

b. How many grams of sugar are in 2 cups of apples?

2 × 13 = 26 grams

c. Are there more grams of sugar in 3 cups of strawberries or 2 cups of apples? Explain.

There are more grams of sugar in 2 cups of apples.

3 × 7 = 21 and 2 × 13 = 26. 26 > 21.

C **5** Look at the table in problem 4. Madeleine made a strawberry-banana smoothie to share with her friends. She put 4 cups of strawberries and 2 cups of bananas in a blender. How many total grams of sugar are in the smoothie?

Show your work.
Strawberries: 4 × 7 = 28
Bananas: 2 × 18 = 36
28 + 36 = 64

Solution: ___64 grams of sugar___

Key

B Basic   **M** Medium   **C** Challenge

Lesson 23

Name: _____

Convert Units of Weight and Mass

Study the example showing how to convert from a larger unit to a smaller unit of weight and mass. Then solve problems 1–7.

Example

Eleanor bought a 3-pound watermelon and 32 ounces of strawberries. How much more does the watermelon weigh than the strawberries?

$\boxed{\text{1 pound (lb) = 16 ounces (oz)}}$

Write an expression to convert pounds to ounces.
Let p stand for the number of pounds.

$p \times 16$

Find the weight of the watermelon in ounces.
The watermelon weighs 48 ounces.

Substitute 3 for p.
$3 \times 16 = 48$

$48 - 32 = 16$

The watermelon weighs 16 ounces more than the strawberries.

B 1 John has a watermelon with a mass of 3 kilograms. Complete the bar model. Then write the mass of the watermelon in grams.

3 kilograms (kg)

1 kg	1 kg	1 kg
1,000 g	1,000 g	1,000 g

__3,000__ grams (g)

M 2 Write an expression that shows how to convert kilograms to grams. Use K to stand for the number of kilograms.

$K \times 1,000$

M 3 Convert the units of mass.

2 kg = __2,000__ g   4 kg = __4,000__ g

Vocabulary

convert to change from one unit to another unit.

1 kilogram = 1,000 grams

unit ← → unit

Lesson 23 Convert Measurements **251**

Solve.

M 4 Complete the table to convert from a larger unit to a smaller unit of weight.

Pounds (lb)	1	2	3	4	5	6	7
Ounces (oz)	16	32	48	64	80	96	112

M 5 Neil brought 2 pounds of grapes for fruit salad at the class picnic. There are 8 ounces of grapes left. How many ounces of grapes were used? Look at the table in problem 4 to help you answer the question.

Show your work.

Possible work:
2 pounds = 32 ounces
$32 - 8 = 24$

Solution: __24 ounces__

M 6 Choose *Yes* or *No* to tell whether the given weight is equal to 6 pounds.

a. 22 ounces   ☐ Yes   ☒ No
b. 96 ounces   ☒ Yes   ☐ No
c. 4 pounds, 32 ounces   ☒ Yes   ☐ No
d. 5 pounds, 16 ounces   ☒ Yes   ☐ No

C 7 An adult bottlenose dolphin has a mass of 200 kilograms. What is the mass of an adult bottlenose dolphin in grams?

Show your work.

Possible work:
$200 \times 1,000 = 200,000$

Solution: __200,000 grams__

$\boxed{\text{1 kilogram = 1,000 grams}}$

252 Lesson 23 Convert Measurements

Lesson 23

Convert Units of Liquid Volume

Study the example showing how to convert from a larger unit to a smaller unit of liquid volume. Then solve problems 1–7.

Example

Josie made 4 quarts of iced tea for a family picnic.
Her sister made 14 cups of punch for the picnic.
Who made a greater amount of beverages?

Use a table to convert
quarts to cups.

Quarts	1	2	3	4	5
Cups	4	8	12	16	20

1 quart = 4 cups

Josie made 4 quarts, or 16 cups of iced tea.

16 > 14

Josie made a greater amount of beverages.

B **1** The soccer coach has a container that holds 5 liters of water. How many milliliters of water does the container hold?

Fill in the table to answer the question.

Liters (L)	1	2	3	4	5
Milliliters (mL)	1,000	2,000	3,000	4,000	5,000

The container holds __5,000 milliliters__ of water.

B **2** Write an expression that shows how to convert liters to milliliters. Use L to stand for the number of liters.

__L × 1,000__

M **3** Convert the units of liquid volume.

6 L = __6,000__ mL $\frac{1}{2}$ L = __500__ mL

Vocabulary

convert to change from one unit to another unit.

1 liter = 1,000 milliliters

unit ← → unit

unit ← → unit

Solve.

M **4** Carla had 2 liters of juice to share. She and her 3 friends each drank an equal amount of the juice. How many milliliters of juice did each friend have?

1 liter = 1,000 milliliters

Show your work.   Possible work shown.

2 × 1,000 = 2,000

2,000 ÷ 4 = 500

Solution: __500 milliliters__

M **5** Theo filled up a 3-liter watering can to water the garden. He has 750 milliliters of water left in the watering can. How many milliliters of water did Theo use?

Show your work.   Possible work shown.

3 × 1,000 = 3,000

3,000 − 750 = 2,250

Solution: __2,250 milliliters__

M **6** A small bottle contains 2 cups of juice. Do 5 small bottles of juice have a greater amount of juice than a 1-quart bottle of juice? Explain.

1 quart = 4 cups

Possible explanation: 2 cups in each small bottle × 5 bottles = 10 cups.

So, 5 small bottles = 10 cups of juice. 1 quart = 4 cups of juice. 10 > 4,

so 5 small bottles of juice have a greater amount of juice than a 1-quart bottle.

C **7** Rachel has a 4-liter jug of water. She fills 3 small vases each with 900 mL of water. How much water did she use? How much water is left in the jug?

Show your work.   Possible work shown.

4 L = 4,000 mL

3 × 900 = 2,700 mL used

4,000 − 2,700 = 1,300 mL left in the jug

Solution: __2,700 mL used and 1,300 mL left__

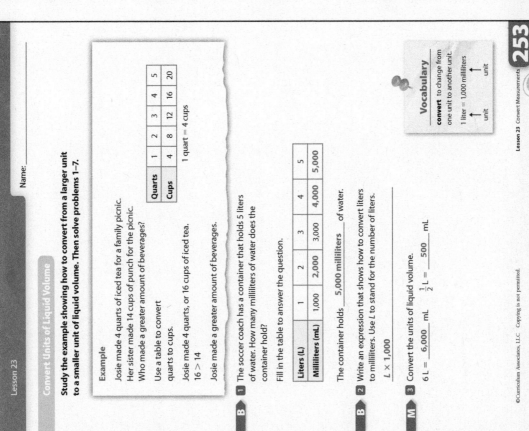
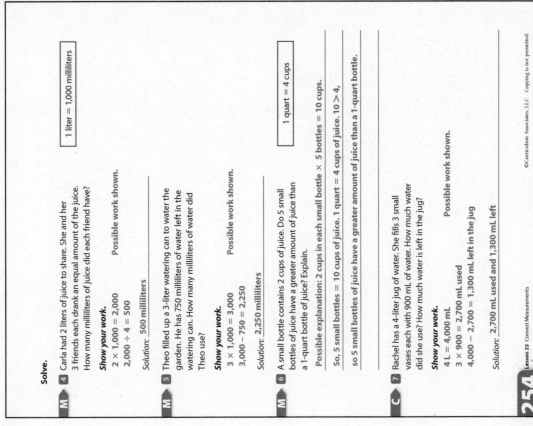

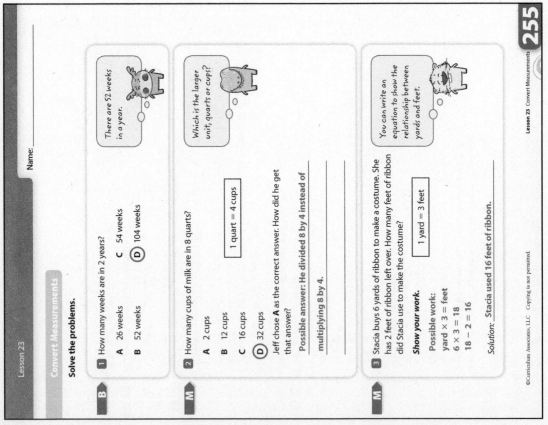

Solve.

4 Which of the following is equal to 2 days, 12 hours? Circle the letter for all that apply.

  A 48 hours

  B 60 hours

  C 1 day, 36 hours

  D 1 day, 24 hours

1 day = 24 hours

5 Jason is 5 foot 11 inches tall. Amy is 63 inches tall. Who is taller and by how much?

Do you compare the heights in inches or feet?

  $1 \text{ foot} = 12 \text{ inches}$

Show your work.

Possible work:
5 feet = 60 inches
60 + 11 = 71 inches for Jason's height
71 − 63 = 8 inches

Solution: Jason is taller than Amy by 8 inches.

6 How many 250 mL glasses can be filled with 2 L of water?

A picture or a table can help you understand and solve this problem.

  $1 \text{ liter} = 1,000 \text{ milliliters}$

Show your work.

Possible work:
2 L = 2,000 mL

Students might draw a picture or a table, or write and solve an equation to solve this problem.

Glasses	1	2	3	4	5	6	7	8
mL per glass	250	500	750	1,000	1,250	1,500	1,750	2,000

Solution: 8 glasses

Lesson 23 Convert Measurements   ©Curriculum Associates, LLC   Copying is not permitted.

256

Name: _____

Lesson 23

Convert Measurements

Solve the problems.

1 How many weeks are in 2 years?

  A 26 weeks   **C** 54 weeks

  B 52 weeks   **D** 104 weeks

There are 52 weeks in a year.

2 How many cups of milk are in 8 quarts?

  A 2 cups

  B 12 cups

  C 16 cups

  D 32 cups

Which is the larger unit, quarts or cups?

  $1 \text{ quart} = 4 \text{ cups}$

Jeff chose **A** as the correct answer. How did he get that answer?

Possible answer: He divided 8 by 4 instead of

multiplying 8 by 4.

3 Stacia buys 6 yards of ribbon to make a costume. She has 2 feet of ribbon left over. How many feet of ribbon did Stacia use to make the costume?

You can write an equation to show the relationship between yards and feet.

  $1 \text{ yard} = 3 \text{ feet}$

Show your work.

Possible work:
yard × 3 = feet
6 × 3 = 18
18 − 2 = 16

Solution: Stacia used 16 feet of ribbon.

©Curriculum Associates, LLC   Copying is not permitted.   Lesson 23 Convert Measurements

255

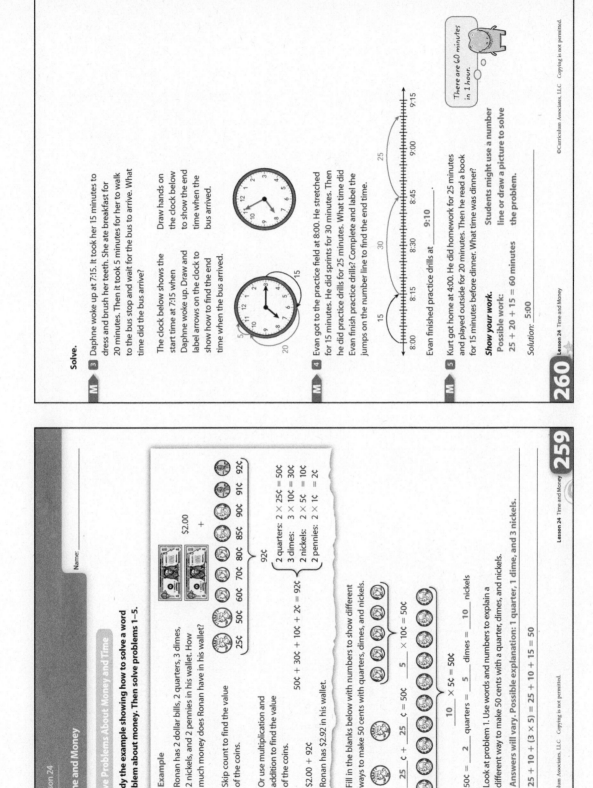

Name: _____

Lesson 24

Time and Money

Solve Problems About Money and Time

Study the example showing how to solve a word problem about money. Then solve problems 1–5.

Example

Ronan has 2 dollar bills, 2 quarters, 3 dimes, 2 nickels, and 2 pennies in his wallet. How much money does Ronan have in his wallet?

Skip count to find the value of the coins.

25¢　50¢　60¢　70¢　80¢　85¢　90¢　91¢　92¢

Or use multiplication and addition to find the value of the coins.

2 quarters: $2 \times 25¢ = 50¢$
3 dimes: $3 \times 10¢ = 30¢$
2 nickels: $2 \times 5¢ = 10¢$
2 pennies: $2 \times 1¢ = 2¢$

$50¢ + 30¢ + 10¢ + 2¢ = 92¢$

$2.00
+ 92¢

$2.00 + 92¢
Ronan has $2.92 in his wallet.

M 1 Fill in the blanks below with numbers to show different ways to make 50 cents with quarters, dimes, and nickels.

__25__ ¢ + __25__ ¢ = 50¢　　__2__ × 25¢ = 50¢

__10__ × 5¢ = 50¢

50¢ = __2__ quarters = __5__ dimes = __10__ nickels

M 2 Look at problem 1. Use words and numbers to explain a different way to make 50 cents with a quarter, dimes, and nickels.

Answers will vary. Possible explanation: 1 quarter, 1 dime, and 3 nickels.

$25 + 10 + (3 \times 5) = 25 + 10 + 15 = 50$

259

Solve.

M 3 Daphne woke up at 7:15. It took her 15 minutes to dress and brush her teeth. She ate breakfast for 20 minutes. Then it took 5 minutes for her to walk to the bus stop and wait for the bus to arrive. What time did the bus arrive?

The clock below shows the start time at 7:15 when Daphne woke up. Draw and label arrows on the clock to show how to find the end time when the bus arrived.

Draw hands on the clock below to show the end time when the bus arrived.

M 4 Evan got to the practice field at 8:00. He stretched for 15 minutes. He did sprints for 30 minutes. Then he did practice drills for 25 minutes. What time did Evan finish practice drills? Complete and label the jumps on the number line to find the end time.

8:00　8:15　8:30　8:45　9:00　9:15

15　30　25

Evan finished practice drills at __9:10__.

M 5 Kurt got home at 4:00. He did homework for 25 minutes and played outside for 20 minutes. Then he read a book for 15 minutes before dinner. What time was dinner?

Show your work.
Possible work:
$25 + 20 + 15 = 60$ minutes

Students might use a number line or draw a picture to solve the problem.

Solution: __5:00__

There are 60 minutes in 1 hour.

260

Key

B Basic　　**M** Medium　　**C** Challenge

Lesson 24

Name: _____

Solve Problems About Time

Study the example showing how to solve a problem about time. Then solve problems 1–6.

Example

Amy had 1 hour to do activities. She talked on the phone for 5 minutes. She rode her bike for 15 minutes. She played a game with her brother for 25 minutes. How much time did Amy have left to spend painting a picture?

Amy had 60 minutes to do activities. 1 hour = 60 minutes

Add the minutes for the known activities. 5 + 15 + 25 = 45 minutes

Write an equation to find how much time 45 + P = 60 or P = 60 − 45
Amy had left to paint a picture. P = 15 P = 15

Amy had 15 minutes left to paint a picture.

B **1** Complete the labels on the number line to represent the example problem.

game   bike   phone

0   10   20   30   40   50   60
        Minutes

B **2** Look at the number line in problem 1. What does the dot at 15 represent?

15 minutes that Amy has left to paint a picture

M **3** Milo visited an amusement park for 3 hours. He rode rides for 50 minutes, played carnival games for 40 minutes, and ate food for 30 minutes. He spent the rest of the time waiting in lines. How much time did Milo spend waiting in lines? Write and solve an equation to find the answer.

3 hours = __180__ minutes

Known activities = __50__ + __40__ + __30__ = __120__ minutes

Equation: __120 + w = 180 or w = 180 − 120__ Students may use any letter for
the variable in the equation.

Milo spent __60__ minutes waiting in lines.

Solve.

M **4** Tell whether each amount of time is equivalent to 2 hours and 10 minutes.

a. 210 minutes ☐ Yes ☒ No

b. 130 minutes ☒ Yes ☐ No

c. 1 hour, 70 minutes ☒ Yes ☐ No

M **5** One of the fastest times for a 1,500-meter race is 3 minutes and 34 seconds. How many seconds is this time?

Show your work.

Possible work:
3 × 60 = 180 seconds
180 + 34 = 214

Solution: __214 seconds__

C **6** Bennett spent 4 hours at school today. He attended three 70-minute classes. There is a 5-minute break between classes. Then he ate lunch before going home. How long did Bennett spend eating lunch?

Show your work.

Possible work:
4 hours = 4 × 60 = 240 minutes
Time in class: 3 × 70 = 210 minutes
Time between classes: 2 × 5 = 10 minutes
210 + 10 = 220
240 − 220 = 20 minutes

Students might draw a bar model, use a number line, or write and solve an equation to solve the problem.

Solution: __20 minutes__

Lesson 24

Name: _____

Solve Problems About Money

Study the example showing how to solve a problem about money. Then solve problems 1–7.

Example

Rita bought milk for $0.50, a sandwich for $2.50, and a fruit salad for $1.25. She paid for her lunch with a $5.00 bill. How much change did Rita get?

$1.00 = 100 cents
$5.00 = 500 cents

Rita spent: 50 + 250 + 125 = 425 cents

500 cents − 425 cents = 75 cents

Rita got 75 cents, or $0.75, in change.

B **1** The picture below shows that $5.00 is the same as $3.00 in bills plus 8 quarters. Cross out the bills and coins to show the amount that Rita spent on lunch in the example above.

1 dollar = 4 quarters
1 quarter = 25 cents

B **2** How can you find the change Rita gets by looking at the picture above? Explain. Possible explanation: Skip count or multiply to find the value of the 3 quarters that are not crossed out: 25, 50, 75 or 3 × 25 = 75 cents.

M **3** Josh bought 4 movie tickets and 2 large popcorns. Each movie ticket is $8. Each popcorn is $5. How much money did Josh spend?

Tickets: 4 × 8 = $32   Popcorn: 2 × 5 = $10

Tickets and popcorn: 32 + 10 = $42

Josh spent $42 .

Solve.

M **4** Mandy has a total of $2.00 in change in her purse. Complete each set of coins below to show amounts equivalent to $2.00.

a. 4 quarters, 5 dimes, 10 nickels

b. 10 pennies, 9 dimes, 3 quarters, 5 nickels

c. 2 quarters, 12 dimes, 3 nickels, 15 pennies

d. 5 quarters, 4 dimes, 6 nickels, 5 pennies

M **5** A pound of apples costs $1.30. Sawyer bought $2\frac{1}{2}$ pounds of apples. How much did Sawyer pay?

Show your work.

Possible work: 130 cents a pound

2 × 130 = 260

Half of 130 cents is 65 cents

260 + 65 = 325 cents

Solution: $3.25

M **6** Brie earns $3,000 a month. Every month, she spends $1,400 on rent and bills, $700 on groceries, $200 on a car payment, and $100 on gas. She saves the rest. How much money does Brie save?

Show your work.

Possible work: Money spent: 1,400 + 700 + 200 + 100 = 2,400

Money to save: 3,000 − 2,400 = 600

Solution: $600

C **7** Regular bananas cost $0.20 each at the supermarket. Organic bananas cost $0.30 each. If you have $3.00, how many more regular bananas than organic bananas can you buy?

Show your work.

Possible work: $3.00 = 300 cents

Regular bananas: 15 × 20 cents = 300 cents

Organic bananas: 10 × 30 cents = 300 cents

15 − 10 = 5

Solution: 5 more regular bananas

Name: _____

Lesson 24

Time and Money

Solve the problems.

1 How many days are in 1 year and 5 weeks?

A 372 days

B 378 days

C 400 days *(circled)*

D 1,825 days

There are 365 days in a year. There are 7 days in a week.

2 Rowan bought 2 comic books for $2.50 each, a fiction book for $7, and a poster for $1.25 at the book fair. Rowan paid with a $20.00 bill. How much change did he get?

A $6.75 *(circled)*   C $13.25

B $12.75   D $17.75

What operation do you use to represent the cost of the 2 comic books?

Courtney chose **C** as the correct answer. How did she get that answer?

Possible answer: She found the amount Rowan spent, instead of subtracting that amount from $20 to find the change.

3 How many minutes are there in one day?

Show your work.

Possible work:

1 day has 24 hours. 1 hour has 60 minutes.

$24 \times 60 = 1{,}440$ minutes

There are 24 hours in one day.

Solution: 1,440 minutes

Solve.

4 A private music lesson at Parker Music costs $40 for 1 hour. A private music lesson at Joelle Music costs $25 for 30 minutes. How much more does a 1-hour private lesson cost at Joelle Music than at Parker Music?

What's the cost for 60 minutes of lessons at each store?

Show your work.

Possible work:

1 hour = 60 minutes

The cost at Parker Music is $40 for 60 minutes.

The cost for 60 minutes at Joelle Music is $2 \times \$25 = \$50$.

$40 < $50, so the cost is less at Parker Music.

$50 - $40 = $10

Solution: $10 more

5 Susan bought 4 boxes of granola bars and 2 cartons of milk. Each box of granola bars cost $2.50 and each carton of milk cost $2.75, including tax. Susan gave the clerk a $20.00 bill. What did she get in change? List two different ways Susan could have received change.

What coins are equal in value to 1 dollar?

Show your work.

Possible work:

$20 - (4 \times $2.50) - (2 \times $2.75)

$20 - ($10) - ($5.50) = $4.50

Answers will vary. Bills and coins should total $4.50.

Solution: bills: 4 one-dollar bills   coins: 2 quarters

bills: 3 one-dollar bills   coins: 2 quarters, 10 dimes

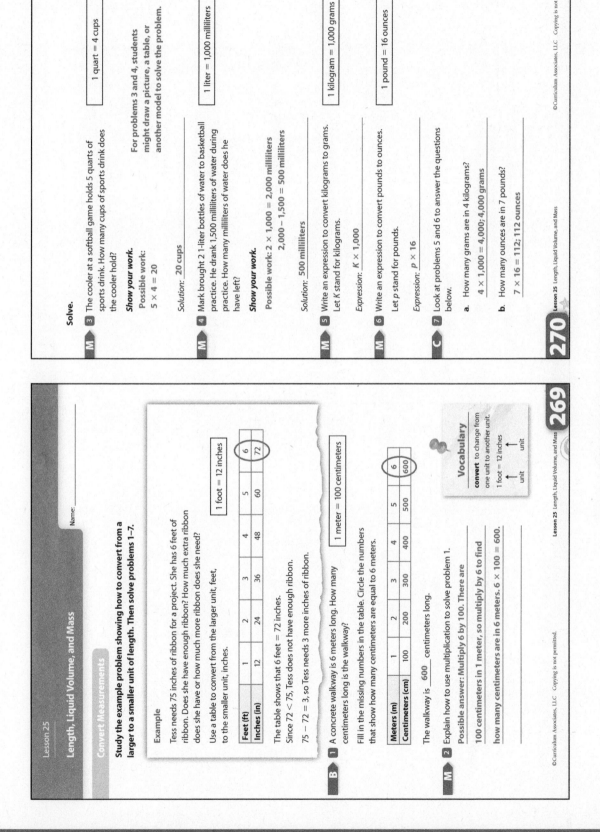

Lesson 25
Length, Liquid Volume, and Mass

Convert Measurements

Study the example problem showing how to convert from a larger to a smaller unit of length. Then solve problems 1–7.

Example
Tess needs 75 inches of ribbon for a project. She has 6 feet of ribbon. Does she have enough ribbon? How much extra ribbon does she have or how much more ribbon does she need?

Use a table to convert from the larger unit, feet, to the smaller unit, inches.

1 foot = 12 inches

Feet (ft)	1	2	3	4	5	6
Inches (in)	12	24	36	48	60	72

The table shows that 6 feet = 72 inches.
Since 72 < 75, Tess does not have enough ribbon.
75 − 72 = 3, so Tess needs 3 more inches of ribbon.

B 1 A concrete walkway is 6 meters long. How many centimeters long is the walkway?

Fill in the missing numbers in the table. Circle the numbers that show how many centimeters are equal to 6 meters.

1 meter = 100 centimeters

Meters (m)	1	2	3	4	5	6
Centimeters (cm)	100	200	300	400	500	600

The walkway is __600__ centimeters long.

M 2 Explain how to use multiplication to solve problem 1.
Possible answer: Multiply 6 by 100. There are 100 centimeters in 1 meter, so multiply by 6 to find how many centimeters are in 6 meters. 6 × 100 = 600.

Vocabulary
convert to change from one unit to another unit.
1 foot = 12 inches
unit ← → unit

Solve.

M 3 The cooler at a softball game holds 5 quarts of sports drink. How many cups of sports drink does the cooler hold?

1 quart = 4 cups

Show your work.
Possible work:
5 × 4 = 20

Solution: __20 cups__

M 4 Mark brought 2 1-liter bottles of water to basketball practice. He drank 1,500 milliliters of water during practice. How many milliliters of water does he have left?

For problems 3 and 4, students might draw a picture, a table, or another model to solve the problem.

1 liter = 1,000 milliliters

Show your work.
Possible work: 2 × 1,000 = 2,000 milliliters
2,000 − 1,500 = 500 milliliters

Solution: __500 milliliters__

M 5 Write an expression to convert kilograms to grams. Let K stand for kilograms.

1 kilogram = 1,000 grams

Expression: __K × 1,000__

M 6 Write an expression to convert pounds to ounces. Let p stand for pounds.

1 pound = 16 ounces

Expression: __p × 16__

C 7 Look at problems 5 and 6 to answer the questions below.
a. How many grams are in 4 kilograms?
   4 × 1,000 = 4,000; 4,000 grams
b. How many ounces are in 7 pounds?
   7 × 16 = 112; 112 ounces

Key

B Basic   **M** Medium   **C** Challenge

269

270

Lesson 25 Length, Liquid Volume, and Mass

©Curriculum Associates, LLC   Copying is not permitted.

Practice and Problem Solving   Unit 5 Measurement and Data   **103**
©Curriculum Associates, LLC   Copying is not permitted.

Lesson 25

Name: _____

Solve Length Problems

Study the example problem showing how to solve a multi-step problem about length. Then solve problems 1–5.

Example
Wendy has a fence that is 10 feet long. Vines cover a section of fence that is $\frac{5}{6}$ foot long. Wendy and 4 friends will each paint an equal length of the rest of the fence. How long is the section of fence that each friend will paint?

| 1 foot = 12 inches |

Length of fence: 10 feet = 120 inches
Length covered with vines: $\frac{5}{6} \times 12$ inches = 10 inches
Length to paint: 120 − 10 = 110 inches
Length of each section: 110 ÷ 5 = 22 inches

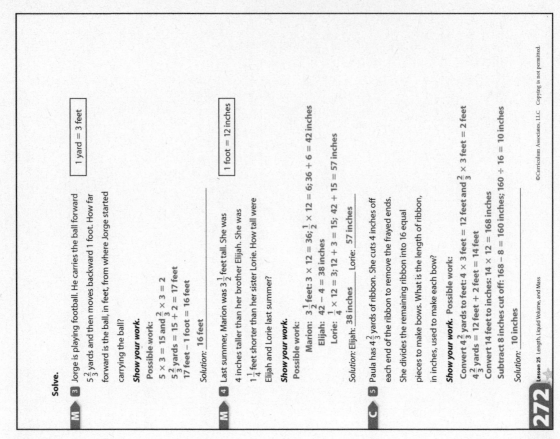

The section of fence each friend will paint is 22 inches.

M 1 Nestor needs 750 centimeters of rope. Rope comes in lengths of $4\frac{1}{2}$ meters and 9 meters at the hardware store. Which length of rope should Nestor buy?

| 1 meter = 100 centimeters |

$4\frac{1}{2}$ meters = __450__ centimeters
9 meters = __900__ centimeters

a. Which length is greater than 750 centimeters? __900__ centimeters

b. Nestor should buy rope with a length of __9 meters__ .

M 2 Which length is greater, $\frac{1}{2}$ meter or 240 centimeters? Explain.

Possible explanation: 1 meter = 100 centimeters, so $\frac{1}{2}$ meter = 50 centimeters.

240 centimeters > 50 centimeters, so 240 centimeters is the greater length.

Lesson 25 Length, Liquid Volume, and Mass

271

Solve.

M 3 Jorge is playing football. He carries the ball forward $5\frac{2}{3}$ yards and then moves backward 1 foot. How far forward is the ball, in feet, from where Jorge started carrying the ball?

| 1 yard = 3 feet |

Show your work.
Possible work:
$5 \times 3 = 15$ and $\frac{2}{3} \times 3 = 2$
$5\frac{2}{3}$ yards $= 15 + 2 = 17$ feet
17 feet − 1 foot = 16 feet

Solution: __16 feet__

M 4 Last summer, Marion was $3\frac{1}{2}$ feet tall. She was 4 inches taller than her brother Elijah. She was $1\frac{1}{4}$ feet shorter than her sister Lorie. How tall were Elijah and Lorie last summer?

| 1 foot = 12 inches |

Show your work.
Possible work:
Marion: $3\frac{1}{2}$ feet: $3 \times 12 = 36$; $\frac{1}{2} \times 12 = 6$; $36 + 6 = 42$ inches
Elijah: $42 - 4 = 38$ inches
Lorie: $1\frac{1}{4} \times 12 = 3$; $12 + 3 = 15$; $42 + 15 = 57$ inches

Solution: Elijah: __38 inches__   Lorie: __57 inches__

C 5 Paula has $4\frac{2}{3}$ yards of ribbon. She cuts 4 inches off each end of the ribbon to remove the frayed ends. She divides the remaining ribbon into 16 equal pieces to make bows. What is the length of ribbon, in inches, used to make each bow?

Show your work. Possible work:
Convert $4\frac{2}{3}$ yards to feet: 4×3 feet = 12 feet and $\frac{2}{3} \times 3$ feet = 2 feet
$4\frac{2}{3}$ yards = 12 feet + 2 feet = 14 feet
Convert 14 feet to inches: $14 \times 12 = 168$ inches
Subtract 8 inches cut off: $168 - 8 = 160$ inches; $160 \div 16 = 10$ inches

Solution: __10 inches__

272 Lesson 25 Length, Liquid Volume, and Mass

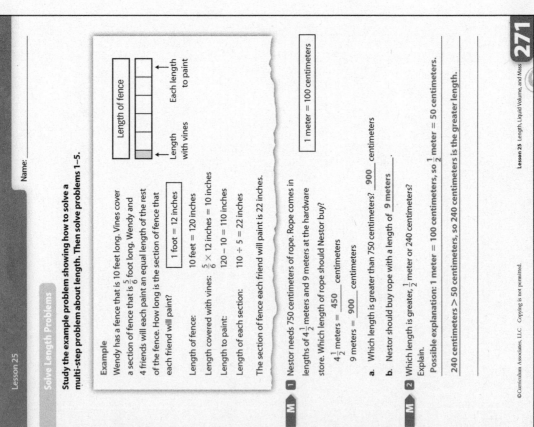

Page 273

Lesson 25

Name: _____

Solve Liquid Volume Problems

Study the example showing how to solve a liquid volume problem. Then solve problems 1–5.

Example

Naomi has a container of water. She uses 4 liters to water her vegetable garden. She uses $3\frac{1}{2}$ liters to water flowers. She uses the remaining 500 milliliters in the container to fill up a bird bath. How many milliliters of water did Naomi have in the container?

| | 1 liter (L) = 1,000 milliliters (mL) |

Write an equation to find the total amount of water. $W = 4\,L + 3\frac{1}{2}\,L + 500\ mL$

Convert liters to milliliters.

$4 \times 1,000\ mL = 4,000\ mL$
$3 \times 1,000\ mL = 3,000\ mL$ and $\frac{1}{2} \times 1,000\ mL = 500\ mL$

Write the equation using milliliters and solve. $W = 4,000\ mL + 3,500\ mL + 500\ mL$
$W = 8,000\ mL$

Naomi had 8,000 milliliters of water in the container.

Benny has two small fish tanks with one fish in each tank. One tank has $3\frac{1}{2}$ quarts of water. The other tank has 12 cups of water. Benny combines the water into one large fish tank with both fish in the large tank.

| | 1 quart = 4 cups |

B   **1** How many cups of water are in the large tank?

$3\frac{1}{2}$ quarts: 3×4 cups = __12__ cups and $\frac{1}{2} \times 4$ cups = __2__ cups

$3\frac{1}{2}$ quarts = __14__ cups; __14__ cups + __12__ cups = __26__ cups

There are __26 cups__ of water in the large tank.

M   **2** At least 5 cups of water are needed for each fish in a tank. How many more fish would Benny be able to put in the large tank? Explain.

Possible explanation: $26 \div 5 = 5$ with a remainder of 1. The tank can hold 5 fish, so

Benny can add 3 more fish to the tank.

Page 274

Solve.

| | 1 gallon = 4 quarts |

M   **3** Tamara prepared fruit punch for a party. She used $\frac{3}{4}$ gallon of pineapple juice, 2 quarts of lemonade, and $1\frac{1}{4}$ gallons of orange juice. How many quarts of punch did Tamara prepare?

Show your work.

Possible work: Pineapple juice: $\frac{3}{4} \times 4$ quarts = 3 quarts

Lemonade: 2 quarts

Orange juice: 1×4 quarts = 4 quarts; $\frac{1}{4} \times 4$ quarts = 1 quart;
4 quarts + 1 quart = 5 quarts

Total number of quarts = $3 + 2 + 5 = 10$

Solution: **10 quarts**

M   **4** Sharon and her cousin are making milkshakes at a family reunion. Sharon brought $2\frac{1}{2}$ gallons of milk. Her cousin brought 2 quarts of milk. The girls used 8 quarts of milk for the milkshakes. How much milk is left? There may be more than one correct answer. Circle the letter for all that apply.

(A) 4 quarts   **(D)** 1 gallon

B 6 quarts   **E** $1\frac{1}{2}$ gallons

C $\frac{1}{2}$ gallon

| | 1 quart = 4 cups |
| | 1 cup = 8 ounces |

C   **5** Rob has 6 quarts of apple cider for the fall fair. He pours the cider into glasses to set on picnic tables. He pours 6 ounces of cider into each glass. How many glasses of cider does Rob set on the tables?

Show your work.

Possible work:
6 quarts = 6×4 cups = 24 cups
24 cups = 24×8 ounces = 192 ounces
$192 \div 6 = 32$

Solution: **32 glasses**

Lesson 25

Name:

Solve Mass and Weight Problems

Study the example problem showing how to solve a mass and weight problem. Then solve problems 1–5.

Example
The softball coach has a box filled with softballs. The weight of the empty box is 3 pounds. When it is filled with softballs, the box weighs 12 pounds. Each softball has a weight of 6 ounces. How many softballs are in the box?

1 pound = 16 ounces

12 pounds

| Weight of softballs (S) | 3 pounds |

Weight of empty container

S = Weight of 1 softball (6 ounces) × number of softballs (n)

Find the weight of the softballs in ounces.
$S = 12$ pounds $- 3$ pounds $= 9$ pounds
$S = 9 \times 16$ ounces $= 144$ ounces

Find the number of softballs.
$S = 6 \times n$
$144 = 6 \times n$
$24 = n$

There are 24 softballs in the box.

1 Look at the example above. Explain why you need to find the weight of the softballs in the box in ounces.
Possible explanation: Because the weight of one softball is given in ounces, you need to know the total weight of all the softballs in ounces. Then you can find the number of softballs by dividing the total weight in ounces by the weight of one softball in ounces.

2 Tyson's baby brother weighed 7 pounds, 3 ounces when he was born. The baby lost 9 ounces after a few days, and then gained 1 pound, 6 ounces by the end of the week. How much did the baby weigh at the end of the week?

Show your work.
Possible work: 7 pounds, 3 ounces = (7 × 16) + 3 = 115 ounces
115 ounces − 9 ounces = 106 ounces; 1 pound, 6 ounces = 16 + 6 = 22 ounces
106 ounces + 22 ounces = 128 ounces

Solution: 128 ounces or 8 pounds

275

Solve.

3 A large truck that moves cars can carry a maximum load of 15,720 pounds. The table below shows the weight of each kind of car that could be loaded onto the truck.

1 ton = 2,000 pounds

Kind of Car	Compact	Mid-size	Full-size
Weight (in tons)	$1\frac{1}{2}$	$2\frac{1}{4}$	3

Choose *Yes* or *No* to tell whether the truck is able to carry each load of cars below.

a. 2 full-size cars, 1 compact car [X] Yes [ ] No
b. 2 compact cars, 2 full-size cars [ ] Yes [X] No
c. 2 mid-size cars, 2 compact cars [X] Yes [ ] No
d. 4 mid-size cars [ ] Yes [X] No

4 Melinda donated fudge for the school bake sale. She wrapped 80 pieces of fudge. Each piece of fudge weighed 1 ounce. How many pounds of fudge did Melinda wrap?

1 pound = 16 ounces

Show your work.
Possible work: 80 × 1 ounce = 80 ounces
$n \times 16 = 80$
$n = 5$

Solution: 5 pounds

5 A paper clip has a mass of 1 gram. A box of paper clips has 100 paper clips. Which equation below can be used to find the number of boxes of paper clips that will have a mass of 1 kilogram? Let n be the number of boxes. Circle the letter for all that apply.

1 kilogram = 1,000 grams

(A) $100 = 1,000 \div n$
(B) $n = 1,000 \times 100$
(C) $n = 1,000 \div 100$
(D) $1,000 = n \times 100$

276 Lesson 25 Length, Liquid Volume, and Mass

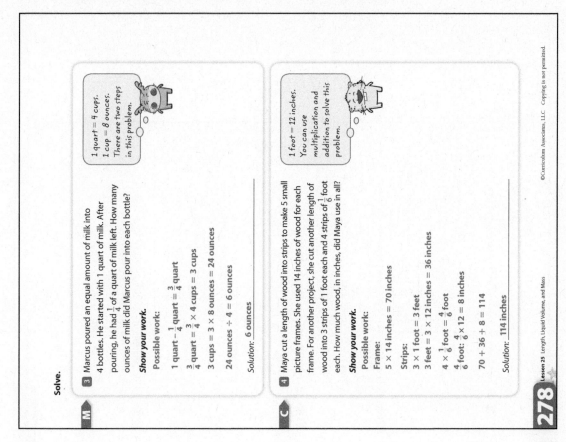

Solve.

M **3** Marcus poured an equal amount of milk into 4 bottles. He started with 1 quart of milk. After pouring, he had $\frac{1}{4}$ of a quart of milk left. How many ounces of milk did Marcus pour into each bottle?

Show your work.

Possible work:

$1\ quart - \frac{1}{4}\ quart = \frac{3}{4}\ quart$

$\frac{3}{4}\ quart = \frac{3}{4} \times 4\ cups = 3\ cups$

$3\ cups = 3 \times 8\ ounces = 24\ ounces$

$24\ ounces \div 4 = 6\ ounces$

Solution: 6 ounces

> 1 quart = 4 cups.
> 1 cup = 8 ounces.
> There are two steps in this problem.

C **4** Maya cut a length of wood into strips to make 5 small picture frames. She used 14 inches of wood for each frame. For another project, she cut another length of wood into 3 strips of 1 foot each and 4 strips of $\frac{1}{6}$ foot each. How much wood, in inches, did Maya use in all?

Show your work.

Possible work:

Frame:

$5 \times 14\ inches = 70\ inches$

Strips:

$3 \times 1\ foot = 3\ feet$

$3\ feet = 3 \times 12\ inches = 36\ inches$

$4 \times \frac{1}{6}\ foot = \frac{4}{6}\ foot$

$\frac{4}{6}\ foot: \frac{4}{6} \times 12 = 8\ inches$

$70 + 36 + 8 = 114$

Solution: 114 inches

> 1 foot = 12 inches.
> You can use multiplication and addition to solve this problem.

Lesson 25

Length, Liquid Volume, and Mass

Name: _____

Solve the problems.

B **1** Miguel and his brother put two 8-foot tables end to end for a graduation party. The tablecloth they plan to use is 5 yards in length. Is the tablecloth long enough to cover both tables?

A Yes, because 8 feet < 10 yards.

B Yes, because the tables are 8 feet long and the tablecloth is 15 feet long.

(C) No, because the tables are 16 feet long and the tablecloth is 15 feet long.

D No, because 8 feet > 5 yards.

> 1 yard = 3 feet.
> What units should you use to compare the length of the tables and the length of the tablecloth?

M **2** Patel bought a 2-pound bag of trail mix. He poured $\frac{1}{2}$ pound of the mix into a bowl and divided the remaining amount into bags. Each bag had 2 ounces of trail mix. How many bags did Patel use?

A 20 bags

B 16 bags

(C) 12 bags

D 8 bags

> 1 pound = 16 ounces.
> How many ounces of trail mix is he dividing into bags?

Jen chose **A** as the correct answer. How did she get that answer?

Possible answer: She added 2 pounds and

$\frac{1}{2}$ pound instead of subtracting $\frac{1}{2}$ pound from

2 pounds to find the remaining amount of trail

mix that Patel divided into bags.

Lesson 26
Perimeter and Area

Name: _____

Connect Area and Perimeter

Study the example showing how to find the area and perimeter of a rectangle. Then solve problems 1–7.

Example
Find the area and perimeter of the rectangle at right.

Area
Count square units or multiply side lengths.
The rectangle is 4 units by 10 units.
$4 \times 10 = 40$ square units
Area = 40 square units

Perimeter
Add the lengths of all the sides.
$4 + 10 + 4 + 10 = 28$ units
Perimeter = 28 units

B 1 Find the area and perimeter of the rectangle at right.
Area = __24__ square units   Perimeter = __20__ units

M 2 Look at the rectangle in problem 1. Draw a rectangle with the same area but a different perimeter.

Possible rectangles: 1×24, 2×12, 3×8, 8×3, 12×2, 24×1

Possible rectangle shown.

What is the perimeter of the rectangle you drew?
Answers will vary. Possible answer: 22 units

M 3 Look at the rectangle in problem 1. Draw a rectangle with the same perimeter but a different area.

Possible rectangles: 7×3, 8×2, 9×1, 3×7, 2×8, 1×9

Possible rectangle shown.

What is the area of the rectangle you drew?
Answers will vary. Possible answer: 16 square units

281 Lesson 26 Perimeter and Area

Solve.

M 4 Look at the shape below. Find the area and perimeter of the shape.

Area = __28__ square units
Perimeter = __32__ units

M 5 What is the area and perimeter of a square with side lengths of 4 units? Draw the square below.

Area = __16__ square units
Perimeter = __16__ units

C 6 Look at the square you drew in problem 5.

a. Draw a rectangle with the same area as the square and a different perimeter than the square.

Possible rectangle shown.
Possible rectangles:
$16 \times 1, 8 \times 2, 2 \times 8, 1 \times 16$

b. What is the perimeter of the rectangle you drew? Is it equal to, greater than, or less than the perimeter of the square you drew in problem 5? Explain.

Possible answer and explanation: 34 units.

The perimeter is greater, 34 > 16.

M 7 The perimeter of each triangle below is 12 centimeters. Write the missing side length on each triangle.

5 cm   4 cm
3 cm   4 cm

4 cm   4 cm   4 cm

282 Lesson 26 Perimeter and Area

Key

B Basic   **M** Medium   **C** Challenge

Lesson 26

Solve Perimeter Problems

Study the example problem showing how to solve a problem about perimeter. Then solve problems 1–6.

Example

The community center has a rectangular kiddie pool. The length of the pool is 25 feet. The width is 15 feet. What is the perimeter of the kiddie pool?

Use a formula for the perimeter of a rectangle.

$P = 2l + 2w$ $P = 2 (l + w)$
$= (2 \times 25) + (2 \times 15)$ $= 2 (25 + 15)$
$= 50 + 30$ $= 2 (40)$
$= 80$ $= 80$

The perimeter of the pool is 80 feet.

[rectangle 25 ft by 15 ft]

B **1** A rectangular photograph has a length of 10 inches and a width of 8 inches. Fill in the numbers in the formulas below to show two ways to find the perimeter of the photograph.

$P = \underline{\quad} 2l \underline{\quad} + \underline{\quad} 2w \underline{\quad}$ $P = 2(l + w)$
$P = (2 \times \underline{10}) + (2 \times \underline{8})$ $P = 2 (\underline{8} + \underline{10})$
$= \underline{20} + \underline{16}$ $= 2 (\underline{18})$
$= \underline{36}$ $= \underline{36}$

The perimeter is $\underline{36}$ inches.

M **2** Jason's rectangular computer screen is 50 centimeters across and 36 centimeters high. What is the perimeter of Jason's computer screen?

Show your work.

Possible work:
$P = (2 \times 50) + (2 \times 36)$
$= 100 + 72$
$= 172$

Solution: $P = \underline{172}$ centimeters

Solve.

M **3** A rectangular garden has a width of 90 feet. The perimeter is 500 feet. What is the length of the garden?

$500 = (2 \times l) + (\underline{\quad 2 \quad} \times \underline{\quad 90 \quad})$
$500 = 2l + \underline{180}$
$\underline{320} = 2l$
$\underline{320} \div 2 = l$
$\underline{160} = l$

The length of the garden is $\underline{160}$ feet.

M **4** What is the perimeter of a square with side lengths of 3 inches?

Show your work.

Possible work:
$P = 3 + 3 + 3 + 3 = 12$

Solution: $\underline{12 \text{ inches}}$

M **5** Amy has a ribbon that is 36 inches long. Choose *Yes* or *No* to tell whether she has enough ribbon to wrap around the perimeter of a picture frame for each frame with the given shape and size.

a. square, side lengths of 9 inches   [X] Yes   [ ] No
b. rectangle, 18 inches by 10 inches   [ ] Yes   [X] No
c. rectangle, 12 inches by 24 inches   [ ] Yes   [X] No
d. square, side lengths of 6 inches   [X] Yes   [ ] No

C **6** The square and the rectangle at the right each have a perimeter of 200 centimeters. What are the side lengths of the square and rectangle? (Hint: First find the side length of the square.)

[square labeled s]   [rectangle labeled $(s + 10)$ and $(s - 10)$]

Show your work.

Possible work:
Square: $4 \times s = 200; s = 50$
Rectangle length: $50 + 10 = 60$
Rectangle width: $50 - 10 = 40$

Square: side length $\underline{50}$ cm   Rectangle: length $\underline{60}$ cm   width $\underline{40}$ cm

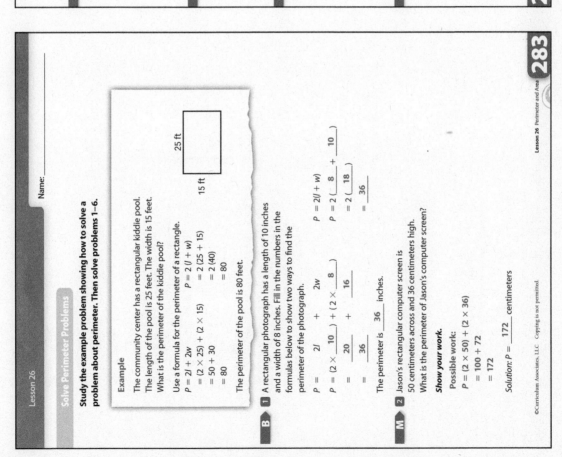

Lesson 26

Name: _____

Solve Area Problems

Study the example showing how to solve a problem about area. Then solve problems 1–6.

Example

Michelle wants to use bricks to make a rectangular patio. She has enough bricks to cover an area of 135 square feet. She wants the length of the patio to be 15 feet. How wide should she make the patio?

Write an equation to represent the area of a rectangle: $A = l \times w$

15 ft

? ft 135 sq ft

$A = 15 \times w$

$135 = 15 \times w$

$135 \div 15 = w$

$9 = w$

Michelle should make the patio 9 feet wide.

B 1 Juan is installing new flooring in a large entryway. The picture at the right shows the length and width of the entryway. How many square feet of flooring does Juan need?

30 ft

25 ft

$A = \underline{30} \times \underline{25}$

$A = \underline{750}$

Juan needs __750__ square feet of flooring.

B 2 Look at the picture at the right. Alyssa wants to tile a room with an area of 480 square feet. The width of the room is 12 feet. What is the length of the room?

? ft

12 ft 480 sq ft

$\underline{480} = l \times \underline{12}$

$480 \div \underline{12} = l$

$\underline{40} = l$

The length of the room is __40__ feet.

Solve.

M 3 Jim is painting the surface of a picnic table. The surface has an area of 2,160 square inches. The width of the table is 30 inches. What is the length of the table?

Show your work.

$2,160 = l \times 30$

$2,160 \div 30 = l; \ 72 = l$

Solution: __72 inches__

M 4 An Olympic floor exercise mat has an area of 144 square meters. Its length is 12 meters. What is the width of the mat?

Show your work.

$144 = 12 \times w$

$144 \div 12 = w; \ 12 = w$

Solution: __12 meters__

M 5 Look at problem 4. What is the shape of the floor exercise mat? Explain how you know.

A square. Possible explanation: The mat is a square because its length and width are the same: 12 meters.

C 6 Melissa has enough paint to cover an area of 250 square feet. She wants to paint two walls. The rectangular wall is 9 feet high and 20 feet wide. The square wall has a height of 9 feet. Does Melissa have enough paint to cover the area of both walls?

Show your work.

Possible work:

Area of one wall: $A = 9 \times 20 = 180$ square feet

Area of other wall: $A = 9 \times 9 = 81$ square feet

Area of both walls: $180 + 81 = 261$ square feet

$261 > 250$

Solution: __No, she does not have enough paint.__

Lesson 26

Name: _____

Solve Perimeter and Area Problems

Solve the problems.

1 The area of a rectangle is 40 square feet. What could be the perimeter of the rectangle? Circle the letter for all that apply.

A 82 ft   **D** 28 ft

B 44 ft   **E** 26 ft

C 40 ft

> $A = l \times w$
> $P = 2(l + w)$
> Find the length and width. Then find the perimeter.

2 Trish had a square garden with side lengths of 8 feet. She expanded her garden to 10 feet by 8 feet. By how many square feet did she expand the area of her garden?

A 144 sq ft   **C** 64 sq ft

B 80 sq ft   **D** 16 sq ft

Kerry chose **A** as the correct answer. How did she get that answer?

Possible answer: She added the areas of the gardens instead of subtracting.

> How much greater is the area of the rectangle than the area of the square?

3 Layla painted the walls of a rectangular room. Two walls are 9 feet by 12 feet. The other two walls are 9 feet by 20 feet. What is the total area of wall that Layla painted?

Show your work.

Possible work: 2 × (9 × 12) = 2 × 108 = 216 sq ft

2 × (9 × 20) = 2 × 180 = 360 sq ft

216 sq ft + 360 sq ft = 576 sq ft

Solution: 576 sq ft

> How do you find the area of all four walls?

Solve.

4 Olivia is putting decorations around the photo in the picture frame shown below. What is the area of the frame that she can decorate?

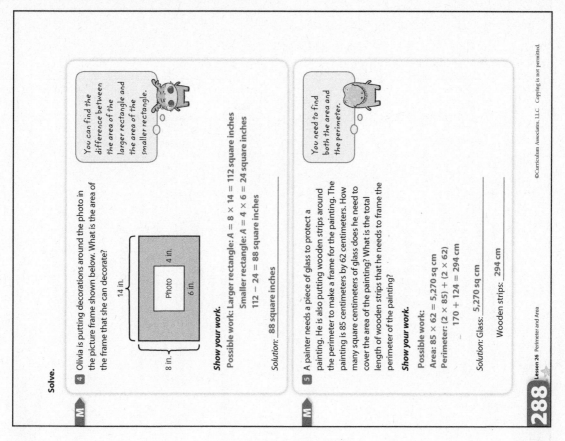

14 in.   8 in.   Photo   4 in.   6 in.

> You can find the difference between the area of the larger rectangle and the area of the smaller rectangle.

Show your work.

Possible work: Larger rectangle: A = 8 × 14 = 112 square inches

Smaller rectangle: A = 4 × 6 = 24 square inches

112 − 24 = 88 square inches

Solution: 88 square inches

5 A painter needs a piece of glass to protect a painting. He is also putting wooden strips around the perimeter to make a frame for the painting. The painting is 85 centimeters by 62 centimeters. How many square centimeters of glass does he need to cover the area of the painting? What is the total length of wooden strips that he needs to frame the perimeter of the painting?

> You need to find both the area and the perimeter.

Show your work.

Possible work:

Area: 85 × 62 = 5,270 sq cm

Perimeter: (2 × 85) + (2 × 62)

170 + 124 = 294 cm

Solution: Glass: 5,270 sq cm

Wooden strips: 294 cm

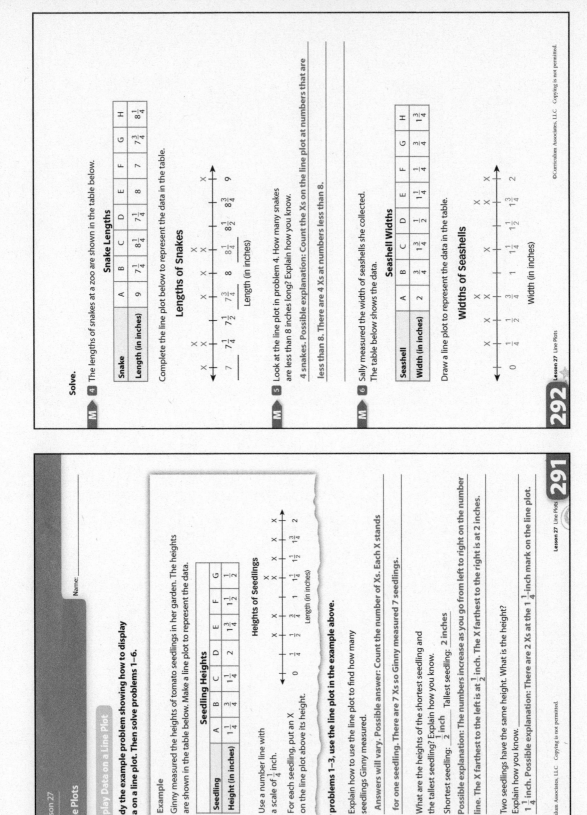

Lesson 27

Line Plots

Display Data on a Line Plot

Study the example problem showing how to display data on a line plot. Then solve problems 1–6.

Example

Ginny measured the heights of tomato seedlings in her garden. The heights are shown in the table below. Make a line plot to represent the data.

Seedling Heights

Seedling	A	B	C	D	E	F	G
Height (in inches)	$1\frac{1}{4}$	$\frac{3}{4}$	$1\frac{1}{4}$	2	$1\frac{3}{4}$	$1\frac{1}{2}$	$\frac{1}{2}$

Use a number line with a scale of $\frac{1}{4}$ inch.

For each seedling, put an X on the line plot above its height.

Heights of Seedlings

0    $\frac{1}{4}$ $\frac{1}{2}$ $\frac{3}{4}$ 1 $1\frac{1}{4}$ $1\frac{1}{2}$ $1\frac{3}{4}$ 2

Length (in inches)

For problems 1–3, use the line plot in the example above.

1 Explain how to use the line plot to find how many seedlings Ginny measured.

Answers will vary. Possible answer: Count the number of Xs. Each X stands for one seedling. There are 7 Xs so Ginny measured 7 seedlings.

2 What are the heights of the shortest seedling and the tallest seedling? Explain how you know.

Shortest seedling: $\frac{1}{2}$ inch   Tallest seedling: 2 inches

Possible explanation: The numbers increase as you go from left to right on the number line. The X farthest to the left is at $\frac{1}{2}$ inch. The X farthest to the right is at 2 inches.

3 Two seedlings have the same height. What is the height? Explain how you know.

$1\frac{1}{4}$ inch. Possible explanation: There are 2 Xs at the $1\frac{1}{4}$-inch mark on the line plot.

Solve.

4 The lengths of snakes at a zoo are shown in the table below.

Snake Lengths

Snake	A	B	C	D	E	F	G	H
Length (in inches)	9	$7\frac{1}{4}$	$8\frac{1}{4}$	$7\frac{1}{4}$	8	7	$7\frac{3}{4}$	$8\frac{1}{4}$

Complete the line plot below to represent the data in the table.

Lengths of Snakes

7    $7\frac{1}{4}$ $7\frac{1}{2}$ $7\frac{3}{4}$ 8 $8\frac{1}{4}$ $8\frac{1}{2}$ $8\frac{3}{4}$ 9

Length (in inches)

5 Look at the line plot in problem 4. How many snakes are less than 8 inches long? Explain how you know.

4 snakes. Possible explanation: Count the Xs on the line plot at numbers that are less than 8. There are 4 Xs at numbers less than 8.

6 Sally measured the width of seashells she collected. The table below shows the data.

Seashell Widths

Seashell	A	B	C	D	E	F	G	H
Width (in inches)	2	$\frac{3}{4}$	$1\frac{3}{4}$	$\frac{1}{2}$	$1\frac{1}{4}$	$\frac{1}{4}$	$\frac{3}{4}$	$1\frac{3}{4}$

Draw a line plot to represent the data in the table.

Widths of Seashells

0    $\frac{1}{4}$ $\frac{1}{2}$ $\frac{3}{4}$ 1 $1\frac{1}{4}$ $1\frac{1}{2}$ $1\frac{3}{4}$ 2

Width (in inches)

Key

B Basic   **M** Medium   **C** Challenge

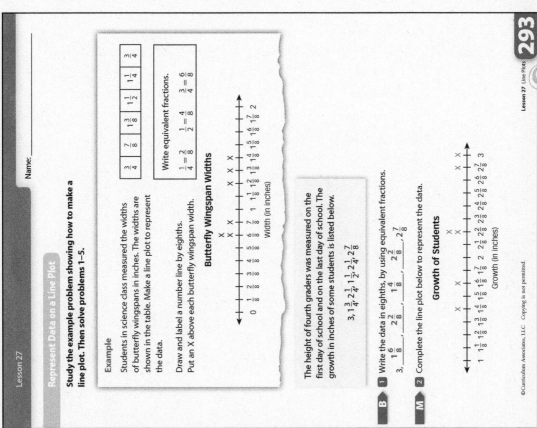

Lesson 27

Name: _____

Represent Data on a Line Plot

Study the example problem showing how to make a line plot. Then solve problems 1–5.

Example

Students in science class measured the widths of butterfly wingspans in inches. The widths are shown in the table. Make a line plot to represent the data.

$\frac{3}{4}$	$\frac{7}{8}$	$1\frac{3}{8}$	$1\frac{1}{2}$	$\frac{3}{4}$
	$\frac{1}{4}$	$1\frac{1}{4}$		

Write equivalent fractions.

$$\frac{1}{4} = \frac{2}{8} \qquad \frac{2}{2} = \frac{4}{8} \qquad \frac{3}{4} = \frac{6}{8}$$

Draw and label a number line by eighths.
Put an X above each butterfly wingspan width.

Butterfly Wingspan Widths

Width (in inches)
$0, \frac{1}{8}, \frac{2}{8}, \frac{3}{8}, \frac{4}{8}, \frac{5}{8}, \frac{6}{8}, \frac{7}{8}, 1, 1\frac{1}{8}, 1\frac{2}{8}, 1\frac{3}{8}, 1\frac{4}{8}, 1\frac{5}{8}, 1\frac{6}{8}, 1\frac{7}{8}, 2$

The height of fourth graders was measured on the first day of school and on the last day of school. The growth in inches of some students is listed below.

$$3, 1\frac{3}{4}, 2\frac{1}{4}, 1\frac{1}{2}, 2\frac{1}{4}, 2\frac{7}{8}$$

B **1** Write the data in eighths, by using equivalent fractions.

$3, 1\frac{6}{8}, \_\_\_, 1\frac{4}{8}, \_\_\_, 2\frac{2}{8}, \_\_\_, 2\frac{7}{8}$

M **2** Complete the line plot below to represent the data.

Growth of Students

Growth (in inches)
$1, 1\frac{1}{8}, 1\frac{2}{8}, 1\frac{3}{8}, 1\frac{4}{8}, 1\frac{5}{8}, 1\frac{6}{8}, 1\frac{7}{8}, 2, 2\frac{1}{8}, 2\frac{2}{8}, 2\frac{3}{8}, 2\frac{4}{8}, 2\frac{5}{8}, 2\frac{6}{8}, 2\frac{7}{8}, 3$

©Curriculum Associates, LLC Copying is not permitted.
Lesson 27 Line Plots **293**

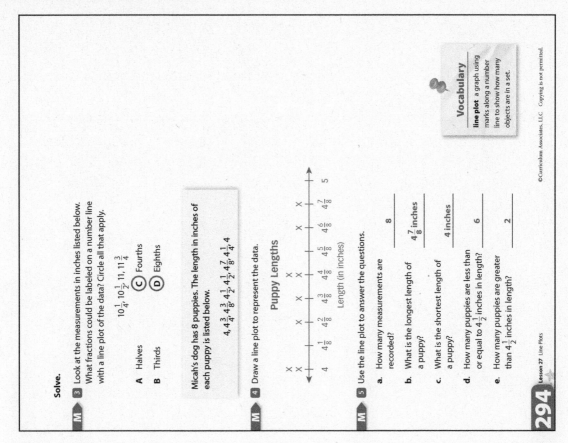

Solve.

M **3** Look at the measurements in inches listed below. What fractions could be labeled on a number line with a line plot of the data? Circle all that apply.

$$10\frac{1}{4}, 10\frac{1}{2}, 11, 11\frac{3}{4}$$

A Halves

B Thirds

C Fourths

D Eighths

Micah's dog has 8 puppies. The length in inches of each puppy is listed below.

$$4, 4\frac{3}{4}, 4\frac{3}{8}, 4\frac{1}{2}, 4\frac{1}{2}, 4\frac{7}{8}, 4\frac{1}{4}, 4$$

M **4** Draw a line plot to represent the data.

Puppy Lengths

Length (in inches)
$4, 4\frac{1}{8}, 4\frac{2}{8}, 4\frac{3}{8}, 4\frac{4}{8}, 4\frac{5}{8}, 4\frac{6}{8}, 4\frac{7}{8}, 5$

M **5** Use the line plot to answer the questions.

a. How many measurements are recorded? _____ 8

b. What is the longest length of a puppy? _____ $4\frac{7}{8}$ inches

c. What is the shortest length of a puppy? _____ 4 inches

d. How many puppies are less than or equal to $4\frac{1}{2}$ inches in length? _____ 6

e. How many puppies are greater than $4\frac{1}{2}$ inches in length? _____ 2

294 Lesson 27 Line Plots

Vocabulary

line plot a graph using marks along a number line to show how many objects are in a set.

©Curriculum Associates, LLC Copying is not permitted.

Lesson 27

Name: _____

Solve Addition Problems with Line Plots

Study the example showing how to solve an addition problem with a line plot. Then solve problems 1–5.

Example

Ashley is decorating a frame with seashells. She wants to know if all the shells will fit along the edge of a 16-inch wide frame. She measures the width of each shell and records the information in a line plot. If Ashley puts all the shells in a row, will the total width of the shells fit on the frame?

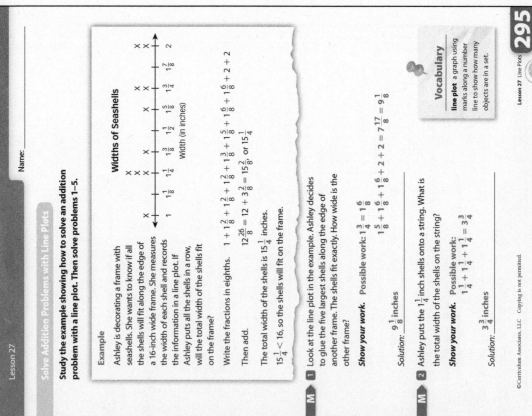

Widths of Seashells

Write the fractions in eighths. $1 + 1\frac{1}{2} + 1\frac{2}{8} + 1\frac{2}{8} + 1\frac{3}{8} + 1\frac{5}{8} + 1\frac{6}{8} + 1\frac{6}{8} + 2 + 2$

Then add. $12\frac{26}{8} = 12 + 3\frac{2}{8} = 15\frac{2}{8}$, or $15\frac{1}{4}$

The total width of the shells is $15\frac{1}{4}$ inches.

$15\frac{1}{4} < 16$, so the shells will fit on the frame.

1 Look at the line plot in the example. Ashley decides to glue the five largest shells along the edge of another frame. The shells fit exactly. How wide is the other frame?

Show your work. Possible work: $1\frac{3}{4} = 1\frac{6}{8}$

$1\frac{5}{8} + 1\frac{6}{8} + 1\frac{6}{8} + 2 + 2 = 7\frac{17}{8} = 9\frac{1}{8}$

Solution: $9\frac{1}{8}$ inches

2 Ashley puts the $1\frac{1}{4}$ inch shells onto a string. What is the total width of the shells on the string?

Show your work. Possible work:

$1\frac{1}{4} + 1\frac{1}{4} + 1\frac{1}{4} = 3\frac{3}{4}$

Solution: $3\frac{3}{4}$ inches

Vocabulary

line plot a graph using marks along a number line to show how many objects are in a set.

Lesson 27 Line Plots   **295**

Solve.

A standard-sized brick should be $7\frac{5}{8}$ inches long. The line plot shows the actual lengths of 12 different bricks.

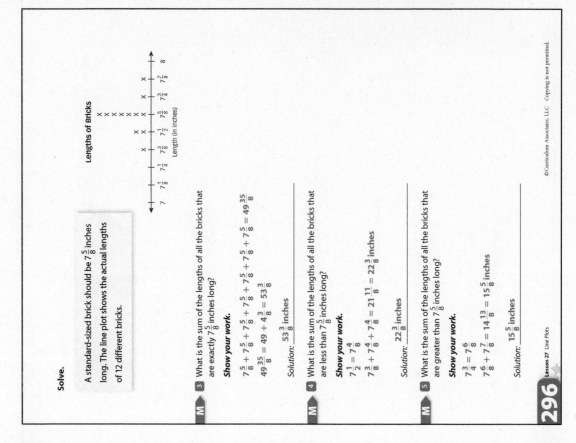

Lengths of Bricks

3 What is the sum of the lengths of all the bricks that are exactly $7\frac{5}{8}$ inches long?

Show your work.

$7\frac{5}{8} + 7\frac{5}{8} + 7\frac{5}{8} + 7\frac{5}{8} + 7\frac{5}{8} + 7\frac{5}{8} + 7\frac{5}{8} = 49\frac{35}{8}$

$49\frac{35}{8} = 49 + 4\frac{3}{8} = 53\frac{3}{8}$

Solution: $53\frac{3}{8}$ inches

4 What is the sum of the lengths of all the bricks that are less than $7\frac{5}{8}$ inches long?

Show your work.

$7\frac{1}{2} = 7\frac{4}{8}$

$7\frac{3}{8} + 7\frac{4}{8} + 7\frac{4}{8} = 21\frac{11}{8} = 22\frac{3}{8}$ inches

Solution: $22\frac{3}{8}$ inches

5 What is the sum of the lengths of all the bricks that are greater than $7\frac{5}{8}$ inches long?

Show your work.

$7\frac{3}{4} = 7\frac{6}{8}$

$7\frac{6}{8} + 7\frac{7}{8} = 14\frac{13}{8} = 15\frac{5}{8}$ inches

Solution: $15\frac{5}{8}$ inches

Lesson 27 Line Plots   **296**

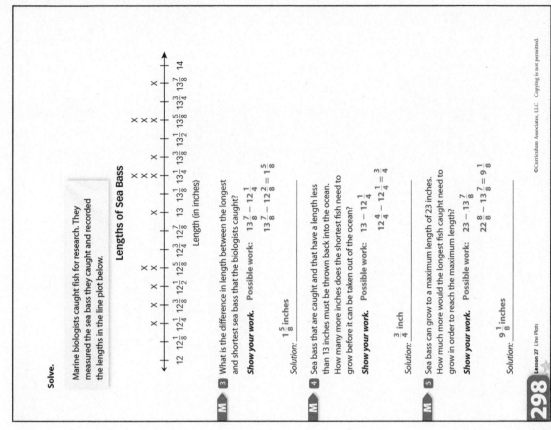

Solve.

Marine biologists caught fish for research. They measured the sea bass they caught and recorded the lengths in the line plot below.

Lengths of Sea Bass

$12 \quad 12\frac{1}{8} \quad 12\frac{1}{4} \quad 12\frac{3}{8} \quad 12\frac{1}{2} \quad 12\frac{5}{8} \quad 12\frac{3}{4} \quad 12\frac{7}{8} \quad 13 \quad 13\frac{1}{8} \quad 13\frac{1}{4} \quad 13\frac{3}{8} \quad 13\frac{1}{2} \quad 13\frac{5}{8} \quad 13\frac{3}{4} \quad 13\frac{7}{8} \quad 14$

Length (in inches)

M 3 What is the difference in length between the longest and shortest sea bass that the biologists caught?

Show your work. Possible work: $13\frac{7}{8} - 12\frac{1}{4}$

$13\frac{7}{8} - 12\frac{2}{8} = 1\frac{5}{8}$

Solution: $1\frac{5}{8}$ inches

M 4 Sea bass that are caught and that have a length less than 13 inches must be thrown back into the ocean. How many more inches does the shortest fish caught need to grow before it can be taken out of the ocean?

Show your work. Possible work: $13 - 12\frac{1}{4}$

$12\frac{4}{4} - 12\frac{1}{4} = \frac{3}{4}$

Solution: $\frac{3}{4}$ inch

M 5 Sea bass can grow to a maximum length of 23 inches. How much more would the longest fish caught need to grow in order to reach the maximum length?

Show your work. Possible work: $23 - 13\frac{7}{8}$

$22\frac{8}{8} - 13\frac{7}{8} = 9\frac{1}{8}$

Solution: $9\frac{1}{8}$ inches

Name: _____

Lesson 27

Solve Subtraction Problems with Line Plots

Study the example showing how to solve a subtraction problem with a line plot. Then solve problems 1–5.

Example

The monthly rainfall in inches for one city is shown in the line plot. What is the difference in inches of rain between the month with the greatest amount of rain and the month with the least amount of rain?

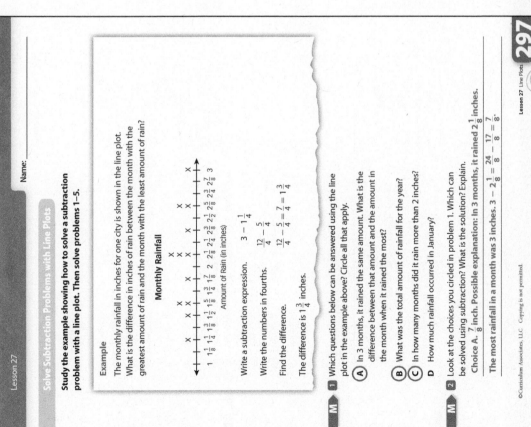

Monthly Rainfall

$1 \quad 1\frac{1}{8} \quad 1\frac{1}{4} \quad 1\frac{3}{8} \quad 1\frac{1}{2} \quad 1\frac{5}{8} \quad 1\frac{3}{4} \quad 1\frac{7}{8} \quad 2 \quad 2\frac{1}{8} \quad 2\frac{1}{4} \quad 2\frac{3}{8} \quad 2\frac{1}{2} \quad 2\frac{5}{8} \quad 2\frac{3}{4} \quad 2\frac{7}{8} \quad 3$

Amount of Rain (in inches)

Write a subtraction expression. $3 - 1\frac{1}{4}$

Write the numbers in fourths. $\frac{12}{4} - \frac{5}{4}$

Find the difference. $\frac{12}{4} - \frac{5}{4} = \frac{7}{4} = 1\frac{3}{4}$

The difference is $1\frac{3}{4}$ inches.

M 1 Which questions below can be answered using the line plot in the example above? Circle all that apply.

(A) In 3 months, it rained the same amount. What is the difference between that amount and the amount in the month when it rained the most?

(B) What was the total amount of rainfall for the year?

(C) In how many months did it rain more than 2 inches?

D How much rainfall occurred in January?

M 2 Look at the choices you circled in problem 1. Which can be solved using subtraction? What is the solution? Explain.

Choice A. $\frac{7}{8}$ inch. Possible explanation: In 3 months, it rained $2\frac{1}{8}$ inches. The most rainfall in a month was 3 inches. $3 - 2\frac{1}{8} = \frac{24}{8} - \frac{17}{8} = \frac{7}{8}$.

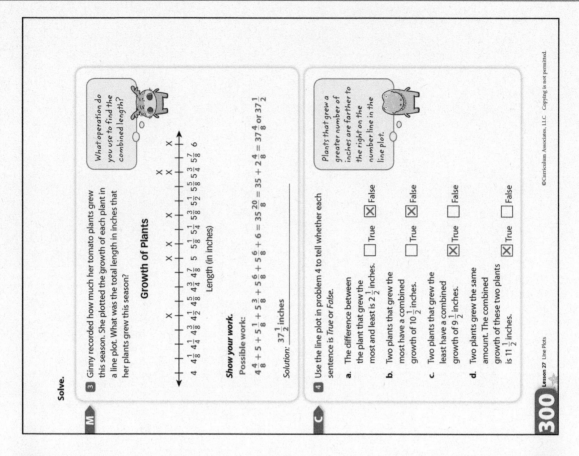

Solve.

M **3** Ginny recorded how much her tomato plants grew this season. She plotted the growth of each plant in a line plot. What was the total length in inches that her plants grew this season?

What operation do you use to find the combined length?

Growth of Plants

$4 \quad 4\frac{1}{8} \quad 4\frac{1}{4} \quad 4\frac{3}{8} \quad 4\frac{1}{2} \quad 4\frac{5}{8} \quad 4\frac{3}{4} \quad 4\frac{7}{8} \quad 5 \quad 5\frac{1}{8} \quad 5\frac{1}{4} \quad 5\frac{3}{8} \quad 5\frac{1}{2} \quad 5\frac{5}{8} \quad 5\frac{3}{4} \quad 5\frac{7}{8} \quad 6$

Length (in inches)

Show your work.
Possible work:

$4\frac{4}{8} + 5 + 5\frac{1}{8} + 5\frac{3}{8} + 5\frac{6}{8} + 5\frac{6}{8} + 6 = 35\frac{20}{8} = 35 + 2\frac{4}{8} = 37\frac{4}{8}$ or $37\frac{1}{2}$

Solution: ___$37\frac{1}{2}$ inches___

C **4** Use the line plot in problem 4 to tell whether each sentence is *True* or *False*.

Plants that grew a greater number of inches are farther to the right on the number line in the line plot.

a. The difference between the plant that grew the most and least is $2\frac{1}{2}$ inches.　☐ True　☒ False

b. Two plants that grew the most have a combined growth of $10\frac{1}{2}$ inches.　☐ True　☒ False

c. Two plants that grew the least have a combined growth of $9\frac{1}{2}$ inches.　☒ True　☐ False

d. Two plants grew the same amount. The combined growth of these two plants is $11\frac{1}{2}$ inches.　☒ True　☐ False

---

Lesson 27

Name: _____

Solve Problems with Line Plots

Solve the problems.

B **1** The line plot shows the finish times of races run by a relay running team. What is the difference in minutes between the team's two fastest times?

Where on the line plot are faster times?

Relay Team Finish Times

$2 \quad 2\frac{1}{8} \quad 2\frac{1}{4} \quad 2\frac{3}{8} \quad 2\frac{1}{2} \quad 2\frac{5}{8} \quad 2\frac{3}{4} \quad 2\frac{7}{8} \quad 3 \quad 3\frac{1}{8} \quad 3\frac{1}{4} \quad 3\frac{3}{8} \quad 3\frac{1}{2} \quad 3\frac{5}{8} \quad 3\frac{3}{4} \quad 3\frac{7}{8} \quad 4$

Time (in minutes)

A　$\frac{1}{8}$ minute

B　$\frac{1}{4}$ minute ⟵ (circled)

C　$1\frac{1}{8}$ minutes

D　$2\frac{7}{8}$ minutes

M **2** Use the line plot in problem 1. What is the total amount of time the team spent running in relay races?

What symbol represents one race on the line plot?

A　17 minutes

B　$17\frac{3}{8}$ minutes

C　20 minutes

D　$20\frac{3}{8}$ minutes ⟵ (circled)

Miriam chose **B** as the correct answer. How did she get that answer?

Possible answer: She added together the race times but she forgot to add 3 twice.

Lesson 28

Understand Angles

What does it mean to multiply with fractions?

Study the example problem showing multiplication with a fraction. Then solve problems 1–6.

Example

4 friends shared a whole pizza. Each person ate an equal amount.

Draw lines on the circle at the right to show the fraction of the pizza that each person ate.

Use multiplication to show that the four parts together equal the whole.

$$4 \times \frac{1}{4} = \frac{4}{1} \times \frac{1}{4} = \frac{4}{4} = 1 \text{ whole}$$

The pizza is divided into 4 parts.
Each part is $\frac{1}{4}$ of the pizza.

B ① 8 friends shared a pizza. Each person ate an equal amount. Draw lines on the circle at the right to show the fraction of the pizza that each person ate.

a. What fraction of the pizza did each person eat? $\frac{1}{8}$

b. Use multiplication to show that all the parts are equal to the whole.

$$8 \times \frac{1}{8} = \frac{8}{1} \times \frac{1}{8} = \frac{8}{8} = 1$$

M ② A pizza is cut into 8 equal slices.

a. What fraction of the pizza is each slice? $\frac{1}{8}$

b. Mandy eats 2 slices. What fraction of the pizza did Mandy eat? $\frac{2}{8} \text{ or } \frac{1}{4}$

c. Use multiplication to explain how you found the answer to **b.** $2 \times \frac{1}{8} = \frac{2}{1} \times \frac{1}{8} = \frac{2}{8} \text{ or } \frac{1}{4}$

Solve.

M ③ Look at the clock at the right. When the minute hand moves from the 12 to the 3, it moves over $\frac{1}{4}$ of a circle.

a. How many minutes are in 1 hour? __60__

b. When the minute hand moves from the 12 to the 3, how many minutes have passed? Use fraction multiplication to show your answer.

$$\frac{1}{4} \times \underline{60} = \underline{15} \text{ minutes}$$

M ④ Look at the clock at the right.

a. When the minute hand moves from the 12 to the 6, what fraction of a circle does it move over? $\frac{1}{2}$ of a circle

b. How many minutes have passed? Use fraction multiplication to show your answer.

$$\frac{1}{2} \times 60 = 30 \text{ minutes}$$

M ⑤ Look at the clock at the right. When the minute hand moves from the 12 to the 4, it moves over $\frac{1}{3}$ of a circle. How many minutes have passed? Use fraction multiplication to show your answer.

$$\frac{1}{3} \times 60 = 20 \text{ minutes}$$

C ⑥ Look at the clock at the right. When the minute hand moves from the 12 to the 1, how many minutes have passed? Use fraction multiplication to show your answer.

$$\frac{1}{12} \times 60 = \frac{1}{12} \times \frac{60}{1} = \frac{60}{12} = 5 \text{ minutes}$$

304 Lesson 28 Understand Angles

Key

B Basic   **M** Medium   **C** Challenge

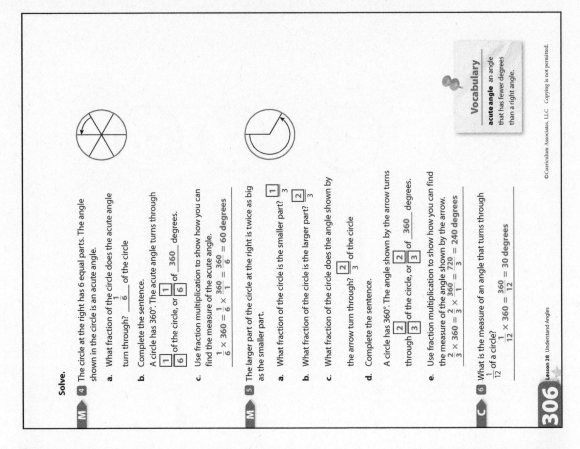

Lesson 28

Name: _____

Show Measures of Angles

**Study the example showing the measure of an angle.
Then solve problems 1–6.**

Example

The drawing below shows an angle that turns through 9 one-degree angles.

1°

The measure of any angle is equal to the number of one-degree angles it turns through.

How many degrees does the angle measure?
The angle measures 9° because it turns through 9 one-degree angles.

B 1 An angle turns through 60 one-degree angles.
What is the measure of the angle? __60__ degrees

B 2 An angle turns through 160 one-degree angles.
What is the measure of the angle? __160__ degrees

M 3 The circle at the right has 4 equal parts. The angle shown in the circle is a right angle.

a. What fraction of the circle does the right angle turn through? __1/4__ of the circle

b. Complete the sentence.
A circle has 360°. A right angle turns through $\frac{1}{4}$ of a circle, or $\frac{1}{4}$ of __360__ degrees.

c. Use fraction multiplication to show how you can find the measure of a right angle.
$\frac{1}{4} \times 360 = \frac{1}{4} \times \frac{360}{1} = \frac{360}{4} = $ **90 degrees**

Lesson 28 Understand Angles **305**

©Curriculum Associates, LLC   Copying is not permitted.

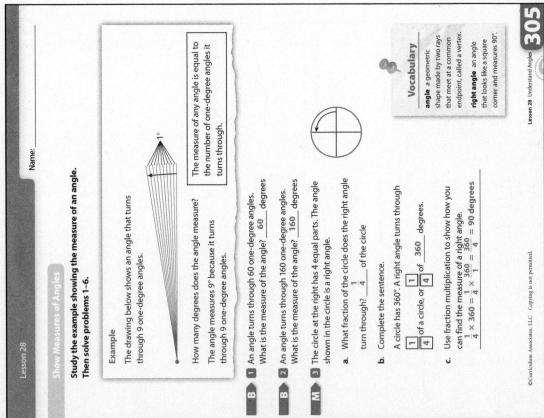

Solve.

M 4 The circle at the right has 6 equal parts. The angle shown in the circle is an acute angle.

a. What fraction of the circle does the acute angle turn through? __1/6__ of the circle

b. Complete the sentence.
A circle has 360°. The acute angle turns through $\frac{1}{6}$ of the circle, or $\frac{1}{6}$ of __360__ degrees.

c. Use fraction multiplication to show how you can find the measure of the acute angle.
$\frac{1}{6} \times 360 = \frac{1}{6} \times \frac{360}{1} = \frac{360}{6} = $ **60 degrees**

M 5 The larger part of the circle at the right is twice as big as the smaller part.

a. What fraction of the circle is the smaller part? $\boxed{1}/3$

b. What fraction of the circle is the larger part? $\boxed{2}/3$

c. What fraction of the circle does the angle shown by the arrow turn through? $\boxed{2}/3$ of the circle

d. Complete the sentence.
A circle has 360°. The angle shown by the arrow turns through $\frac{2}{3}$ of the circle, or $\frac{2}{3}$ of __360__ degrees.

e. Use fraction multiplication to show how you can find the measure of the angle shown by the arrow.
$\frac{2}{3} \times 360 = \frac{2}{3} \times \frac{360}{1} = \frac{720}{3} = $ **240 degrees**

C 6 What is the measure of an angle that turns through $\frac{1}{12}$ of a circle?
$\frac{1}{12} \times 360 = \frac{360}{12} = $ **30 degrees**

Vocabulary

acute angle an angle that has fewer degrees than a right angle.

306 Lesson 28 Understand Angles

©Curriculum Associates, LLC   Copying is not permitted.

Page 307

Name: _____

Reason and Write

Study the example. Underline two parts that you think make it a particularly good answer and a helpful example.

Example
Describe and compare the angles shown by the hands on the clocks below. What kinds of angle are shown? Which angle has a greater measure?

Clock A   Clock B

Show your work. Use numbers and words to explain your answer.

The angle formed by the hands of Clock A turns through 15 minutes out of 60 minutes on the clock.

This is $\frac{15}{60}$, or $\frac{1}{4}$, of the circle on the clock.

$\frac{1}{4}$ of 360 degrees in a circle is the measure of the angle.

$$\frac{1}{4} \times 360 = 90$$

The angle measures 90 degrees, so it is a right angle.

The angle formed by the hands of Clock B turns through 10 minutes out of 60 minutes.

This is $\frac{10}{60}$, or $\frac{1}{6}$, of the circle.

$\frac{1}{6}$ of 360 degrees in a circle is the measure of the angle.

$$\frac{1}{6} \times 360 = 60$$

The angle measures 60 degrees, so it is an acute angle.

The angle in Clock A has a greater measure than the angle in Clock B because 90 degrees > 60 degrees.

Answers will vary. Note whether students incorporate the features they chose in their answer on the next page.

Where does the example . . .
• describe each angle?
• compare the measures of the angles?
• use numbers to explain?
• use words to explain?

Page 308

Solve the problem. Use what you learned from the model.

Describe and compare the angles shown by the hands on the clocks below. What kinds of angle are shown? Which angle has a greater measure?

Clock A   Clock B

Show your work. Use numbers and words to explain your answer.

The angle formed by the hands of Clock A turns through 5 minutes out of 60 minutes on the clock.

This is $\frac{5}{60}$, or $\frac{1}{12}$, of the circle on the clock.

$\frac{1}{12}$ of 360 degrees in a circle is the measure of the angle.

$$\frac{1}{12} \times 360 = 30$$

The angle measures 30 degrees. It is an acute angle.

The angle formed by the hands of Clock B turns through 20 minutes out of 60 minutes.

This is $\frac{20}{60}$, or $\frac{2}{6}$, or $\frac{1}{3}$, of the circle.

$\frac{1}{3}$ of 360 degrees in a circle is the measure of the angle.

$$\frac{1}{3} \times 360 = 120$$

The angle measures 120 degrees. It is an obtuse angle.

The angle in Clock B has a greater measure than the angle in Clock A because 120 > 30.

Did you . . .
• describe each angle?
• compare the measures of the angles?
• use numbers to explain?
• use words to explain?

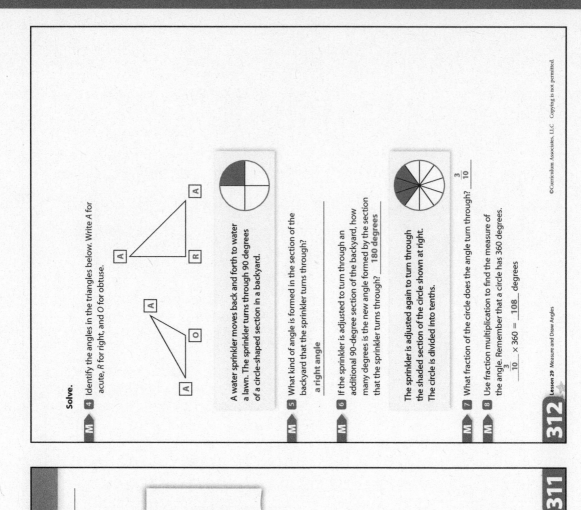

Lesson 29

Measure and Draw Angles

Identify Angles

Study the example problem showing how to identify angles. Then solve problems 1–8.

Example

Logan sketched the front of his townhouse. He labeled the angles in his sketch.

Fill in the table below to identify angles V through Z as acute, right, or obtuse.

Acute angle < 90 degrees	Right angle = 90 degrees	Obtuse angle > 90 degrees
Angle V	Angle X	Angle W
	Angle Y	Angle Z

For problems 1–3, write A for an acute angle, R for a right angle, and O for an obtuse angle.

B 1 Identify and label the three angles in the sign at the right.

B 2 Identify and label the four angles in the sign at the right.

B 3 Identify and label one angle in the sign at the right.

©Curriculum Associates, LLC Copying is not permitted.

Lesson 29 Measure and Draw Angles

311

Solve.

M 4 Identify the angles in the triangles below. Write A for acute, R for right, and O for obtuse.

A water sprinkler moves back and forth to water a lawn. The sprinkler turns through 90 degrees of a circle-shaped section in a backyard.

M 5 What kind of angle is formed in the section of the backyard that the sprinkler turns through?
a right angle

M 6 If the sprinkler is adjusted to turn through an additional 90-degree section of the backyard, how many degrees is the new angle formed by the section that the sprinkler turns through? _180 degrees_

The sprinkler is adjusted again to turn through the shaded section of the circle shown at right. The circle is divided into tenths.

$\frac{3}{10}$

M 7 What fraction of the circle does the angle turn through? $\frac{3}{10}$

M 8 Use fraction multiplication to find the measure of the angle. Remember that a circle has 360 degrees.
$\frac{3}{10} \times 360 = $ _108_ degrees

312 Lesson 29 Measure and Draw Angles

©Curriculum Associates, LLC Copying is not permitted.

Key

B Basic	M Medium	C Challenge

Lesson 29

Use a Protractor to Measure Angles

Study the example showing how to use a protractor to measure an angle. Then solve problems 1–5.

Name: _____

Example

Omar drew the angle at the right. What is the measure of the angle?

Line up the 0° or the 180° mark on a protractor with one ray of the angle.

Line up the center point of the protractor with the vertex of the angle.

Look at the other ray. Read the number of degrees on the protractor. Read the number that is less than 90, since the angle is less than 90°.

The angle measures 70°.

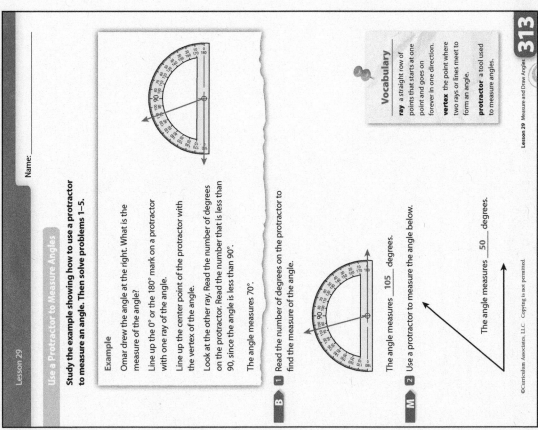

B 1 Read the number of degrees on the protractor to find the measure of the angle.

The angle measures ___105___ degrees.

M 2 Use a protractor to measure the angle below.

The angle measures ___50___ degrees.

Vocabulary

ray a straight row of points that starts at one point and goes on forever in one direction.

vertex the point where two rays or lines meet to form an angle.

protractor a tool used to measure angles.

Lesson 29 Measure and Draw Angles **313**

Solve.

For problems 3–5, use a protractor to measure the angles. Write each measure.

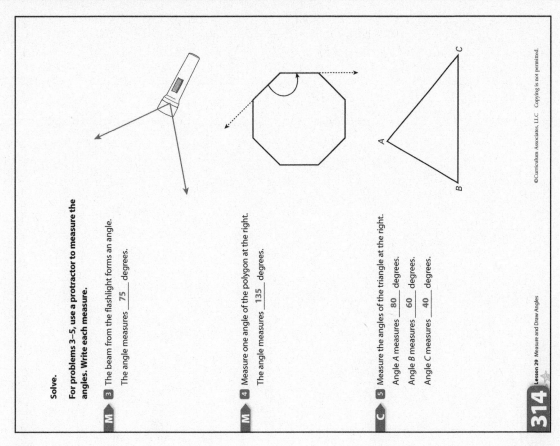

M 3 The beam from the flashlight forms an angle.

The angle measures ___75___ degrees.

M 4 Measure one angle of the polygon at the right.

The angle measures ___135___ degrees.

C 5 Measure the angles of the triangle at the right.

Angle A measures ___80___ degrees.

Angle B measures ___60___ degrees.

Angle C measures ___40___ degrees.

314 **Lesson 29** Measure and Draw Angles

Lesson 29

Draw Angles

Study the example showing how to draw an angle. Then solve problems 1–6.

Example

Stephanie wants to draw a 60° angle. She drew a ray and positioned the endpoint of the ray on a protractor's center point. Then she drew a point at 0° on the ray. How does she draw the other ray to form a 60° angle?

Find 60° on the protractor.

Draw a point at the 60°-degree mark.

Draw a ray from the vertex through this point.

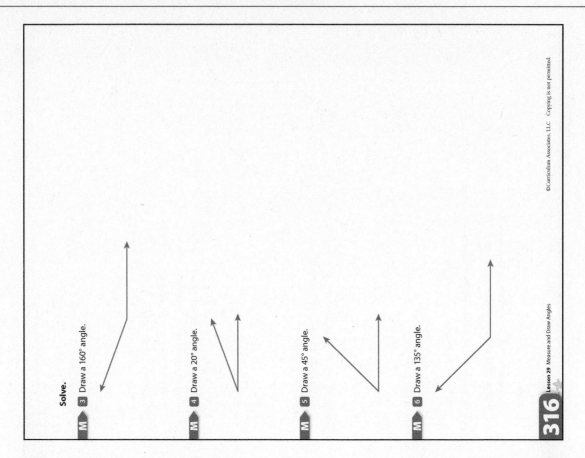

B 1 Draw a ray to show a 70° angle.

B 2 Draw a ray to show a 100° angle.

Vocabulary

ray a straight row of points that starts at one point and goes on forever in one direction.

vertex the point where two rays or lines meet to form an angle.

protractor a tool used to measure angles.

Lesson 29 Measure and Draw Angles **315**

Solve.

M 3 Draw a 160° angle.

M 4 Draw a 20° angle.

M 5 Draw a 45° angle.

M 6 Draw a 135° angle.

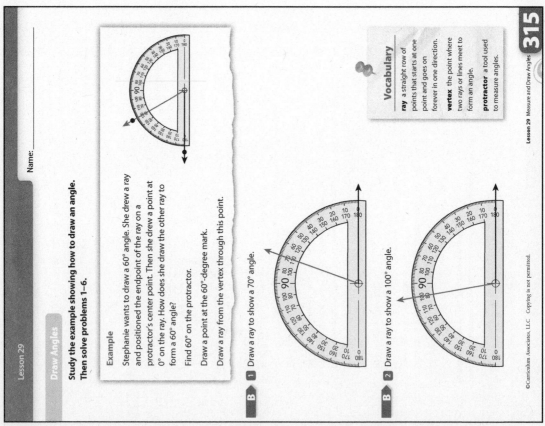

316 Lesson 29 Measure and Draw Angles

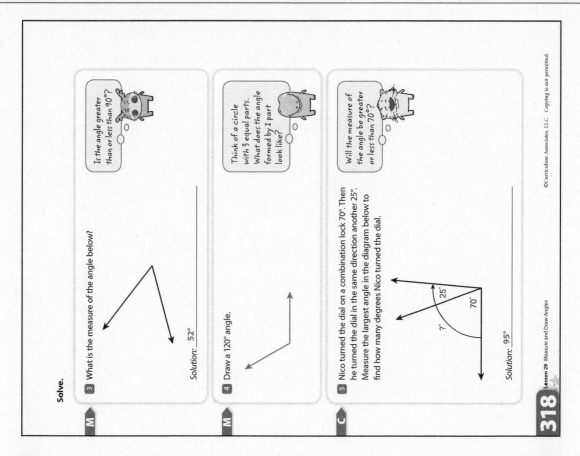

Solve.

3 What is the measure of the angle below?

Is the angle greater than or less than 90°?

Solution: __52°__

4 Draw a 120° angle.

Think of a circle with 3 equal parts. What does the angle formed by 1 part look like?

5 Nico turned the dial on a combination lock 70°. Then he turned the dial in the same direction another 25°. Measure the largest angle in the diagram below to find how many degrees Nico turned the dial.

Will the measure of the angle be greater or less than 70°?

Solution: __95°__

318

Lesson 29

Measure and Draw Angles

Name: _____

Solve the problems.

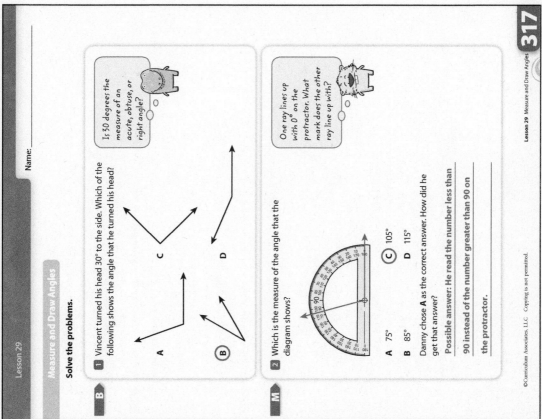

1 Vincent turned his head 30° to the side. Which of the following shows the angle that he turned his head?

Is 30 degrees the measure of an acute, obtuse, or right angle?

2 Which is the measure of the angle that the diagram shows?

One ray lines up with 0° on the protractor. What mark does the other ray line up with?

A 75°   **C** 105°

B 85°   **D** 115°

Danny chose **A** as the correct answer. How did he get that answer?

Possible answer: He read the number less than

90 instead of the number greater than 90 on

the protractor.

317

Lesson 30

Add and Subtract with Angles

Name: _____

Measure and Draw Angles

Study the example explaining how to use a protractor to measure angles to solve a word problem. Then solve problems 1–5.

Example

Charlie is designing a roof for a new building. He draws the angles below to show two roof designs. What is the measure of the angle at the top of each roof in the drawings?

Use a protractor to measure each angle.

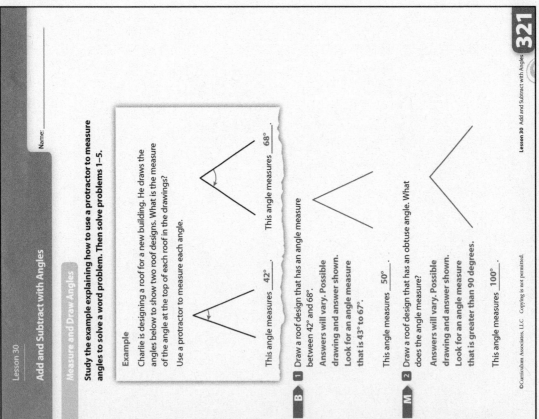

This angle measures 42°.

This angle measures 68°.

B 1 Draw a roof design that has an angle measure between 42° and 68°.

Answers will vary. Possible drawing and answer shown.

Look for an angle measure that is 43° to 67°.

This angle measures 50°.

M 2 Draw a roof design that has an obtuse angle. What does the angle measure?

Answers will vary. Possible drawing and answer shown.

Look for an angle measure that is greater than 90 degrees.

This angle measures 100°.

Lesson 30 Add and Subtract with Angles **321**

Solve.

M 3 Madison drew three rays and realized she had drawn an acute and an obtuse angle.

a. Label the angles *acute* and *obtuse*.

b. Use a protractor to measure each angle. Write the angle measure.

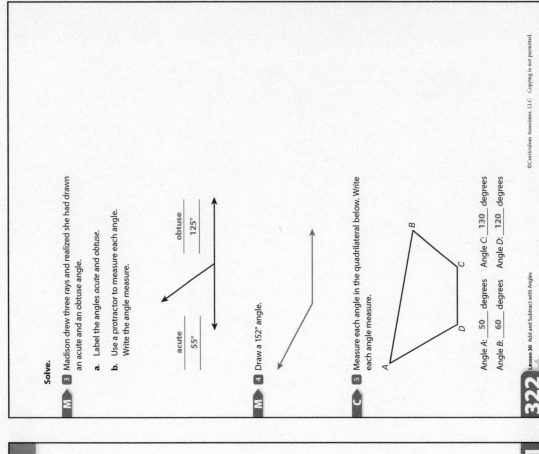

acute 55°

obtuse 125°

M 4 Draw a 152° angle.

C 5 Measure each angle in the quadrilateral below. Write each angle measure.

Angle A: 50 degrees   Angle C: 130 degrees

Angle B: 60 degrees   Angle D: 120 degrees

322 Lesson 30 Add and Subtract with Angles

Key

B Basic   **M** Medium   **C** Challenge

Lesson 30

Combine Angles

Study the example problem showing how to combine smaller angles to form a larger angle. Then solve problems 1–5.

Name: _____

Example

A spotlight in a theater casts a beam that has an angle measure of 24°.

If four spotlights are placed so that they have a common endpoint, what is the measure of the greater angle formed by the beams of all four spotlights?

Four 24° angles compose the greater angle. Use addition to combine the angles.

24° + 24° + 24° + 24° = 96°

The measure of the greater angle is 96°.

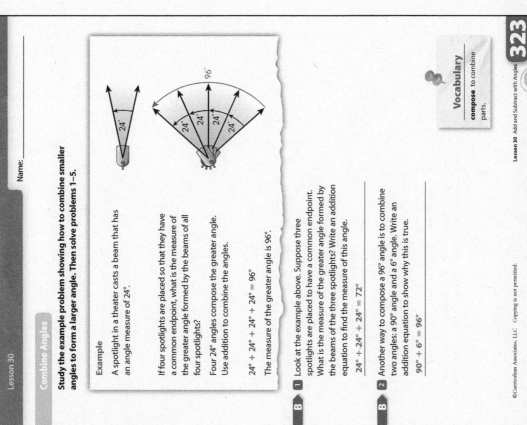

1 Look at the example above. Suppose three spotlights are placed to have a common endpoint. What is the measure of the greater angle formed by the beams of the three spotlights? Write an addition equation to find the measure of this angle.

24° + 24° + 24° = 72°

2 Another way to compose a 96° angle is to combine two angles: a 90° angle and a 6° angle. Write an addition equation to show why this is true.

90° + 6° = 96°

Vocabulary
compose to combine parts.

Solve.

3 Tell whether each statement is *True* or *False*.

a. A 20° angle and a 70° angle can be composed into a 90° angle.   [X] True   [ ] False

b. Three 50° angles compose an angle that measures 350°.   [ ] True   [X] False

c. A 15° angle and a 60° angle compose an angle that measures 75°.   [X] True   [ ] False

d. Four 50° angles can be composed into a 200° angle.   [X] True   [ ] False

4 Look at the drawing of a hand fan at the right. The angle between each wooden stick on the fan is 12°. If 11 of these angles combine to form the open fan, what is the measure of the purple angle on the open fan?

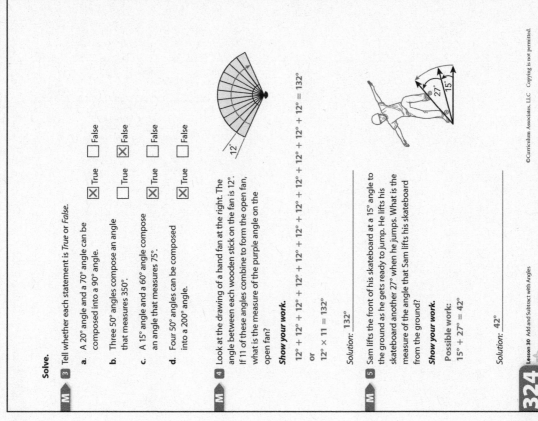

Show your work.

12° + 12° + 12° + 12° + 12° + 12° + 12° + 12° + 12° + 12° + 12° = 132°

or

12° × 11 = 132°

Solution: **132°**

5 Sam lifts the front of his skateboard at a 15° angle to the ground as he gets ready to jump. He lifts his skateboard another 27° when he jumps. What is the measure of the angle that Sam lifts his skateboard from the ground?

Show your work.

Possible work:
15° + 27° = 42°

Solution: **42°**

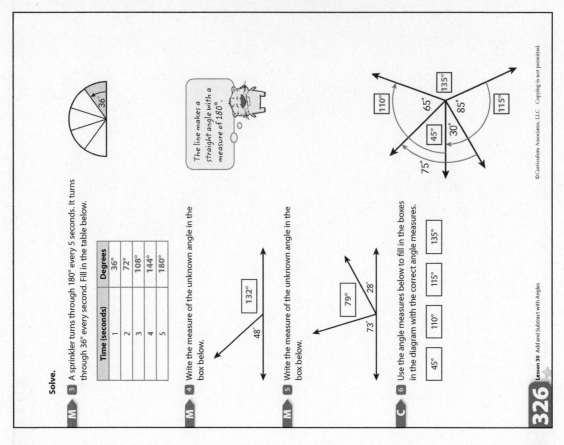

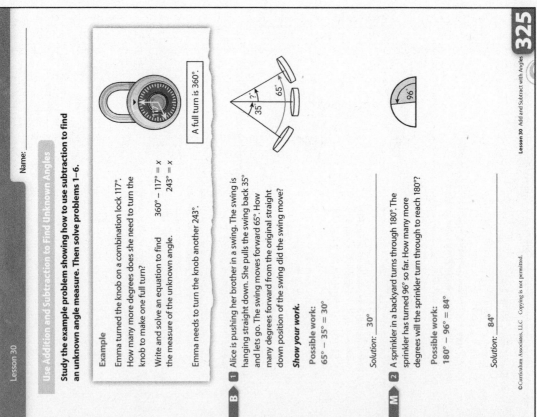

Lesson 30

Name: _____

Use Addition and Subtraction to Find Unknown Angles

Study the example problem showing how to use subtraction to find an unknown angle measure. Then solve problems 1–6.

Example

Emma turned the knob on a combination lock 117°. How many more degrees does she need to turn the knob to make one full turn?

Write and solve an equation to find the measure of the unknown angle.

$$360° – 117° = x$$
$$243° = x$$

Emma needs to turn the knob another 243°.

A full turn is 360°.

B 1 Alice is pushing her brother in a swing. The swing is hanging straight down. She pulls the swing back 35° and lets go. The swing moves forward 65°. How many degrees forward from the original straight down position of the swing did the swing move?

Show your work.

Possible work:
$$65° – 35° = 30°$$

Solution: __30°__

M 2 A sprinkler in a backyard turns through 180°. The sprinkler has turned 96° so far. How many more degrees will the sprinkler turn through to reach 180°?

Possible work:
$$180° – 96° = 84°$$

Solution: __84°__

Lesson 30 Add and Subtract with Angles   **325**

Solve.

M 3 A sprinkler turns through 180° every 5 seconds. It turns through 36° every second. Fill in the table below.

Time (seconds)	Degrees
1	36°
2	72°
3	108°
4	144°
5	180°

M 4 Write the measure of the unknown angle in the box below.

48°   [132°]

The line makes a straight angle with a measure of 180°.

M 5 Write the measure of the unknown angle in the box below.

73°   [79°]   28°

C 6 Use the angle measures below to fill in the boxes in the diagram with the correct angle measures.

110°   65°   [135°]   85°   115°   75°   45°   30°

[45°]   [110°]   [115°]   [135°]

326 Lesson 30 Add and Subtract with Angles

Name:

Lesson 30

Add and Subtract with Angles

Solve the problems.

1 Alex blew on a pinwheel. The pinwheel turned 240°. How many degrees more does the pinwheel need to turn to make one full turn?

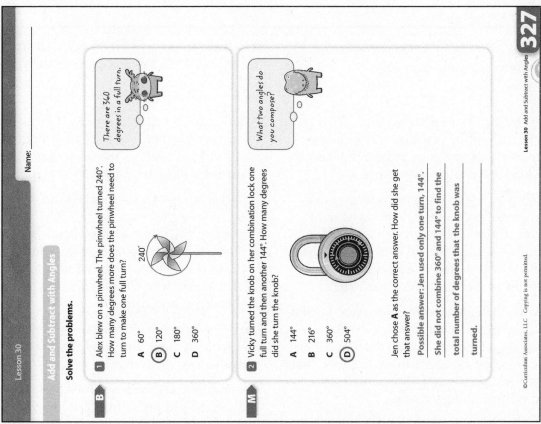

240°

A 60°

B 120°

C 180°

D 360°

There are 360 degrees in a full turn.

2 Vicky turned the knob on her combination lock one full turn and then another 144°. How many degrees did she turn the knob?

A 144°

B 216°

C 360°

D 504°

What two angles do you compose?

Jen chose **A** as the correct answer. How did she get that answer?

Possible answer: Jen used only one turn, 144°.

She did not combine 360° and 144° to find the

total number of degrees that the knob was

turned.

Lesson 30 Add and Subtract with Angles **327**

Solve.

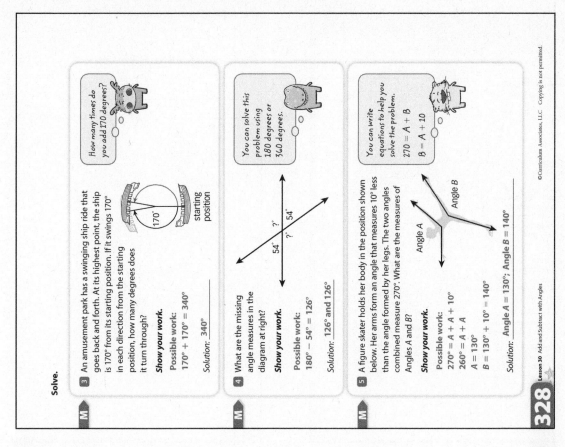

3 An amusement park has a swinging ship ride that goes back and forth. At its highest point, the ship is 170° from its starting position. If it swings 170° in each direction from the starting position, how many degrees does it turn through?

How many times do you add 170 degrees?

170°

starting position

Show your work.

Possible work:

170° + 170° = 340°

Solution: _340°_

4 What are the missing angle measures in the diagram at right?

You can solve this problem using 180 degrees or 360 degrees.

54°　?°

?°　54°

Show your work.

Possible work:

180° − 54° = 126°

Solution: _126° and 126°_

5 A figure skater holds her body in the position shown below. Her arms form an angle that measures 10° less than the angle formed by her legs. The two angles combined measure 270°. What are the measures of Angles A and B?

You can write equations to help you solve the problem.

270° = A + B

B = A + 10

Angle A

Angle B

Show your work.

Possible work:

270° = A + A + 10°

260° = A + A

A = 130°

B = 130° + 10° = 140°

Solution: _Angle A = 130°; Angle B = 140°_

328 Lesson 30 Add and Subtract with Angles

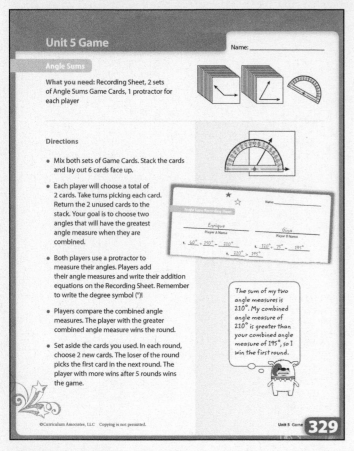

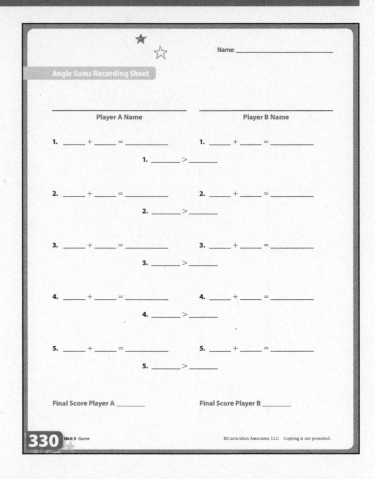

STEP BY STEP

CCSS Focus - 4.MD.C.6, 4.MD.C.7 *Embedded SMPs - 5, 6* **Objective:** Measure angles with a protractor. Add angle measures.	**Materials** For each pair: Recording Sheet (TR 8), 2 sets of Game Cards (TR 9), 2 protractors (1 for each player)

- Read through the directions with students. Point out that the goal in each round is to choose two angles that have a greater angle measure when combined than the two angles the other player chooses.

- Model one round by laying out 6 cards face up and choosing one card. Choose another card and set it aside for the other player. Then choose a second card for yourself and set aside a second card for the other player. Discuss how you made your choices based on your estimates of the measures of each angle.

- Model measuring each angle with a protractor. Review how to line up the center of the protractor with the vertex of the angle and how to line up the 0° mark on the protractor with one ray of the angle. Read the angle measure shown on the protractor. Write both angle measures and model finding the sum.

- Have students play 5 rounds. Tell them to keep the angle cards they choose in each round and to replace the unused cards in the stack. Remind them that the loser of each round goes first in the next round.

- When students have finished the game, ask them to share strategies they used to choose cards. Encourage them to use terms such as *obtuse, acute,* and *right angles* in their responses. Ask: *Why do you think the loser of one round chooses first in the next round?* (The player who chooses first has a chance to pick the largest angle.)

Vary the Game Have students subtract to find the difference in angle measures. The winner is the player with the least difference.

Challenge Have students draw their combined angles and use the protractor to check their work.

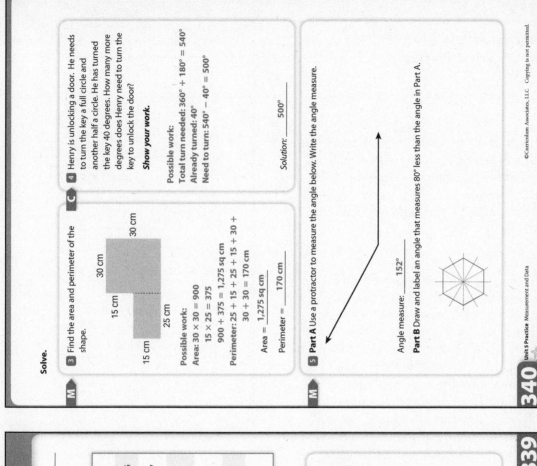

Unit 5 Practice

Measurement and Data

Name: _____

In this unit you learned to:

	Lesson
convert units of length, weight, volume, and time, for example: 5 feet = 60 inches.	23, 24, 25
solve word problems about time, money, distances, volumes, and masses, for example: 4 L of juice + 300 mL of juice = 4,300 mL of juice.	24, 25, 27
use the area formula for rectangles, for example: $A = 3 \times 9$ for a rectangle with a length of 9 and a width of 3.	26
use the perimeter formula for rectangles, for example: $P = (2 \times 12) + (2 \times 5)$ for a rectangle with a length of 12 and a width of 5.	26
measure angles using a protractor, for example: an angle on a stop sign is 135°.	28, 29
solve addition and subtraction problems with angles, for example: 165° − 23° = 142°.	30

Use these skills to solve problems 1–5.

M 1 Tell whether each statement is *True* or *False*.

a. 12 yards = 4 feet   ☐ True   ☒ False

b. 2 kilograms = 2,000 grams   ☒ True   ☐ False

c. 1 hour = 360 seconds   ☐ True   ☒ False

d. 4,000 kilometers = 4 meters   ☐ True   ☒ False

e. 3 pounds = 48 ounces   ☒ True   ☐ False

M 2 The school library is holding a summer reading challenge. Students who meet a goal of reading 16 hours or more receive a prize. There are 10 weeks of summer break. If a student reads 4 days a week, how many minutes does a student need to read each day to meet the goal?

Show your work.

Possible work: Reading goal:
16 hours × 60 = 960 minutes
Number of days: 4 × 10 = 40 days
960 ÷ 40 = 24

Solution: _____ 24 minutes

Solve.

M 3 Find the area and perimeter of the shape.

30 cm
15 cm
30 cm
15 cm
25 cm

Possible work:
Area: 30 × 30 = 900
15 × 25 = 375
900 + 375 = 1,275 sq cm
Perimeter: 25 + 15 + 25 + 15 + 30 +
30 + 30 = 170 cm

Area = _____ 1,275 sq cm
Perimeter = _____ 170 cm

C 4 Henry is unlocking a door. He needs to turn the key a full circle and another half a circle. He has turned the key 40 degrees. How many more degrees does Henry need to turn the key to unlock the door?

Show your work.

Possible work:
Total turn needed: 360° + 180° = 540°
Already turned: 40°
Need to turn: 540° − 40° = 500°

Solution: _____ 500°

M 5 Part A Use a protractor to measure the angle below. Write the angle measure.

Angle measure: _____ 152°

Part B Draw and label an angle that measures 80° less than the angle in Part A.

Key

B Basic   **M** Medium   **C** Challenge

TEACHER NOTES

Common Core Standards: 4.MD.A.1, 4.MD.A.3
Standards for Mathematical Practice: 1, 2, 3, 4, 6
DOK: 3
Materials: none

About the Task

To complete this task, students use their understanding of area and intervals of time to solve a multi-step word problem. Students analyze information provided in a table, apply the area formula, convert units of time and calculate elapsed time, make a plan, and explain their reasoning.

Getting Students Started

Read the problem out loud with students and go over the checklist. Discuss the tasks that Joey can do in 10 minutes: mow 100 square meters of lawn or weed a flower garden border that is 5 meters long. Point out the area measurement is in square meters and the linear measurement is in meters. Discuss the chart. Ask students how they could find the area of lawn to mow for each yard. If students need prompting, remind them of the area formula. Ask how they could find the size of each flower border (calculate it using the length or width measurement in the chart). Finally, ask students whether they think Joey has time to finish all the neighbors' yards before going to soccer practice (he does not). **(SMP 1, 2)**

Completing the Task

Some students may make a diagram of each yard and label the dimensions of the yard and flower border. Students should first find the area of each yard and then calculate the time needed to mow. Students can use their knowledge of multiplying by 10 to make this calculation (e.g., 40 minutes to mow 400 square meters). **(SMP 4, 6)**

Students next calculate the length of each flower border and the time it takes to weed. Students can then add this time to the time it takes to mow that neighbor's yard to find the total amount of time to complete yard work for each neighbor. **(SMP 4, 6)**

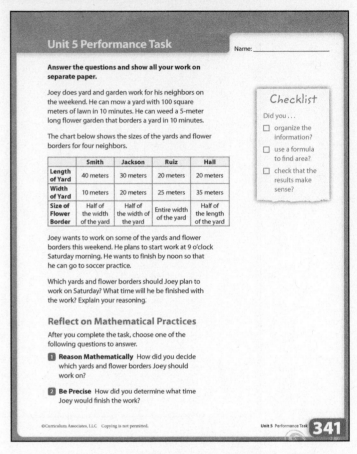

Students should compare the time it would take to do yard work for each neighbor to the time Joey has available in order to decide which yards to work on. Students need to determine how much time Joey works in all and tell what time it will be when he finishes. Finally, students explain how they arrived at their solutions. **(SMP 2, 3)**

Extension

If some students have more time to spend on this problem, you can have them solve this extension:

Soccer practice is delayed 1 hour. Which yard(s) should Joey work on, and what time will he finish?

SAMPLE RESPONSES AND RUBRIC

4-Point Solution

I calculated the area of each yard and the time needed to mow. It takes 10 minutes to mow 100 square meters, so it takes 40 minutes to mow 400 square meters. The table shows the information for each yard. Next, I calculated the size of each garden and time to weed: Smith: 5 meters; 10 minutes. Jackson: 10 meters; 20 minutes. Ruiz: 25 meters; 50 minutes. Hall: 10 meters; 20 minutes.

Neighbor	Length	Width	Area	Minutes
Smith	40	10	400	40
Jackson	30	20	600	60
Ruiz	20	25	500	50
Hall	20	35	700	70

I added to find the total time to mow and weed each neighbor's yard. Smith: 40 + 10 = 50 minutes. Jackson: 60 + 20 = 80 minutes. Ruiz: 50 + 50 = 100 minutes. Hall: 70 + 20 = 90 minutes. Joey has 3 hours, or 180 minutes, to work. He should do Jackson's and Ruiz's yards because the work will take exactly 180 minutes. 80 + 100 = 180. Joey will finish the work at 12 noon.

REFLECT ON MATHEMATICAL PRACTICES

1. Look for an explanation that includes calculating total times for yard and garden work for each neighbor and comparing these times to the time available to do the work. **(SMP 2)**

2. Students should indicate that they started at 9:00 and added the time (hours and minutes, or minutes) for the chosen neighbors to find the time Joey would finish. **(SMP 6)**

SCORING RUBRIC

4 points   The student has completed all parts of the problem and shows understanding of the problem. The calculations for areas, garden size, and times are correct and are clearly explained. The student provides a complete, clear explanation for the choice of jobs.

3 points   The student has completed all parts of the problem with one or two errors. Some area calculations, garden sizes, and times may be incorrect. The explanation for the jobs that were selected is unclear or incomplete.

2 points   The student has attempted all parts of the problem with several errors. There are mistakes in the area calculations, garden sizes, and/or times. The explanation for the jobs that were selected may not be clear or may be incomplete.

1 point   The student has not completed all parts of the problem. There are a number of errors and/or missing elements. The student may not have calculated the areas or garden sizes and/or times. The explanation of the calculations may be incomplete, incorrect, or missing. The explanation for the jobs that were selected is incorrect or not provided.

SOLUTION TO THE EXTENSION

Possible Solution

Joey has 60 minutes more to work. He should work on Smith's yard and garden because that will take 50 minutes. 50 < 60. Joey will finish at 12:50 P.M.

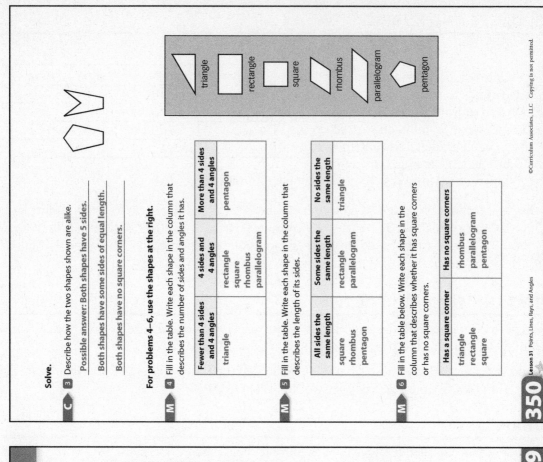

Lesson 31

Points, Lines, Rays, and Angles

Name: _____

Describe the Properties of Shapes

Study the example showing how to describe the sides and angles in shapes. Then solve problems 1–6.

Example
Compare the triangles below. What is the same and different about the shapes?

Same
Both triangles have 3 sides.
Both triangles have 3 angles.

Different
Triangle A has 1 square corner and Triangle B has no square corners.
Triangle A has 0 sides the same length and Triangle B has 2 sides the same length.

B 1 Look at the shapes below. Read the descriptions in the table. Draw each shape in the column that describes it.

All square corners and all sides the same length	Square corners and some sides the same length	No square corners and no sides the same length

M 2 Describe the sides and angles of the pentagon at the right.
Possible answer: 5 sides all the same length, no square corners.

349 Lesson 31 Points, Lines, Rays, and Angles

Solve.

C 3 Describe how the two shapes shown are alike.
Possible answer: Both shapes have 5 sides.
Both shapes have some sides of equal length.
Both shapes have no square corners.

For problems 4–6, use the shapes at the right.

triangle	rectangle	square	rhombus	parallelogram	pentagon

M 4 Fill in the table. Write each shape in the column that describes the number of sides and angles it has.

Fewer than 4 sides and 4 angles	4 sides and 4 angles	More than 4 sides and 4 angles
triangle	rectangle square rhombus parallelogram	pentagon

M 5 Fill in the table. Write each shape in the column that describes the length of its sides.

All sides the same length	Some sides the same length	No sides the same length
square rhombus pentagon	rectangle parallelogram	triangle

M 6 Fill in the table below. Write each shape in the column that describes whether it has square corners or has no square corners.

Has a square corner	Has no square corners
triangle rectangle square	rhombus parallelogram pentagon

350 Lesson 31 Points, Lines, Rays, and Angles

Key
B Basic   **M** Medium   **C** Challenge

Name: _____

Lesson 31

Identify Points, Lines, Line Segments, and Rays

Study the example that shows a drawing with points, lines, line segments, and rays. Then solve problems 1–9.

Example

Amy made a drawing of a letter "A" in her math notebook. Use geometry words to describe the drawing.

There are 4 points on the drawing: point A, point B, point C, and point D.

There is a line segment from point B to point D. $\overline{BD}$

There is a line through points A and C. $\overleftrightarrow{AC}$

There is a ray from point B through point A. $\overrightarrow{BA}$

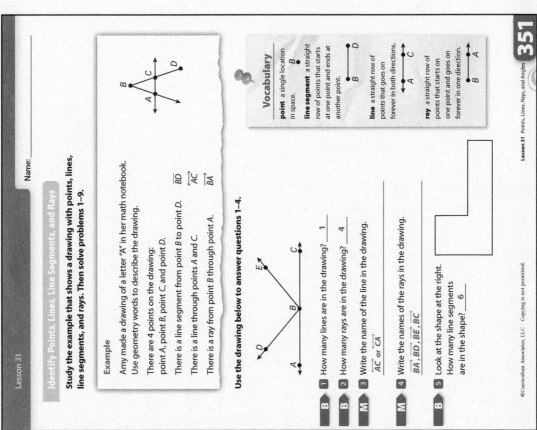

Use the drawing below to answer questions 1–4.

1 How many lines are in the drawing? **1**

2 How many rays are in the drawing? **4**

3 Write the name of the line in the drawing. $\overleftrightarrow{AC}$ or $\overleftrightarrow{CA}$

4 Write the names of the rays in the drawing. $\overrightarrow{BA}, \overrightarrow{BD}, \overrightarrow{BE}, \overrightarrow{BC}$

5 Look at the shape at the right. How many line segments are in the shape? **6**

Vocabulary

point a single location in space.

line segment a straight row of points that starts at one point and ends at another point.

line a straight row of points that goes on forever in both directions.

ray a straight row of points that starts on one point and goes on forever in one direction.

Lesson 31 Points, Lines, Rays, and Angles **351**

Solve.

6 Label each sign below. Write *line*, *line segment*, or *ray*.

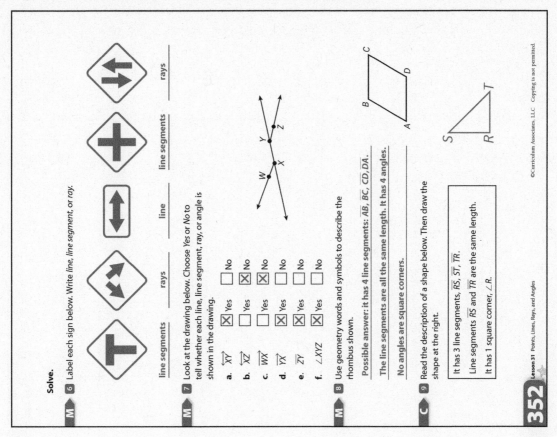

line segments | rays | line | line segments | rays

7 Look at the drawing below. Choose *Yes* or *No* to tell whether each line, line segment, ray, or angle is shown in the drawing.

a. $\overleftrightarrow{XY}$ [X] Yes [ ] No

b. $\overleftrightarrow{XZ}$ [ ] Yes [X] No

c. $\overrightarrow{WX}$ [ ] Yes [X] No

d. $\overrightarrow{YX}$ [X] Yes [ ] No

e. $\overline{ZY}$ [X] Yes [ ] No

f. ∠XYZ [X] Yes [ ] No

8 Use geometry words and symbols to describe the rhombus shown.

Possible answer: it has 4 line segments: $\overline{AB}, \overline{BC}, \overline{CD}, \overline{DA}$.

The line segments are all the same length. It has 4 angles.

No angles are square corners.

9 Read the description of a shape below. Then draw the shape at the right.

> It has 3 line segments, $\overline{RS}, \overline{ST}, \overline{TR}$.
> Line segments $\overline{RS}$ and $\overline{TR}$ are the same length.
> It has 1 square corner, ∠R.

352 Lesson 31 Points, Lines, Rays, and Angles

Lesson 31

Identify Angles

Study the example identifying angles in a shape. Then solve problems 1–10.

Example

Name and describe the angles in the shape below.

∠A is a right angle. It has a shape like a square corner.

∠B is also a right angle.

∠C is an obtuse angle. It has a wider opening than a right angle.

∠D is an acute angle. It has a smaller opening than a right angle.

The shape has 2 right angles, 1 acute angle, and 1 obtuse angle.

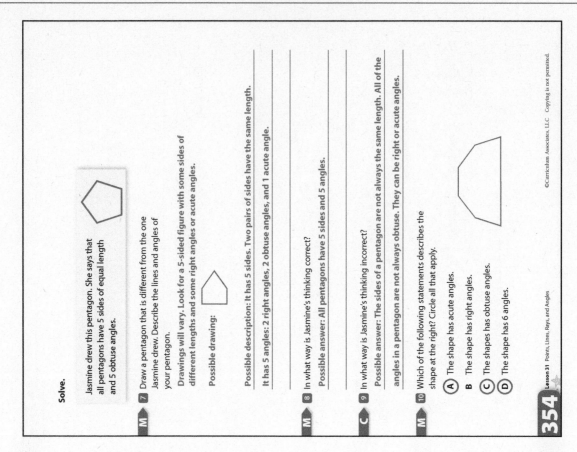

Use the shape at the right to answer questions 1–5.

B 1. How many right angles are in this shape? __0__

B 2. How many acute angles are in this shape? __2__

B 3. How many obtuse angles are in this shape? __2__

M 4. Name the acute angles in the shape.

∠M, ∠K or ∠JML, ∠JKL or ∠LMJ, ∠LKJ

M 5. Name the obtuse angles in the shape.

∠J, ∠L or ∠KJM, ∠KLM or ∠MJK, ∠MLK

M 6. Look at the shape at the right. Describe the number and kind of angles it has.

The shape has 8 obtuse angles.

Solve.

Jasmine drew this pentagon. She says that all pentagons have 5 sides of equal length and 5 obtuse angles.

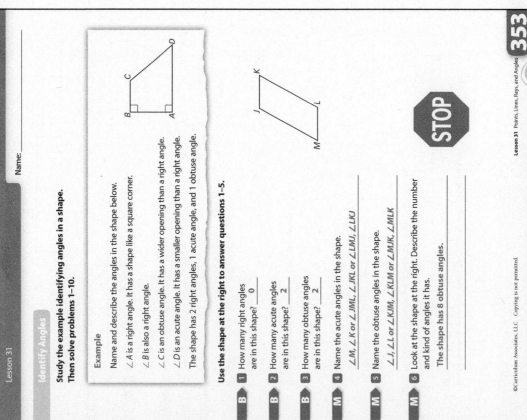

M 7. Draw a pentagon that is different from the one Jasmine drew. Describe the lines and angles of your pentagon.

Drawings will vary. Look for a 5-sided figure with some sides of different lengths and some right angles or acute angles.

Possible drawing:

Possible description: It has 5 sides. Two pairs of sides have the same length. It has 5 angles: 2 right angles, 2 obtuse angles, and 1 acute angle.

M 8. In what way is Jasmine's thinking correct?

Possible answer: All pentagons have 5 sides and 5 angles.

C 9. In what way is Jasmine's thinking incorrect?

Possible answer: The sides of a pentagon are not always the same length. All of the angles in a pentagon are not always obtuse. They can be right or acute angles.

M 10. Which of the following statements describes the shape at the right? Circle all that apply.

A The shape has acute angles.

B The shape has right angles.

C The shapes has obtuse angles.

D The shape has 6 angles.

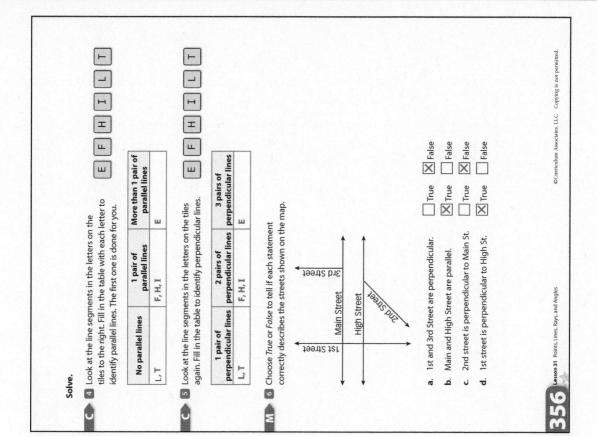

Solve.

C 4 Look at the line segments in the letters on the tiles to the right. Fill in the table with each letter to identify parallel lines. The first one is done for you.

E F H I L T

No parallel lines	1 pair of parallel lines	More than 1 pair of parallel lines
L, T	F, H, I	E

C 5 Look at the line segments in the letters on the tiles again. Fill in the table to identify perpendicular lines.

E F H I L T

1 pair of perpendicular lines	2 pairs of perpendicular lines	3 pairs of perpendicular lines
L, T	F, H, I	E

M 6 Choose *True* or *False* to tell if each statement correctly describes the streets shown on the map.

3rd Street
Main Street
High Street
2nd Street
1st Street

a. 1st and 3rd Street are perpendicular.   True ☐   False ☒
b. Main and High Street are parallel.   True ☒   False ☐
c. 2nd street is perpendicular to Main St.   True ☐   False ☒
d. 1st street is perpendicular to High St.   True ☒   False ☐

356   Lesson 31 Points, Lines, Rays, and Angles   ©Curriculum Associates, LLC Copying is not permitted.

Lesson 31

Name: _____

Identify Parallel and Perpendicular Lines

Study the example identifying parallel and perpendicular lines and segments. Then solve problems 1–6.

Example

Colby drew parallel and perpendicular lines to place the bases and pitcher's mound on a drawing of a baseball field.

$\overleftrightarrow{SF}$ and $\overleftrightarrow{TH}$ are parallel lines.
$\overleftrightarrow{ST}$ and $\overleftrightarrow{FH}$ are parallel lines.

The pitcher's mound is one place where perpendicular lines cross. At what point do perpendicular lines cross at the pitcher's mound?

They cross at point P, where $\overleftrightarrow{TF}$ crosses $\overleftrightarrow{SH}$.

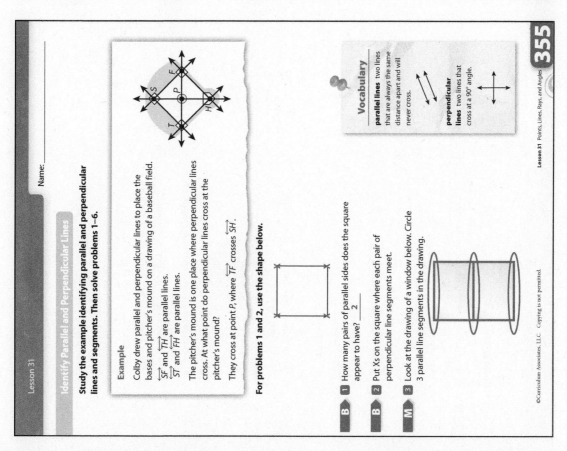

Vocabulary

parallel lines two lines that are always the same distance apart and will never cross.

perpendicular lines two lines that cross at a 90° angle.

For problems 1 and 2, use the shape below.

B 1 How many pairs of parallel sides does the square appear to have?   2

B 2 Put Xs on the square where each pair of perpendicular line segments meet.

M 3 Look at the drawing of a window below. Circle 3 parallel line segments in the drawing.

©Curriculum Associates, LLC Copying is not permitted.   Lesson 31 Points, Lines, Rays, and Angles   **355**

Left page (357)

Name:

Lesson 31

Points, Lines, Rays, and Angles

Solve the problems.

B

1 Which of the following describes the drawing below? Circle the letter for all that apply.

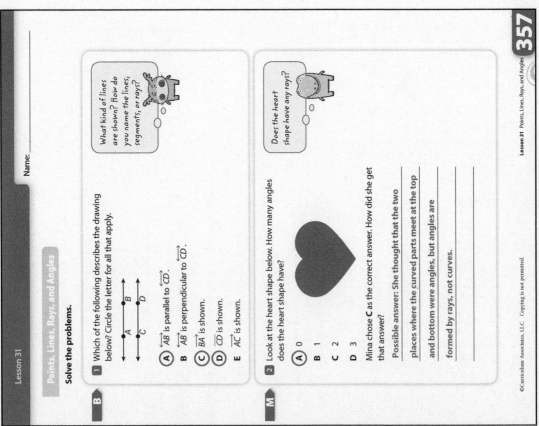

A $\overleftrightarrow{AB}$ is parallel to $\overleftrightarrow{CD}$.

B $\overleftrightarrow{AB}$ is perpendicular to $\overleftrightarrow{CD}$.

C $\overleftrightarrow{CD}$ is shown.

D $\overleftrightarrow{CD}$ is shown.

E $\overleftrightarrow{AC}$ is shown.

What kind of lines are shown? How do you name the lines, segments, or rays?

M

2 Look at the heart shape below. How many angles does the heart shape have?

Ⓐ 0

B 1

C 2

D 3

Does the heart shape have any rays?

Mina chose **C** as the correct answer. How did she get that answer?

Possible answer: She thought that the two
places where the curved parts meet at the top
and bottom were angles, but angles are
formed by rays, not curves.

Lesson 31 Points, Lines, Rays, and Angles **357**

Right page (358)

Solve.

M

3 Name and describe all the angles in the drawing below.

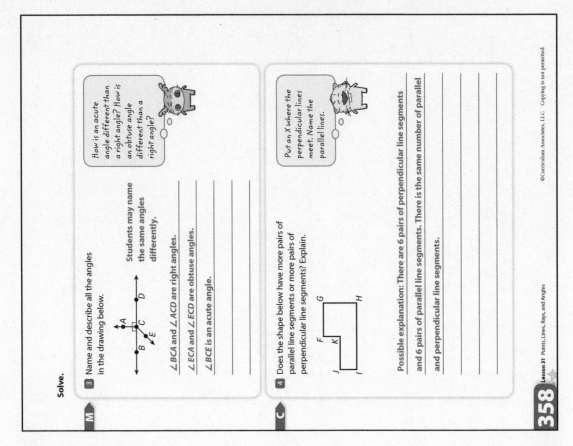

How is an acute angle different than a right angle? How is an obtuse angle different than a right angle?

Students may name the same angles differently.

∠BCA and ∠ACD are right angles.

∠ECA and ∠ECD are obtuse angles.

∠BCE is an acute angle.

C

4 Does the shape below have more pairs of parallel line segments or more pairs of perpendicular line segments? Explain.

Put an X where the perpendicular lines meet. Name the parallel lines.

Possible explanation: There are 6 pairs of perpendicular line segments
and 6 pairs of parallel line segments. There is the same number of parallel
and perpendicular line segments.

Lesson 32

Classify Two-Dimensional Figures

Name: _____

Classify Quadrilaterals

Study the example showing how to classify and compare quadrilaterals. Then solve problems 1–7.

Example

Is every square also a rectangle and a rhombus?
Use a table to compare quadrilaterals.

Quadrilateral	4 sides 4 angles	4 square corners	2 pairs of parallel sides	2 pairs of sides that are the same length	4 sides that are the same length
square	✓	✓	✓	✓	✓
rectangle	✓	✓	✓	✓	sometimes
rhombus	✓	sometimes	✓	✓	✓

Yes. Every square can be named as a rectangle and a rhombus.

B **1** A parallelogram is a quadrilateral with 2 pairs of parallel sides and 2 pairs of sides that are the same length. Circle the quadrilaterals below that are parallelograms.

A   B   C   D   E

B **2** Look at problem 1. Is quadrilateral B a parallelogram? Explain.

No. Possible explanation: Quadrilateral B has only 1 pair of parallel sides.

A parallelogram has 2 pairs of parallel sides.

M **3** A rectangle is a quadrilateral. Describe a rectangle by telling about its sides and its corners.

Possible answer: A rectangle has 4 square corners. It has 2 pairs of parallel sides and 2 pairs of sides that are the same length.

Solve.

M **4** Use the words in the box. Name each shape below. Use as many words from the box as apply. Describe the sides and corners of each shape.

| quadrilateral |
| parallelogram |
| rectangle |
| rhombus |
| square |

a.   b.

a. Names: _Quadrilateral, parallelogram_

Description: Possible answer: The shape has 4 sides. It has no square corners, 2 pairs of parallel sides, and 2 pairs of sides that are the same length.

b. Names: _Square, rhombus, rectangle, parallelogram, quadrilateral_

Description: Possible answer: The shape has 4 square corners, 2 pairs of parallel sides, and 4 sides that are the same length.

M **5** Draw a quadrilateral that has at least 1 pair of parallel sides, but no square corners.
Possible drawings:

or

Drawings may vary. Drawings should show a trapezoid or a parallelogram.

M **6** Draw a quadrilateral that has at least 1 square corner, but is not a rectangle.
Possible drawings:

or

Drawings may vary. Drawings should show a quadrilateral with at least 1 square corner that has no pairs of parallel sides or 1 pair of parallel sides.

C **7** Draw a quadrilateral that does not have pairs of parallel sides or sides of the same length.

Drawings will vary. Drawings should show a 4-sided shape with no parallel sides and side lengths that are all different.

Key

B Basic   **M** Medium   **C** Challenge

Lesson 32

Name: _____

Sort Shapes Based on Sides

Study the example showing how to sort shapes into groups based on parallel and perpendicular sides. Then solve problems 1–4.

Example

Sort the shapes in the box based on parallel and perpendicular sides. Put the shapes in the Venn diagram below.

rhombus   triangle   square   hexagon   rectangle

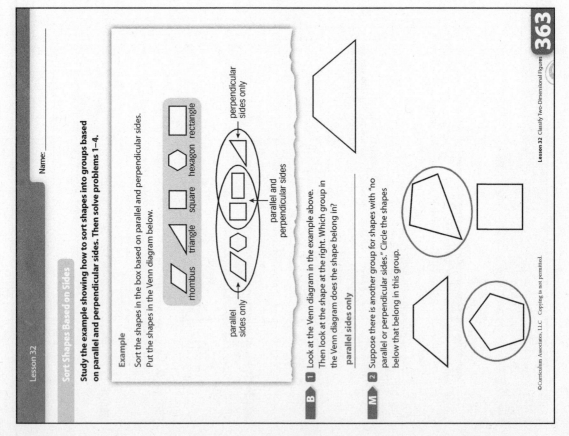

parallel sides only

parallel and perpendicular sides

perpendicular sides only

B 1 Look at the Venn diagram in the example above. Then look at the shape at the right. Which group in the Venn diagram does the shape belong in?

parallel sides only

M 2 Suppose there is another group for shapes with "no parallel or perpendicular sides." Circle the shapes below that belong in this group.

Solve.

M 3 Look at each shape below. Choose *Yes* or *No* to tell whether the shape has parallel sides. Then choose *Yes* or *No* to tell whether it has perpendicular sides.

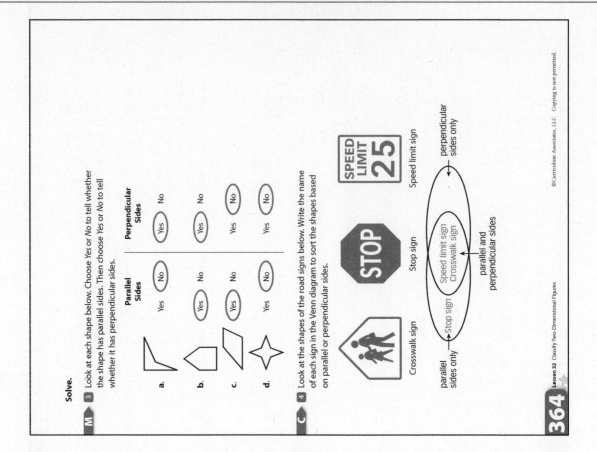

	Parallel Sides	Perpendicular Sides
a.	Yes No	Yes No
b.	Yes No	Yes No
c.	Yes No	Yes No
d.	Yes No	Yes No

C 4 Look at the shapes of the road signs below. Write the name of each sign in the Venn diagram to sort the shapes based on parallel or perpendicular sides.

Crosswalk sign   Stop sign   Speed limit sign

parallel sides only — Stop sign

parallel and perpendicular sides — Speed limit sign / Crosswalk sign

perpendicular sides only

Lesson 32

Name: _____

Sort Shapes Based on Angles

Study the example showing how to sort shapes into groups based on angles. Then solve problems 1–5.

Example
Label each angle in the shapes below with "a" for acute, "r" for right, and "o" for obtuse.
Then draw an arrow from each shape to the group it belongs to.

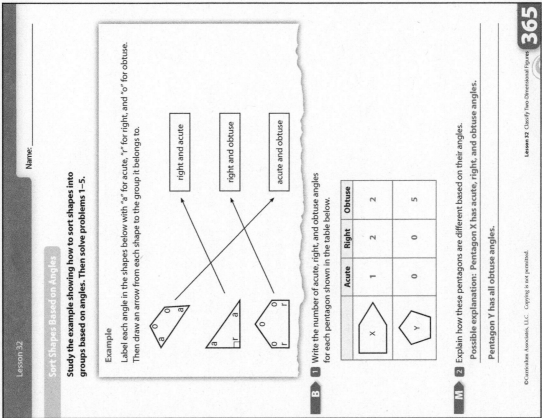

- right and acute
- right and obtuse
- acute and obtuse

B 1 Write the number of acute, right, and obtuse angles for each pentagon shown in the table below.

	Acute	Right	Obtuse
X	1	2	2
Y	0	0	5

M 2 Explain how these pentagons are different based on their angles.
Possible explanation: Pentagon X has acute, right, and obtuse angles.
Pentagon Y has all obtuse angles.

©Curriculum Associates, LLC   Copying is not permitted.

Lesson 32 Classify Two-Dimensional Figures **365**

Solve.

M 3 Choose *Yes* or *No* to tell whether each shape belongs in the group described.

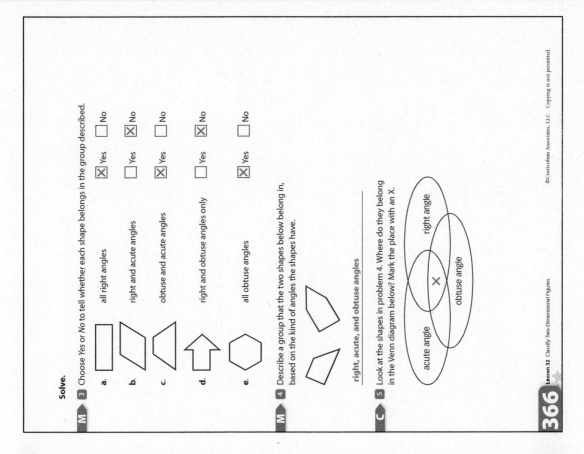

a. all right angles — ☒ Yes ☐ No

b. right and acute angles — ☐ Yes ☒ No

c. obtuse and acute angles — ☒ Yes ☐ No

d. right and obtuse angles only — ☐ Yes ☒ No

e. all obtuse angles — ☒ Yes ☐ No

M 4 Describe a group that the two shapes below belong in, based on the kind of angles the shapes have.

right, acute, and obtuse angles

C 5 Look at the shapes in problem 4. Where do they belong in the Venn diagram below? Mark the place with an X.

acute angle   right angle   obtuse angle

366 Lesson 32 Classify Two-Dimensional Figures

©Curriculum Associates, LLC   Copying is not permitted.

Practice Lesson 32 Classify Two-Dimensional Figures

Unit 6

Lesson 32

Name: _____

Sort Triangles Based on Sides and Angles

Study the example showing how to sort triangles into groups based on kinds of angles and lengths of sides. Then solve problems 1–4.

Example

What is the same about the two triangles shown at the right? What is different?

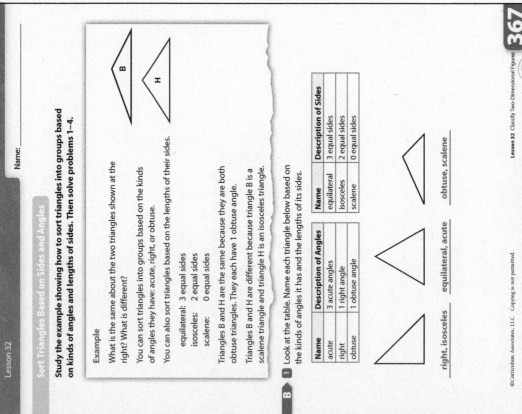

You can sort triangles into groups based on the kinds of angles they have: acute, right, or obtuse.

You can also sort triangles based on the lengths of their sides.

equilateral: 3 equal sides
isosceles: 2 equal sides
scalene: 0 equal sides

Triangles B and H are the same because they are both obtuse triangles. They each have 1 obtuse angle.

Triangles B and H are different because triangle B is a scalene triangle and triangle H is an isosceles triangle.

B 1 Look at the table. Name each triangle below based on the kinds of angles it has and the lengths of its sides.

Name	Description of Angles
acute	3 acute angles
right	1 right angle
obtuse	1 obtuse angle

Name	Description of Sides
equilateral	3 equal sides
isosceles	2 equal sides
scalene	0 equal sides

right, isosceles   equilateral, acute   obtuse, scalene

©Curriculum Associates, LLC   Copying is not permitted.

Lesson 32 Classify Two-Dimensional Figures **367**

Solve.

M 2 Look at the name of each triangle below. Then use the numbers in the boxes to write the missing length for one side of each triangle.

9 cm   10 cm   11 cm

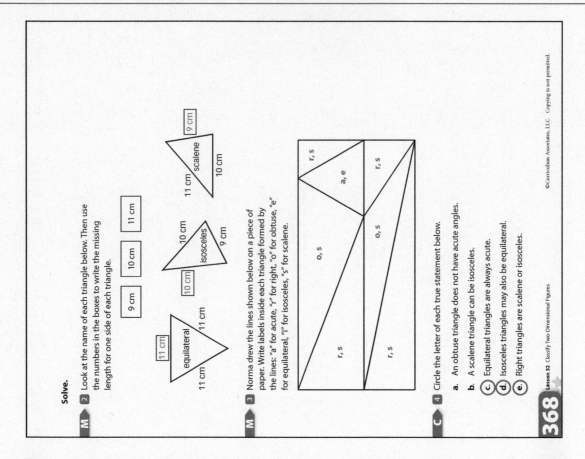

M 3 Norma drew the lines shown below on a piece of paper. Write labels inside each triangle formed by the lines: "a" for acute, "r" for right, "o" for obtuse, "e" for equilateral, "i" for isosceles, "s" for scalene.

C 4 Circle the letter of each true statement below.

a. An obtuse triangle does not have acute angles.

b. A scalene triangle can be isosceles.

c. Equilateral triangles are always acute.

d. Isosceles triangles may also be equilateral.

e. Right triangles are scalene or isosceles.

©Curriculum Associates, LLC   Copying is not permitted.

368 Lesson 32 Classify Two-Dimensional Figures

140 Practice and Problem Solving

Unit 6 Geometry

©Curriculum Associates, LLC   Copying is not permitted.

Lesson 32

Name: ____________________

Classify Two-Dimensional Figures

Solve the problems.

B

1 Which is the best name for the group of triangles below?

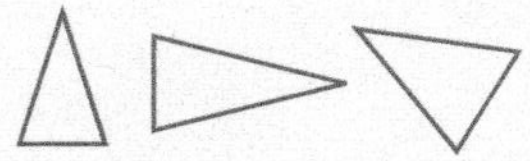

How are all the angles similar? How are the sides similar?

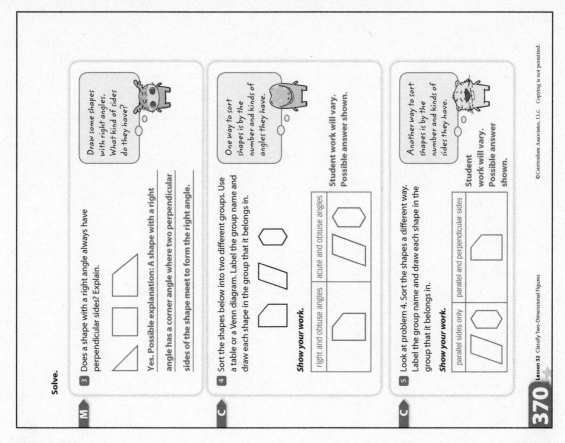

A acute, scalene **C** obtuse, scalene

(B) acute, isosceles **D** obtuse, isosceles

M

2 Which choice best describes the group this shape belongs in, based on the kinds of sides and angles it has?

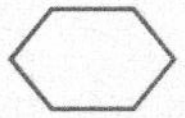

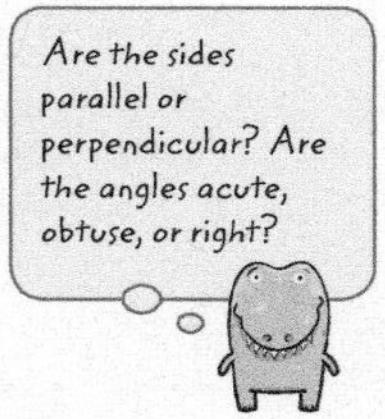
Are the sides parallel or perpendicular? Are the angles acute, obtuse, or right?

A parallel sides, acute angles

B perpendicular sides, acute angles

(C) parallel sides, obtuse angles

D perpendicular sides, obtuse angles

Angela chose **A** as the correct answer. How did she get that answer?

Possible answer: She correctly identified parallel sides, but thought the angles larger than a square corner were acute instead of obtuse.

Solve.

M

3 Does a shape with a right angle always have perpendicular sides? Explain.

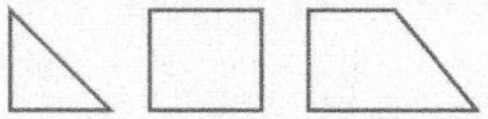

Draw some shapes with right angles. What kind of sides do they have?

Yes. Possible explanation: A shape with a right angle has a corner angle where two perpendicular sides of the shape meet to form the right angle.

C

4 Sort the shapes below into two different groups. Use a table or a Venn diagram. Label the group name and draw each shape in the group that it belongs in.

One way to sort shapes is by the number and kinds of angles they have.

Show your work.

right and obtuse angles	acute and obtuse angles

Student work will vary. Possible answer shown.

C

5 Look at problem 4. Sort the shapes a different way. Label the group name and draw each shape in the group that it belongs in.

Another way to sort shapes is by the number and kinds of sides they have.

Show your work.

parallel sides only	parallel and perpendicular sides

Student work will vary. Possible answer shown.

Lesson 33

Symmetry

Divide Shapes into Equal Parts

Study the example showing how to divide a shape into equal parts. Then solve problems 1–5.

Example

Show two different ways to divide a square into 4 equal parts.

Each part is $\frac{1}{4}$ of the square.

Each equal part is the same shape.

The 4 equal parts are rectangles.

The 4 equal parts are squares.

B 1 Show another way to divide a square into 4 equal parts. Then complete the sentence.

Possible dividing lines shown. Students may also draw vertical lines to divide the square into 4 equal parts.

Each part is $\frac{1}{4}$ of the square.

M 2 Divide the rectangle below into 2 equal parts. Then complete the sentence.

Possible dividing lines shown. Students may also draw a vertical line or a diagonal line to divide the rectangle into 2 equal parts.

Each part is $\frac{1}{2}$ of the rectangle.

Solve.

M 3 The rectangle below at the left is divided into 8 equal parts. Draw lines on the rectangle at the right to show a different way to divide the rectangle into 8 equal parts.

a.

b. What fraction of the rectangle is each part? $\frac{1}{8}$

M 4 Draw a rectangle and divide it into 4 equal parts. What fraction of the rectangle is each part?

Each part is $\frac{1}{4}$ of the rectangle.

C 5 Liam is making a game board. He wants the game board to have 20 equal sections. Show one way that he could divide the board into 20 equal sections. How many rows are there and how many equal parts in each row?

Show your work.

Possible drawing:

Solution: Answers will vary. Possible answer: There are 5 rows with 4 equal parts in each row.

Key

B Basic   **M** Medium   **C** Challenge

Lesson 33

Find a Line of Symmetry

Study the example showing how to find a line of symmetry. Then solve problems 1–5.

Example

Which shape has more lines of symmetry—a rectangle, an equilateral triangle, or a square?

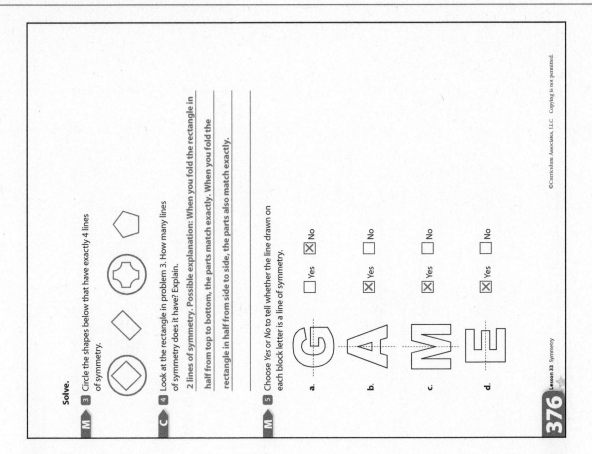

A rectangle has 2 lines of symmetry.

An equilateral triangle has 3 lines of symmetry.

A square has 4 lines of symmetry.

A square has more lines of symmetry than a rectangle and an equilateral triangle.

Vocabulary

line of symmetry a line dividing a shape into two matching parts.

B 1 Circle the shapes below that have at least one line of symmetry.

M 2 Circle the shape below that has a greater number of lines of symmetry.

Solve.

M 3 Circle the shapes below that have exactly 4 lines of symmetry.

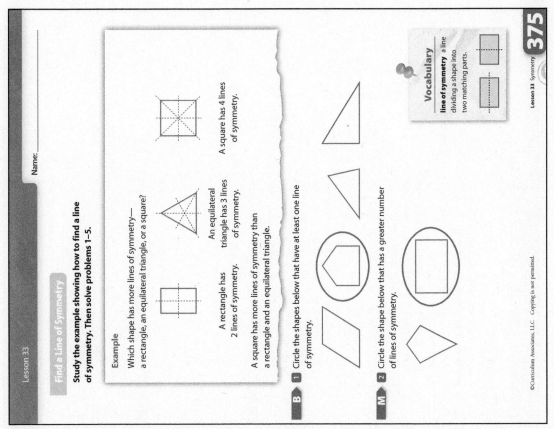

C 4 Look at the rectangle in problem 3. How many lines of symmetry does it have? Explain.

2 lines of symmetry. Possible explanation: When you fold the rectangle in half from top to bottom, the parts match exactly. When you fold the rectangle in half from side to side, the parts also match exactly.

M 5 Choose *Yes* or *No* to tell whether the line drawn on each block letter is a line of symmetry.

a. G ☐ Yes ☒ No

b. A ☒ Yes ☐ No

c. M ☒ Yes ☐ No

d. E ☒ Yes ☐ No

Lesson 33

Draw a Line of Symmetry

Study the example showing how to draw a line of symmetry. Then solve problems 1–5.

Example

Draw all of the lines of symmetry for each star shape.
How many lines of symmetry does each shape have?
Where do all the lines of symmetry cross?

The 6-pointed star has 6 lines of symmetry.

The 5-pointed star has 5 lines of symmetry.

All the lines of symmetry cross at the center point of each shape.

B **1** Draw all the lines of symmetry on the tree shape below.

How many lines of symmetry does the tree shape have? 1

B **2** Draw all the lines of symmetry on the X shape below.

How many lines of symmetry does the X shape have? 4

Name: _____

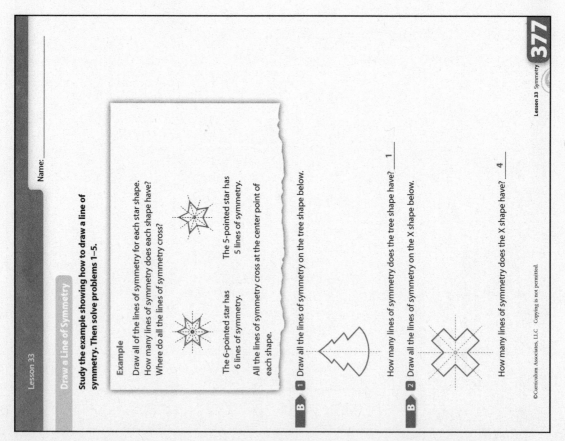

Solve.

M **3** Draw all the lines of symmetry on each pentagon below.
Write how many lines of symmetry each pentagon has.

5 line(s) of symmetry   1 line(s) of symmetry

M **4** Titus drew a hexagon with 6 lines of symmetry. He says that all hexagons have 6 sides of symmetry. Use words and a drawing to explain why Titus's thinking is incorrect.

Drawings will vary. Look for a hexagon with fewer than 6 lines of symmetry.

Answers will vary. Possible answer: A hexagon that has sides of the same length has 6 lines of symmetry, but hexagons with sides of different lengths have a different number of lines of symmetry. The drawing shows an example of a hexagon with 2 lines of symmetry.

C **5** Draw all the lines of symmetry that the design in each flag below has. Then write how many lines of symmetry that the design in each flag below has.

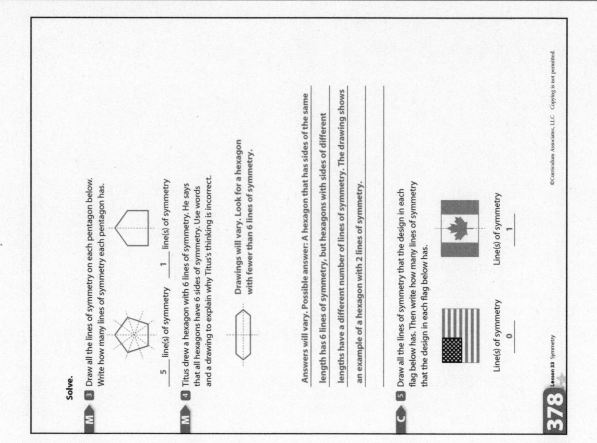

Line(s) of symmetry   Line(s) of symmetry
0   1

Lesson 33

Symmetry

Solve the problems.

B 1 Which figure below shows a correct line of symmetry?
Circle the letter for all that apply.

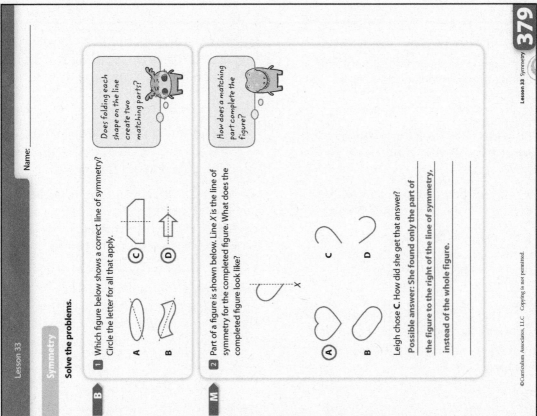

Does folding each shape on the line create two matching parts?

M 2 Part of a figure is shown below. Line X is the line of symmetry for the completed figure. What does the completed figure look like?

How does a matching part complete the figure?

Leigh chose **C**. How did she get that answer?

Possible answer: She found only the part of the figure to the right of the line of symmetry, instead of the whole figure.

Solve.

M 3 Draw all the lines of symmetry on the figure below.
How many lines of symmetry are there?

Show your work.

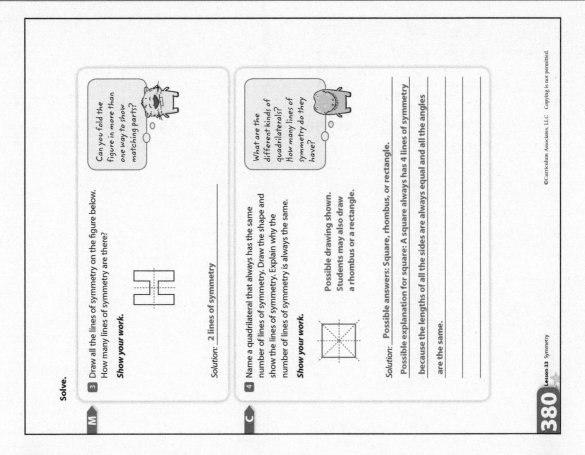

Can you fold the figure in more than one way to show matching parts?

Solution: ___2 lines of symmetry___

C 4 Name a quadrilateral that always has the same number of lines of symmetry. Draw the shape and show the lines of symmetry. Explain why the number of lines of symmetry is always the same.

Show your work.

What are the different kinds of quadrilaterals? How many lines of symmetry do they have?

Possible drawing shown. Students may also draw a rhombus or a rectangle.

Solution: ___Possible answers: Square, rhombus, or rectangle.___

Possible explanation for square: A square always has 4 lines of symmetry because the lengths of all the sides are always equal and all the angles are the same.

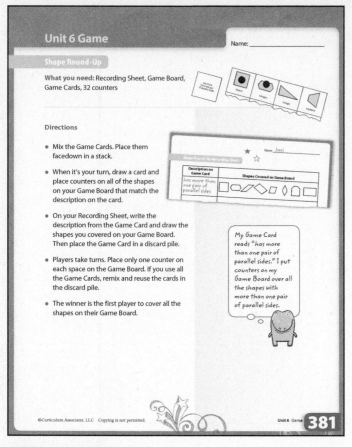

STEP BY STEP

CCSS Focus - 4.G.A.2 *Embedded SMPs* - 4, 6, 7 **Objective:** Identify types of angles in two-dimensional figures. Identify parallel and perpendicular sides in two-dimensional figures.	**Materials** For each pair: Recording Sheet (TR 10), 1 set of Game Cards (TR 11), Game Board (1 for each player) (TR 12), 32 counters (16 for each player)

- Read through the directions with students. Point out that the goal is to cover all your game board spaces with counters.

- Review parallel and perpendicular sides and types of angles for several shapes on the game board.

- Model playing the game. Choose a game card and read aloud the description on the card. Model looking for shapes on the game board that match the description.

- Cover each shape that matches the description with a counter. Display the Recording Sheet and point to the two columns where students write the description and draw the shapes.

- Remind students that they can remix and use the cards in the discard pile if necessary. Provide additional copies of the recording sheets if needed.

Vary the Game Play 5 rounds without the game board. Draw one card. Players record as many different kinds of shapes as they can that fit the description. The player with more shapes wins the round.

Extra Support Players take turns choosing a card. They work together to find and cover one shape on their game boards that matches the description. Each player records the description and shape on their recording sheet. Provide additional copies of the recording sheets.

Unit 6 Practice

Geometry

Name: _____

In this unit you learned to:

	Lesson
draw and identify points, lines, line segments, rays, and perpendicular and parallel lines, for example: a plus sign has perpendicular lines.	31
draw and identify angles (right, acute, obtuse), for example: a square has 4 right angles.	31
classify two-dimensional figures based on sides and angles, for example: regular pentagons and hexagons have all obtuse angles.	32
draw and identify lines of symmetry, for example: a square has 4 lines of symmetry.	33

Use these skills to solve problems 1–4.

B | **1** Tell whether each sentence is *True* or *False*.

    a. An acute angle has a larger opening than a right angle.   ☐ True   ☒ False

    b. Any shape with more than 4 sides has only obtuse angles.   ☐ True   ☒ False

    c. A triangle can have 1 right angle or 1 obtuse angle, but not both.   ☒ True   ☐ False

    d. An angle is formed by 2 rays.   ☒ True   ☐ False

M | **2** Name each triangle below based on the kinds of angles it has and the length of its sides.

right, isosceles   right, scalene   acute, equilateral

Unit 6 Practice Geometry **387**

Solve.

M | **3** Compare the two triangles below. How are the triangles the same? How are they different?

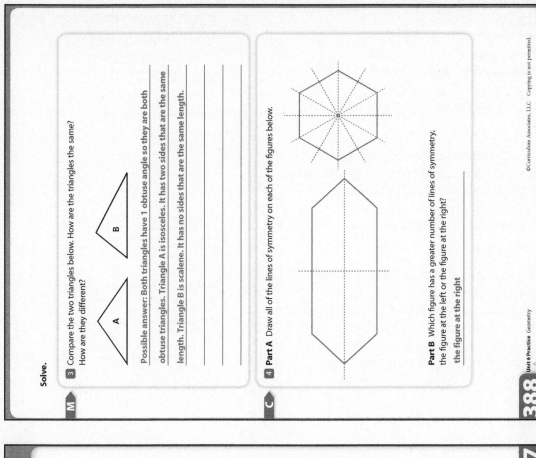

A   B

Possible answer: Both triangles have 1 obtuse angle so they are both obtuse triangles. Triangle A is isosceles. It has two sides that are the same length. Triangle B is scalene. It has no sides that are the same length.

C | **4** **Part A** Draw all of the lines of symmetry on each of the figures below.

Part B Which figure has a greater number of lines of symmetry, the figure at the left or the figure at the right? **the figure at the right**

388 Unit 6 Practice Geometry

Key

B Basic   **M** Medium   **C** Challenge

TEACHER NOTES

Common Core Standards: 4.G.A.1, 4.G.A.2
Standards for Mathematical Practice: 1, 2, 3, 5, 6
DOK: 3
Materials: pattern blocks, rulers, grid paper (optional)

About the Task

To complete this task, students draw shapes and use precise geometric vocabulary to describe the properties of the shapes' sides and angles. This task requires students to analyze shapes' properties and draw composite shapes that meet given parameters.

Getting Students Started

Read the problem out loud and go over the checklist. Review geometric vocabulary and have students give examples of shapes that have parallel and perpendicular lines and each kind of angle (acute, obtuse, right). Talk about the shapes shown in the flower design. Discuss the sides and angles. Ask how those properties influence how you might decide to use the shape in a design. **(SMP 6)**

Completing the Task

Students will begin by choosing the shapes to use in their flower designs. Have students use pattern blocks to help design their flowers before they begin to draw. Point out the shape models on the student page and encourage students to use other shapes they have learned. **(SMP 1, 2)**

Next, students draw the geometric shapes to create their designs. Students may find it helpful to use rulers and grid paper. Some students might prefer to draw the shapes—with or without grid paper—and then cut out the shapes and manipulate them to finalize their designs. Encourage students to draw carefully and accurately. **(SMP 5, 6)**

Finally, students make a list of their shapes, along with a description of the properties of each shape. Make sure students understand that they should include terms such as *parallel, perpendicular, line segment, acute, obtuse,* and *right angles* in their descriptions. Have students read their descriptions aloud and point to the various parts of each shape as they describe it. **(SMP 1, 3)**

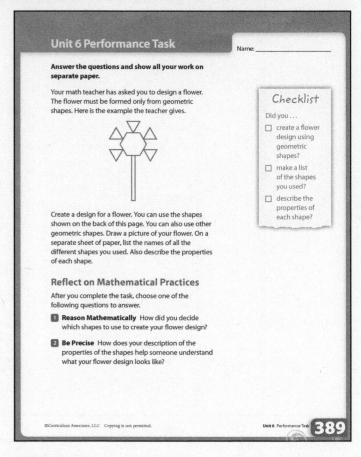

Extension

If some students have more time to spend on this problem, you can have them solve this extension:

Make another flower design using at least two shapes that are different from your original design. Use geometric vocabulary to describe the properties of the new shapes in the design.

SAMPLE RESPONSES AND RUBRIC

4-Point Solution

My flower design is made of 6 shapes: 1 trapezoid, 1 rectangle, and 4 isosceles triangles. The trapezoid has 2 parallel sides at the top and bottom. It has 2 obtuse angles at the bottom corners and 2 acute angles at the top corners. The flower stem is a rectangle. It has 2 pairs of parallel sides and 4 right angles. The 4 right angles form perpendicular lines. I used 4 isosceles triangles for the flower petals. Each isosceles triangle has 2 same-length sides and one side that is a shorter length. Each isosceles triangle has 3 acute angles.

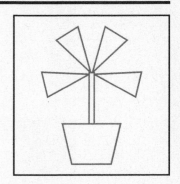

REFLECT ON MATHEMATICAL PRACTICES

1. Students' explanations should show an understanding that the sides and angles of their chosen shapes should look like features and shapes seen in real-life flowers. **(SMP 2)**

2. Students' explanations should include an understanding of how real-life objects can be described as geometric shapes using geometric vocabulary terms. **(SMP 6)**

SCORING RUBRIC

4 points   The student has drawn a reasonable flower design. The student has used geometric shapes in the design. The student lists each shape used and describes the properties of its sides and angles. The student accurately uses geometric vocabulary terms in the description.

3 points   The student has drawn a reasonable flower design. The student has used geometric shapes in the design. The student lists each shape used but may give incomplete descriptions of the shapes' properties. Some geometric vocabulary terms may be incorrect.

2 points   The student has attempted to draw a flower design. The student has used some geometric shapes in the design. The list of shapes is incomplete. There is little description of shapes' properties. Geometric vocabulary terms are used incorrectly or not used at all.

1 point   The student has not drawn a flower design or has not used geometric shapes in the design. The student does not list the shapes or describe the shapes' properties. There are few or no geometric vocabulary terms used.

SOLUTION TO THE EXTENSION

Possible Solution

I used a hexagon and 3 equilateral triangles for the flower petals. The hexagon has 3 pairs of parallel sides and 6 obtuse angles. Each equilateral triangle has 3 sides of the same length and 3 acute angles.

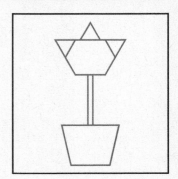

Multi-Digit Addition—Skills Practice

Form A

Name: _____

Add within 10,000.

#			#			#			#		
1	2,145 + 653 2,798		**2**	5,260 + 417 5,677		**3**	1,083 + 2,513 3,596		**4**	2,864 + 7,135 9,999	
5	1,248 + 532 1,780		**6**	3,709 + 152 3,861		**7**	4,561 + 1,054 5,615		**8**	5,726 + 3,742 9,468	
9	3,750 + 456 4,206		**10**	2,538 + 167 2,705		**11**	1,659 + 3,291 4,950		**12**	4,806 + 3,255 8,061	
13	6,725 + 385 7,110		**14**	5,218 + 938 6,156		**15**	6,002 + 2,999 9,001		**16**	8,375 + 1,625 10,000	
17	4,278 + 3,956 8,234		**18**	9,407 + 396 9,803		**19**	3,098 + 2,574 5,672		**20**	2,710 + 5,690 8,400	

Multi-Digit Addition—Skills Practice

Form B

Name: _____

Add within 10,000.

#			#			#			#		
1	1,247 + 532 1,779		**2**	3,415 + 243 3,658		**3**	1,068 + 1,510 2,578		**4**	4,037 + 5,062 9,099	
5	2,653 + 412 3,065		**6**	1,087 + 637 1,724		**7**	1,960 + 3,204 5,164		**8**	6,723 + 1,238 7,961	
9	4,058 + 852 4,910		**10**	2,718 + 534 3,252		**11**	3,605 + 2,795 6,400		**12**	2,806 + 6,294 9,100	
13	6,725 + 385 7,110		**14**	5,218 + 938 6,156		**15**	7,538 + 2,462 10,000		**16**	3,999 + 4,006 8,005	
17	7,092 + 1,865 8,957		**18**	8,444 + 565 9,009		**19**	5,146 + 3,175 8,321		**20**	8,470 + 1,525 9,995	

Fluency Practice

Form B

Multi-Digit Addition—Skills Practice

Name: _____

Add within 100,000.

1	10,943 + 2,035 12,978	2	17,342 + 1,340 18,682	3	12,453 + 20,143 32,596	4	61,238 + 24,501 85,739
5	34,210 + 1,399 35,609	6	72,643 + 8,142 80,785	7	15,920 + 63,254 79,174	8	45,806 + 54,159 99,965
9	94,627 + 987 95,614	10	68,254 + 2,438 70,692	11	26,513 + 25,974 52,487	12	21,942 + 38,657 60,599
13	23,658 + 8,467 32,125	14	47,652 + 27,836 75,488	15	29,999 + 3,999 33,998	16	84,316 + 15,684 100,000
17	74,895 + 16,395 91,290	18	57,918 + 25,896 83,814	19	42,968 + 20,947 63,915	20	45,163 + 27,989 73,152

Fluency Practice **399**

Form A

Multi-Digit Addition—Skills Practice

Name: _____

Add within 100,000.

1	10,352 + 1,430 11,782	2	16,164 + 1,325 17,489	3	20,753 + 10,104 30,857	4	50,618 + 24,350 74,968
5	15,200 + 999 16,199	6	32,145 + 4,625 36,770	7	64,102 + 17,254 81,356	8	24,390 + 56,180 80,570
9	93,752 + 598 94,350	10	46,250 + 23,805 70,055	11	12,643 + 52,794 65,437	12	54,622 + 34,588 89,210
13	23,856 + 15,246 39,102	14	47,423 + 19,836 67,259	15	49,999 + 3,999 53,998	16	90,187 + 9,783 99,970
17	84,678 + 6,395 91,073	18	27,329 + 15,896 43,225	19	52,098 + 28,107 80,205	20	48,365 + 51,635 100,000

398 Fluency Practice

Multi-Digit Addition—Repeated Reasoning

Name: _____

Find place value patterns in the hundreds.

Set A

1. $190 + 210 = \underline{400}$
2. $290 + 210 = \underline{500}$
3. $1{,}290 + 210 = \underline{1{,}500}$
4. $190 + 220 = \underline{410}$
5. $290 + 220 = \underline{510}$
6. $1{,}290 + 220 = \underline{1{,}510}$
7. $190 + 230 = \underline{420}$
8. $290 + 230 = \underline{520}$
9. $1{,}290 + 230 = \underline{1{,}520}$
10. $190 + 240 = \underline{430}$
11. $290 + 240 = \underline{530}$
12. $1{,}290 + 240 = \underline{1{,}530}$

Set B

1.
$$\begin{array}{r} 102 \\ +\ 298 \\ \hline 400 \end{array}$$
2.
$$\begin{array}{r} 112 \\ +\ 298 \\ \hline 410 \end{array}$$
3.
$$\begin{array}{r} 118 \\ +\ 292 \\ \hline 410 \end{array}$$
4.
$$\begin{array}{r} 202 \\ +\ 298 \\ \hline 500 \end{array}$$
5.
$$\begin{array}{r} 212 \\ +\ 298 \\ \hline 510 \end{array}$$
6.
$$\begin{array}{r} 218 \\ +\ 292 \\ \hline 510 \end{array}$$
7.
$$\begin{array}{r} 302 \\ +\ 298 \\ \hline 600 \end{array}$$
8.
$$\begin{array}{r} 312 \\ +\ 298 \\ \hline 610 \end{array}$$
9.
$$\begin{array}{r} 318 \\ +\ 292 \\ \hline 610 \end{array}$$

Describe a pattern you see in one of the sets of problems above.

Answers will vary. Students may see in set A that when one addend increases by 10 the sum increases by 10.

Fluency Practice **401**

Multi-Digit Addition—Repeated Reasoning

Name: _____

Find place value patterns in the tens.

Set A

1. $201 + 109 = \underline{310}$
2. $1{,}201 + 109 = \underline{1{,}310}$
3. $2{,}201 + 109 = \underline{2{,}310}$
4. $202 + 109 = \underline{311}$
5. $1{,}202 + 109 = \underline{1{,}311}$
6. $2{,}202 + 109 = \underline{2{,}311}$
7. $203 + 109 = \underline{312}$
8. $1{,}203 + 109 = \underline{1{,}312}$
9. $2{,}203 + 109 = \underline{2{,}312}$
10. $204 + 109 = \underline{313}$
11. $1{,}204 + 109 = \underline{1{,}313}$
12. $2{,}204 + 109 = \underline{2{,}313}$

Set B

1.
$$\begin{array}{r} 1{,}325 \\ +\ 25 \\ \hline 1{,}350 \end{array}$$
2.
$$\begin{array}{r} 1{,}326 \\ +\ 25 \\ \hline 1{,}351 \end{array}$$
3.
$$\begin{array}{r} 1{,}327 \\ +\ 25 \\ \hline 1{,}352 \end{array}$$
4.
$$\begin{array}{r} 1{,}325 \\ +\ 125 \\ \hline 1{,}450 \end{array}$$
5.
$$\begin{array}{r} 1{,}326 \\ +\ 125 \\ \hline 1{,}451 \end{array}$$
6.
$$\begin{array}{r} 1{,}327 \\ +\ 125 \\ \hline 1{,}452 \end{array}$$
7.
$$\begin{array}{r} 1{,}326 \\ +\ 126 \\ \hline 1{,}452 \end{array}$$
8.
$$\begin{array}{r} 1{,}327 \\ +\ 126 \\ \hline 1{,}453 \end{array}$$
9.
$$\begin{array}{r} 1{,}328 \\ +\ 126 \\ \hline 1{,}454 \end{array}$$

Describe a pattern you see in one of the sets of problems above.

Answers will vary. Students may see that when the ones and tens digits in the addends stay the same, the ones and tens digits in the sum stay the same.

400 Fluency Practice

Multi-Digit Subtraction—Skills Practice

Name: _____

Form A

Subtract within 10,000.

1
```
  4,865
- 2,341
-------
  2,524
```

2
```
  1,788
- 1,263
-------
    525
```

3
```
  2,592
- 1,271
-------
  1,321
```

4
```
  7,342
- 4,132
-------
  3,210
```

5
```
  8,790
- 6,688
-------
  2,102
```

6
```
  3,743
-   626
-------
  3,117
```

7
```
  9,487
- 1,394
-------
  8,093
```

8
```
  6,427
- 2,515
-------
  3,912
```

9
```
  2,637
- 2,419
-------
    218
```

10
```
  3,780
-   671
-------
  3,109
```

11
```
  8,618
- 3,425
-------
  5,193
```

12
```
  4,756
- 3,813
-------
    943
```

13
```
  8,403
- 6,520
-------
  1,883
```

14
```
  1,438
-   839
-------
    599
```

15
```
  4,725
- 1,439
-------
  3,286
```

16
```
  7,275
- 4,188
-------
  3,087
```

17
```
  5,274
- 2,778
-------
  2,496
```

18
```
  2,923
- 1,976
-------
    947
```

19
```
  5,824
- 2,948
-------
  2,876
```

20
```
  6,743
- 2,878
-------
  3,865
```

Multi-Digit Subtraction—Skills Practice

Name: _____

Form B

Subtract within 10,000.

1
```
  5,647
- 3,210
-------
  2,437
```

2
```
  2,748
-   312
-------
  2,436
```

3
```
  5,429
- 4,003
-------
  1,426
```

4
```
  6,918
- 4,105
-------
  2,813
```

5
```
  8,263
- 1,453
-------
  6,810
```

6
```
  1,397
- 1,239
-------
    158
```

7
```
  4,131
- 2,051
-------
  2,080
```

8
```
  7,382
- 2,581
-------
  4,801
```

9
```
  2,732
- 1,108
-------
  1,624
```

10
```
  4,803
-   615
-------
  4,188
```

11
```
  8,652
- 3,481
-------
  5,171
```

12
```
  3,607
- 2,801
-------
    806
```

13
```
  8,275
- 2,391
-------
  5,884
```

14
```
  3,120
- 1,052
-------
  2,068
```

15
```
  9,253
-   198
-------
  9,055
```

16
```
  6,732
- 5,587
-------
  1,145
```

17
```
  4,366
- 1,568
-------
  2,798
```

18
```
  1,812
-   945
-------
    867
```

19
```
  7,493
- 2,594
-------
  4,899
```

20
```
  7,423
- 2,846
-------
  4,577
```

Multi-Digit Subtraction—Skills Practice

Name: _____

Form A

Subtract within 100,000.

1 47,863
    −   251
    47,612

2 19,038
    − 11,018
     8,020

3 28,682
    − 3,270
    25,412

4 76,429
    − 20,306
    56,123

5 81,235
    − 20,017
    61,218

6 36,725
    − 1,582
    35,143

7 94,130
    − 20,125
    74,005

8 64,728
    − 3,914
    60,814

9 28,236
    − 8,915
    19,321

10 58,623
     − 26,374
     32,249

11 72,160
     − 2,087
     70,073

12 38,412
     − 25,651
     12,761

13 34,210
     − 8,105
     26,105

14 10,714
     − 9,456
      1,258

15 63,258
     − 21,399
     41,859

16 40,805
     − 15,912
     24,893

17 53,126
     − 45,928
      7,198

18 80,052
     − 71,963
      8,089

19 24,350
     − 9,582
     14,768

20 100,000
     − 86,932
      13,068

Multi-Digit Subtraction—Skills Practice

Name: _____

Form B

Subtract within 100,000.

1 53,641
    − 1,320
    52,231

2 85,472
    − 82,302
     3,170

3 93,245
    − 32,025
    61,220

4 43,619
    − 20,301
    23,318

5 30,582
    −   156
    30,426

6 12,987
    − 2,793
    10,194

7 82,056
    − 50,330
    31,726

8 73,542
    − 25,402
    48,140

9 27,810
    − 15,675
    12,135

10 94,321
     − 4,255
     90,066

11 65,852
     − 23,890
     41,962

12 18,376
     − 8,953
      9,423

13 15,008
     − 2,409
     12,599

14 20,530
     − 19,790
        740

15 99,325
     − 38,547
     60,778

16 50,364
     − 37,148
     13,216

17 36,825
     − 28,967
      7,858

18 38,972
     − 19,999
     18,973

19 45,000
     − 37,955
      7,045

20 100,000
     − 23,871
      76,129

Multi-Digit Subtraction—Repeated Reasoning

Name: _____

Find patterns in subtracting small numbers.

Set A

1 897 − 1 = 896

2 897 − 2 = 895

3 898 − 1 = 897

4 898 − 2 = 896

5 899 − 1 = 898

6 899 − 2 = 897

7 900 − 1 = 899

8 900 − 2 = 898

9 901 − 1 = 900

10 901 − 2 = 899

Set B

1
```
  650
−  10
  640
```

2
```
  650
−  20
  630
```

3
```
  650
−  30
  620
```

4
```
  320
−  10
  310
```

5
```
  320
−  20
  300
```

6
```
  320
−  30
  290
```

7
```
  400
−  10
  390
```

8
```
  400
−  20
  380
```

9
```
  400
−  30
  370
```

Describe a pattern you see in one of the sets of problems above.

Answers will vary. Students may see in Set B that when the amount you subtract

increases by ten the difference decreases by ten.

Multi-Digit Subtraction—Repeated Reasoning

Name: _____

Find place value patterns in subtracting hundreds.

Set A

1 156 − 104 = 52

2 256 − 104 = 152

3 156 − 105 = 51

4 256 − 105 = 151

5 156 − 106 = 50

6 256 − 106 = 150

7 156 − 107 = 49

8 256 − 107 = 149

9 156 − 108 = 48

10 256 − 108 = 148

Set B

1
```
  625
− 101
  524
```

2
```
  625
− 102
  523
```

3
```
  625
− 103
  522
```

4
```
  625
− 201
  424
```

5
```
  625
− 202
  423
```

6
```
  625
− 203
  422
```

7
```
  625
− 301
  324
```

8
```
  625
− 302
  323
```

9
```
  625
− 303
  322
```

Describe a pattern you see in one of the sets of problems above.

Answers will vary. Students may see in Set B that when the amount you subtract

increases by 100, the difference decreases by 100.

Fraction Addition—Skills Practice

Name: _____

Form A

Add fractions.

1. $\frac{1}{4} + \frac{1}{4} = \frac{2}{4}$ or $\frac{1}{2}$

2. $\frac{1}{6} + \frac{1}{6} = \frac{2}{6}$ or $\frac{1}{3}$

3. $\frac{1}{3} + \frac{2}{3} = \frac{3}{3}$ or 1

4. $\frac{1}{10} + \frac{2}{10} = \frac{3}{10}$

5. $\frac{1}{5} + \frac{3}{5} = \frac{4}{5}$

6. $\frac{5}{8} + \frac{2}{8} = \frac{7}{8}$

7. $\frac{3}{12} + \frac{5}{12} = \frac{8}{12}$ or $\frac{2}{3}$

8. $\frac{5}{100} + \frac{5}{100} = \frac{10}{100}$ or $\frac{1}{10}$

9. $\frac{6}{10} + \frac{3}{10} = \frac{9}{10}$

10. $\frac{4}{3} + \frac{1}{3} = \frac{5}{3}$ or $1\frac{2}{3}$

11. $\frac{4}{8} + \frac{5}{8} = \frac{9}{8}$ or $1\frac{1}{8}$

12. $\frac{1}{2} + \frac{1}{2} = \frac{2}{2}$ or 1

13. $\frac{2}{6} + \frac{5}{6} = \frac{7}{6}$ or $1\frac{1}{6}$

14. $\frac{3}{12} + \frac{7}{12} = \frac{10}{12}$ or $\frac{5}{6}$

15. $\frac{80}{100} + \frac{8}{100} = \frac{88}{100}$ or $\frac{22}{25}$

16. $\frac{1}{4} + \frac{4}{4} = \frac{5}{4}$ or $1\frac{1}{4}$

17. $\frac{3}{4} + \frac{5}{4} = \frac{8}{4}$ or 2

18. $\frac{2}{8} + \frac{3}{8} = \frac{5}{8}$

19. $\frac{8}{5} + \frac{2}{5} = \frac{10}{5}$ or 2

20. $\frac{8}{10} + \frac{3}{10} = \frac{11}{10}$ or $1\frac{1}{10}$

21. $\frac{1}{3} + \frac{2}{3} + \frac{1}{3} = \frac{4}{3}$ or $1\frac{1}{3}$

22. $\frac{4}{5} + \frac{2}{5} + \frac{3}{5} = \frac{9}{5}$ or $1\frac{4}{5}$

23. $\frac{2}{6} + \frac{1}{6} + \frac{2}{6} = \frac{5}{6}$

24. $\frac{5}{8} + \frac{2}{8} + \frac{1}{8} = \frac{8}{8}$ or 1

25. $\frac{2}{10} + \frac{1}{10} + \frac{5}{10} = \frac{8}{10}$ or $\frac{4}{5}$

26. $\frac{1}{2} + \frac{1}{2} + \frac{1}{2} = \frac{3}{2}$ or $1\frac{1}{2}$

27. $\frac{7}{12} + \frac{1}{12} + \frac{3}{12} = \frac{11}{12}$

Fraction Addition—Skills Practice

Name: _____

Form B

Add fractions.

1. $\frac{1}{3} + \frac{1}{3} = \frac{2}{3}$

2. $\frac{1}{5} + \frac{2}{5} = \frac{3}{5}$

3. $\frac{1}{2} + \frac{1}{2} = \frac{2}{2}$ or 1

4. $\frac{3}{10} + \frac{2}{10} = \frac{5}{10}$ or $\frac{1}{2}$

5. $\frac{2}{12} + \frac{5}{12} = \frac{7}{12}$

6. $\frac{2}{4} + \frac{1}{4} = \frac{3}{4}$

7. $\frac{3}{6} + \frac{2}{6} = \frac{5}{6}$

8. $\frac{2}{100} + \frac{8}{100} = \frac{10}{100}$ or $\frac{1}{10}$

9. $\frac{60}{100} + \frac{30}{100} = \frac{90}{100}$ or $\frac{9}{10}$

10. $\frac{9}{10} + \frac{3}{10} = \frac{12}{10}$ or $1\frac{1}{5}$

11. $\frac{3}{5} + \frac{4}{5} = \frac{7}{5}$ or $1\frac{2}{5}$

12. $\frac{5}{2} + \frac{1}{2} = \frac{6}{2}$ or 3

13. $\frac{3}{8} + \frac{2}{8} = \frac{5}{8}$

14. $\frac{4}{3} + \frac{1}{3} = \frac{5}{3}$ or $1\frac{2}{3}$

15. $\frac{30}{100} + \frac{3}{1} = \frac{330}{100}$ or $3\frac{3}{10}$

16. $\frac{4}{12} + \frac{5}{12} = \frac{9}{12}$ or $\frac{3}{4}$

17. $\frac{7}{10} + \frac{2}{10} = \frac{9}{10}$

18. $\frac{2}{5} + \frac{3}{5} = \frac{5}{5}$ or 1

19. $\frac{3}{2} + \frac{4}{2} = \frac{7}{2}$ or $3\frac{1}{2}$

20. $\frac{5}{4} + \frac{2}{4} = \frac{7}{4}$ or $1\frac{3}{4}$

21. $\frac{3}{10} + \frac{5}{10} + \frac{1}{10} = \frac{9}{10}$

22. $\frac{1}{4} + \frac{2}{4} + \frac{3}{4} = \frac{6}{4}$ or $1\frac{1}{2}$

23. $\frac{2}{8} + \frac{1}{8} + \frac{4}{8} = \frac{7}{8}$

24. $\frac{2}{12} + \frac{3}{12} + \frac{5}{12} = \frac{10}{12}$ or $\frac{5}{6}$

25. $\frac{1}{2} + \frac{1}{2} + \frac{1}{2} = \frac{3}{2}$ or $1\frac{1}{2}$

26. $\frac{9}{10} + \frac{3}{10} + \frac{1}{10} = \frac{13}{10}$ or $1\frac{3}{10}$

27. $\frac{4}{5} + \frac{3}{5} + \frac{2}{5} = \frac{9}{5}$ or $1\frac{4}{5}$

Fraction Addition—Skills Practice

Name: _____ Form A

Add mixed numbers.

1. $2\frac{1}{3} + 1\frac{1}{3} = 3\frac{2}{3}$
2. $2\frac{1}{5} + 1\frac{3}{5} = 3\frac{4}{5}$
3. $1\frac{1}{2} + 1\frac{1}{2} = 3$
4. $2\frac{5}{12} + 3\frac{1}{12} = 5\frac{6}{12}$ or $5\frac{1}{2}$
5. $3\frac{2}{4} + 2\frac{1}{4} = 5\frac{3}{4}$
6. $\frac{5}{6} + 4\frac{1}{6} = 5$
7. $3\frac{20}{100} + 4\frac{5}{100} = 7\frac{25}{100}$ or $7\frac{1}{4}$
8. $9\frac{2}{10} + 3\frac{7}{10} = 12\frac{9}{10}$
9. $2\frac{3}{5} + 4\frac{1}{5} = 6\frac{4}{5}$
10. $10\frac{3}{8} + 2\frac{3}{8} = 12\frac{6}{8}$ or $12\frac{3}{4}$
11. $9\frac{1}{3} + \frac{2}{3} = 10$
12. $7\frac{10}{100} + \frac{7}{100} = 7\frac{17}{100}$
13. $5\frac{4}{10} + 1\frac{6}{10} = 7$
14. $4\frac{2}{5} + 5\frac{4}{5} = 10\frac{1}{5}$
15. $3\frac{1}{2} + 4\frac{1}{2} = 8$
16. $3\frac{5}{10} + 5\frac{1}{10} = 8\frac{6}{10}$ or $8\frac{3}{5}$
17. $6\frac{3}{4} + 4\frac{2}{4} = 11\frac{1}{4}$
18. $6\frac{2}{8} + 2\frac{5}{8} = 8\frac{7}{8}$
19. $\frac{8}{12} + 2\frac{7}{12} = 3\frac{3}{12}$ or $3\frac{1}{4}$
20. $3\frac{2}{10} + 4\frac{1}{10} = 7\frac{3}{10}$
21. $10\frac{1}{5} + 8\frac{3}{5} = 18\frac{4}{5}$
22. $5\frac{3}{4} + 2\frac{3}{4} = 8\frac{2}{4}$ or $8\frac{1}{2}$
23. $7\frac{90}{100} + 7\frac{10}{100} = 15$
24. $6\frac{2}{3} + 4\frac{2}{3} = 11\frac{1}{3}$

Fraction Addition—Skills Practice

Name: _____ Form B

Add mixed numbers.

1. $2\frac{1}{4} + 3\frac{1}{4} = 5\frac{2}{4}$ or $5\frac{1}{2}$
2. $3\frac{4}{6} + 4\frac{1}{6} = 7\frac{5}{6}$
3. $2\frac{1}{3} + 6\frac{2}{3} = 9$
4. $1\frac{4}{5} + 2\frac{3}{5} = 4\frac{2}{5}$
5. $5\frac{3}{8} + 7\frac{2}{8} = 12\frac{5}{8}$
6. $2\frac{3}{12} + 3\frac{9}{12} = 6$
7. $6\frac{9}{10} + 3\frac{2}{10} = 10\frac{1}{10}$
8. $4\frac{2}{3} + 1\frac{2}{3} = 6\frac{1}{3}$
9. $4\frac{3}{8} + 5\frac{4}{8} = 9\frac{7}{8}$
10. $2\frac{5}{6} + 8\frac{4}{6} = 11\frac{3}{6}$ or $11\frac{1}{2}$
11. $1\frac{3}{12} + 6\frac{5}{12} = 7\frac{8}{12}$ or $7\frac{2}{3}$
12. $15\frac{80}{100} + 4\frac{20}{100} = 20$
13. $5\frac{3}{4} + 6\frac{2}{4} = 12\frac{1}{4}$
14. $3\frac{1}{8} + 7\frac{4}{8} = 10\frac{5}{8}$
15. $8\frac{1}{5} + 7\frac{2}{5} = 15\frac{3}{5}$
16. $3\frac{2}{3} + 3\frac{2}{3} = 7\frac{1}{3}$
17. $3\frac{4}{5} + 5\frac{2}{5} = 9\frac{1}{5}$
18. $2\frac{5}{6} + 9\frac{3}{6} = 12\frac{2}{6}$ or $12\frac{1}{3}$
19. $7\frac{8}{10} + 5\frac{9}{10} = 13\frac{7}{10}$
20. $20\frac{1}{2} + 10\frac{1}{2} = 31$
21. $7\frac{3}{12} + 2\frac{11}{12} = 10\frac{2}{12}$ or $10\frac{1}{6}$
22. $3\frac{7}{8} + 4\frac{5}{8} = 8\frac{4}{8}$ or $8\frac{1}{2}$
23. $\frac{32}{100} + 3\frac{55}{100} = 3\frac{87}{100}$
24. $3\frac{5}{6} + 8\frac{3}{6} = 12\frac{2}{6}$ or $12\frac{1}{3}$

Fraction Subtraction—Skills Practice

Name: _____ Form A

Subtract fractions.

1. $\frac{3}{4} - \frac{1}{4} = \frac{2}{4}$ or $\frac{1}{2}$

2. $\frac{5}{6} - \frac{1}{6} = \frac{4}{6}$ or $\frac{2}{3}$

3. $\frac{2}{3} - \frac{1}{3} = \frac{1}{3}$

4. $\frac{7}{10} - \frac{3}{10} = \frac{4}{10}$ or $\frac{2}{5}$

5. $\frac{4}{5} - \frac{3}{5} = \frac{1}{5}$

6. $\frac{5}{8} - \frac{2}{8} = \frac{3}{8}$

7. $\frac{13}{12} - \frac{5}{12} = \frac{8}{12}$ or $\frac{2}{3}$

8. $\frac{50}{100} - \frac{5}{100} = \frac{45}{100}$ or $\frac{9}{20}$

9. $\frac{6}{10} - \frac{3}{10} = \frac{3}{10}$

10. $\frac{5}{3} - \frac{1}{3} = \frac{4}{3}$ or $1\frac{1}{3}$

11. $\frac{10}{8} - \frac{5}{8} = \frac{5}{8}$

12. $\frac{5}{2} - \frac{1}{2} = \frac{4}{2}$ or 2

13. $\frac{9}{6} - \frac{1}{6} = \frac{8}{6}$ or $1\frac{1}{3}$

14. $\frac{7}{12} - \frac{3}{12} = \frac{4}{12}$ or $\frac{1}{3}$

15. $\frac{80}{100} - \frac{20}{100} = \frac{60}{100}$ or $\frac{3}{5}$

16. $\frac{7}{4} - \frac{4}{4} = \frac{3}{4}$

17. $\frac{7}{4} - \frac{3}{4} = \frac{4}{4}$ or 1

18. $\frac{7}{8} - \frac{1}{8} = \frac{6}{8}$ or $\frac{3}{4}$

19. $\frac{8}{5} - \frac{2}{5} = \frac{6}{5}$ or $1\frac{1}{5}$

20. $\frac{8}{10} - \frac{3}{10} = \frac{5}{10}$ or $\frac{1}{2}$

21. $\frac{6}{3} - \frac{2}{3} = \frac{4}{3}$ or $1\frac{1}{3}$

22. $\frac{4}{5} - \frac{2}{5} = \frac{2}{5}$

23. $\frac{7}{6} - \frac{5}{6} = \frac{2}{6}$ or $\frac{1}{3}$

24. $\frac{10}{8} - \frac{3}{8} = \frac{7}{8}$

25. $\frac{12}{10} - \frac{5}{10} = \frac{7}{10}$

26. $\frac{3}{2} - \frac{3}{2} = 0$

27. $\frac{6}{12} - \frac{3}{12} = \frac{3}{12}$ or $\frac{1}{4}$

©Curriculum Associates, LLC   Copying is permitted for classroom use.

Fraction Addition—Repeated Reasoning

Name: _____

Find patterns in adding fractions.

Set A

1. $1\frac{1}{2} + \frac{1}{2} = 2$

2. $2\frac{1}{2} + \frac{1}{2} = 3$

3. $3\frac{1}{2} + \frac{1}{2} = 4$

4. $1\frac{1}{2} + 1\frac{1}{2} = 3$

5. $2\frac{1}{2} + 1\frac{1}{2} = 4$

6. $3\frac{1}{2} + 1\frac{1}{2} = 5$

7. $1\frac{2}{3} + \frac{1}{3} = 2$

8. $2\frac{2}{3} + \frac{1}{3} = 3$

9. $3\frac{2}{3} + \frac{1}{3} = 4$

10. $1\frac{2}{3} + 1\frac{1}{3} = 3$

11. $2\frac{2}{3} + 1\frac{1}{3} = 4$

12. $3\frac{2}{3} + 1\frac{1}{3} = 5$

Set B

1. $2\frac{1}{2} + 1\frac{1}{2} = 4$

2. $2\frac{1}{2} + 1\frac{1}{2} + 1 = 5$

3. $3\frac{2}{3} + 1\frac{1}{3} = 4$

4. $2\frac{1}{3} + 1\frac{1}{3} + 1\frac{1}{3} = 5$

5. $2\frac{1}{4} + 1\frac{2}{4} + \frac{1}{4} = 4$

6. $2\frac{1}{4} + 1\frac{2}{4} + 1\frac{1}{4} = 5$

Describe a pattern you see in one of the sets of problems above.

Answers will vary. Students may see in Set A that in each case the fractions add to one whole so the sum is one more than the sum of the whole numbers.

_____

©Curriculum Associates, LLC   Copying is permitted for classroom use.

©Curriculum Associates, LLC   Copying is not permitted.

Fraction Subtraction—Skills Practice — Form A

Name: _____

Subtract mixed numbers.

1. $2\frac{2}{3} - 1\frac{1}{3} = 2$
2. $2\frac{3}{5} - 1\frac{1}{5} = 1\frac{2}{5}$
3. $3\frac{1}{2} - \frac{3}{2} = 0$
4. $4\frac{5}{12} - 1\frac{3}{12} = 3\frac{2}{12}$ or $3\frac{1}{6}$
5. $5\frac{3}{4} - 2\frac{1}{4} = 1\frac{1}{4}$
6. $4\frac{5}{6} - 3\frac{3}{6} = 1\frac{4}{6}$ or $1\frac{2}{3}$
7. $7\frac{15}{100} - 2\frac{5}{100} = 5\frac{10}{100}$ or $5\frac{1}{10}$
8. $8\frac{2}{10} - 3\frac{7}{10} = 4\frac{5}{10}$ or $4\frac{1}{2}$
9. $9\frac{4}{5} - 2\frac{3}{5} = 1\frac{3}{5}$
10. $10\frac{3}{8} - 2\frac{3}{8} = 8$
11. $10\frac{1}{3} - \frac{2}{3} = 9\frac{2}{3}$
12. $2\frac{10}{100} - \frac{7}{100} = 2\frac{3}{100}$
13. $5\frac{6}{10} - 1\frac{3}{10} = 4\frac{3}{10}$
14. $6\frac{2}{5} - 5\frac{4}{5} = \frac{3}{5}$
15. $9\frac{1}{2} - 4\frac{1}{2} = 5$
16. $7\frac{5}{10} - 5\frac{1}{10} = 2\frac{4}{10}$ or $2\frac{2}{5}$
17. $6\frac{3}{4} - 4\frac{2}{4} = 2\frac{1}{4}$
18. $6\frac{2}{8} - 2\frac{5}{8} = 3\frac{5}{8}$
19. $2\frac{8}{12} - 2\frac{7}{12} = \frac{1}{12}$
20. $6\frac{6}{10} - 4\frac{7}{10} = 1\frac{5}{10}$ or $1\frac{1}{2}$
21. $10\frac{1}{5} - 8\frac{4}{5} = 1\frac{2}{5}$
22. $5\frac{1}{4} - 2\frac{3}{4} = 2\frac{2}{4}$ or $2\frac{1}{2}$
23. $7\frac{90}{100} - 7\frac{10}{100} = \frac{80}{100}$ or $\frac{4}{5}$
24. $6\frac{1}{3} - 4\frac{2}{3} = 1\frac{2}{3}$

Fluency Practice **415**

Fraction Subtraction—Skills Practice — Form B

Name: _____

Subtract fractions.

1. $\frac{3}{3} - \frac{1}{3} = \frac{2}{3}$
2. $\frac{5}{5} - \frac{2}{5} = \frac{3}{5}$
3. $\frac{1}{2} - \frac{1}{2} = 0$
4. $\frac{6}{10} - \frac{2}{10} = \frac{4}{10}$ or $\frac{2}{5}$
5. $\frac{11}{12} - \frac{5}{12} = \frac{6}{12}$ or $\frac{1}{2}$
6. $\frac{5}{4} - \frac{1}{4} = \frac{4}{4}$ or 1
7. $\frac{7}{6} - \frac{3}{6} = \frac{4}{6}$ or $\frac{2}{3}$
8. $\frac{12}{100} - \frac{8}{100} = \frac{4}{100}$ or $\frac{1}{25}$
9. $\frac{60}{100} - \frac{30}{100} = \frac{30}{100}$ or $\frac{3}{10}$
10. $\frac{12}{10} - \frac{3}{10} = \frac{9}{10}$
11. $\frac{13}{5} - \frac{4}{5} = \frac{9}{5}$ or $1\frac{4}{5}$
12. $\frac{6}{2} - \frac{1}{2} = \frac{5}{2}$ or $2\frac{1}{2}$
13. $\frac{7}{8} - \frac{1}{8} = \frac{6}{8}$ or $\frac{3}{4}$
14. $\frac{5}{3} - \frac{1}{3} = \frac{4}{3}$ or $1\frac{1}{3}$
15. $\frac{56}{100} - \frac{6}{100} = \frac{50}{100}$ or $\frac{1}{2}$
16. $\frac{15}{12} - \frac{3}{12} = \frac{12}{12}$ or 1
17. $\frac{7}{10} - \frac{2}{10} = \frac{5}{10}$ or $\frac{1}{2}$
18. $\frac{7}{5} - \frac{3}{5} = \frac{4}{5}$
19. $\frac{4}{2} - \frac{3}{2} = \frac{1}{2}$
20. $\frac{7}{4} - \frac{2}{4} = \frac{5}{4}$ or $1\frac{1}{4}$
21. $\frac{30}{10} - \frac{5}{10} = \frac{25}{10}$ or $2\frac{1}{2}$
22. $\frac{10}{4} - \frac{2}{4} = \frac{8}{4}$ or 2
23. $\frac{7}{8} - \frac{4}{8} = \frac{3}{8}$
24. $\frac{12}{12} - \frac{3}{12} = \frac{9}{12}$ or $\frac{3}{4}$
25. $\frac{7}{2} - \frac{5}{2} = \frac{2}{2}$ or 1
26. $\frac{9}{10} - \frac{3}{10} = \frac{6}{10}$ or $\frac{3}{5}$
27. $\frac{8}{5} - \frac{1}{5} = \frac{7}{5}$ or $1\frac{2}{5}$

414 Fluency Practice

Fraction Subtraction—Repeated Reasoning

Name: _____

Find patterns in subtracting fractions.

Set A

1 $1 - \frac{1}{2} = \frac{1}{2}$

2 $2 - \frac{1}{2} = 1\frac{1}{2}$

3 $3 - \frac{1}{2} = 2\frac{1}{2}$

4 $1 - \frac{1}{3} = \frac{2}{3}$

5 $2 - \frac{1}{3} = 1\frac{2}{3}$

6 $3 - \frac{1}{3} = 2\frac{2}{3}$

7 $1 - \frac{1}{4} = \frac{3}{4}$

8 $2 - \frac{1}{4} = 1\frac{3}{4}$

9 $3 - \frac{1}{4} = 2\frac{3}{4}$

10 $1 - \frac{1}{10} = \frac{9}{10}$

11 $2 - \frac{1}{10} = 1\frac{9}{10}$

12 $3 - \frac{1}{10} = 2\frac{9}{10}$

Set B

1 $5 - 1\frac{1}{2} = 3\frac{1}{2}$

2 $5 - 2\frac{1}{2} = 2\frac{1}{2}$

3 $5 - 3\frac{1}{2} = 1\frac{1}{2}$

4 $5 - 1\frac{1}{3} = 3\frac{2}{3}$

5 $5 - 2\frac{1}{3} = 2\frac{2}{3}$

6 $5 - 3\frac{1}{3} = 1\frac{2}{3}$

7 $5 - 1\frac{1}{4} = 3\frac{3}{4}$

8 $5 - 2\frac{1}{4} = 2\frac{3}{4}$

9 $5 - 3\frac{1}{4} = 1\frac{3}{4}$

10 $5 - 1\frac{1}{10} = 3\frac{9}{10}$

11 $5 - 2\frac{1}{10} = 2\frac{9}{10}$

12 $5 - 3\frac{1}{10} = 1\frac{9}{10}$

Describe a pattern you see in one of the sets of problems above.

Answers will vary. Students may see in Set B that when the amount subtracted increases by one whole, the difference decrease by one whole.

Fraction Subtraction—Skills Practice

Name: _____   **Form B**

Subtract mixed numbers.

1 $3\frac{2}{5} - \frac{1}{5} = 3\frac{1}{5}$

2 $6\frac{3}{4} - 1\frac{1}{4} = 5\frac{2}{4}$ or $5\frac{1}{2}$

3 $7\frac{1}{2} - \frac{1}{2} = 7$

4 $4\frac{6}{10} - 1\frac{2}{10} = 3\frac{4}{10}$ or $3\frac{2}{5}$

5 $5\frac{2}{3} - 2\frac{1}{3} = 3\frac{1}{3}$

6 $4\frac{5}{6} - 3\frac{1}{6} = 1\frac{4}{6}$ or $1\frac{2}{3}$

7 $9\frac{20}{100} - 5\frac{2}{100} = 4\frac{18}{100}$ or $4\frac{9}{50}$

8 $8\frac{7}{10} - 3\frac{1}{10} = 5\frac{6}{10}$ or $5\frac{3}{5}$

9 $10\frac{4}{5} - 3\frac{1}{5} = 7\frac{3}{5}$

10 $1\frac{1}{8} - \frac{3}{8} = \frac{6}{8}$ or $\frac{3}{4}$

11 $4\frac{1}{3} - \frac{3}{3} = 3\frac{1}{3}$

12 $8\frac{60}{100} - 2\frac{10}{100} = 6\frac{50}{100}$ or $6\frac{1}{2}$

13 $6\frac{5}{10} - 1\frac{9}{10} = 4\frac{6}{10}$ or $4\frac{3}{5}$

14 $8\frac{2}{5} - 5\frac{4}{5} = 2\frac{3}{5}$

15 $7\frac{1}{2} - 4\frac{1}{2} = 3$

16 $5\frac{7}{10} - 3\frac{9}{10} = 1\frac{8}{10}$ or $1\frac{4}{5}$

17 $1\frac{3}{4} - \frac{2}{4} = 1\frac{1}{4}$

18 $16\frac{2}{8} - 12\frac{5}{8} = 3\frac{5}{8}$

19 $5\frac{3}{12} - 2\frac{7}{12} = 2\frac{8}{12}$ or $2\frac{2}{3}$

20 $7\frac{2}{10} - 2\frac{7}{10} = 4\frac{5}{10}$ or $4\frac{1}{2}$

21 $9\frac{1}{5} - 8\frac{4}{5} = \frac{2}{5}$

22 $3\frac{1}{4} - \frac{3}{4} = 2\frac{2}{4}$ or $2\frac{1}{2}$

23 $9\frac{70}{100} - 4\frac{10}{100} = 5\frac{60}{100}$ or $5\frac{3}{5}$

24 $14\frac{1}{3} - 9\frac{2}{3} = 4\frac{2}{3}$

Multi-Digit Multiplication—Skills Practice

Name: _____

Form A

Multiply a 2-digit number by a 1-digit number.

1 12 ×2 = 24	**2** 10 ×3 = 30	**3** 21 ×4 = 84	**4** 23 ×1 = 23	**5** 33 ×2 = 66
6 11 ×8 = 88	**7** 35 ×4 = 140	**8** 46 ×5 = 230	**9** 51 ×3 = 153	**10** 70 ×5 = 350
11 10 ×9 = 90	**12** 88 ×4 = 352	**13** 78 ×5 = 390	**14** 29 ×6 = 174	**15** 61 ×6 = 366
16 12 ×7 = 84	**17** 26 ×8 = 208	**18** 58 ×9 = 522	**19** 81 ×7 = 567	**20** 75 ×3 = 225
21 72 ×3 = 216	**22** 92 ×3 = 276	**23** 49 ×7 = 343	**24** 31 ×6 = 186	**25** 56 ×4 = 224
26 34 ×6 = 204	**27** 58 ×5 = 290	**28** 37 ×7 = 259	**29** 64 ×8 = 512	**30** 98 ×9 = 882

Multi-Digit Multiplication—Skills Practice

Name: _____

Form B

Multiply a 2-digit number by a 1-digit number.

1 21 ×2 = 42	**2** 10 ×6 = 60	**3** 41 ×3 = 123	**4** 32 ×1 = 32	**5** 22 ×4 = 88
6 11 ×7 = 77	**7** 54 ×9 = 486	**8** 64 ×5 = 320	**9** 55 ×8 = 440	**10** 75 ×5 = 375
11 12 ×9 = 108	**12** 84 ×8 = 672	**13** 57 ×4 = 228	**14** 96 ×7 = 672	**15** 41 ×6 = 246
16 82 ×7 = 574	**17** 26 ×5 = 130	**18** 92 ×6 = 552	**19** 81 ×3 = 243	**20** 35 ×7 = 245
21 62 ×8 = 496	**22** 43 ×8 = 344	**23** 98 ×2 = 196	**24** 36 ×9 = 324	**25** 28 ×4 = 112
26 53 ×4 = 212	**27** 38 ×5 = 190	**28** 24 ×7 = 168	**29** 48 ×3 = 144	**30** 99 ×9 = 891

Multi-Digit Multiplication—Skills Practice

Name: _____

Form A

Multiply 2-digit numbers.

1 21 ×35 = 735

2 18 ×16 = 288

3 24 ×12 = 288

4 32 ×15 = 480

5 12 ×37 = 444

6 11 ×77 = 847

7 54 ×92 = 4,968

8 64 ×35 = 2,240

9 75 ×28 = 2,100

10 43 ×15 = 645

11 42 ×96 = 4,032

12 40 ×88 = 3,520

13 57 ×64 = 3,648

14 96 ×70 = 6,720

15 61 ×54 = 3,294

16 82 ×27 = 2,214

17 26 ×45 = 1,170

18 82 ×34 = 2,788

19 63 ×36 = 2,268

20 35 ×27 = 945

21 20 ×16 = 320

22 41 ×30 = 1,230

23 98 ×20 = 1,960

24 36 ×79 = 2,844

25 28 ×49 = 1,372

Multi-Digit Multiplication

Name: _____

Form B

Multiply 2-digit numbers.

1 12 ×53 = 636

2 86 ×11 = 946

3 55 ×43 = 2,365

4 23 ×15 = 345

5 12 ×83 = 996

6 11 ×66 = 726

7 94 ×25 = 2,350

8 46 ×53 = 2,438

9 37 ×62 = 2,294

10 78 ×18 = 1,404

11 24 ×96 = 2,304

12 14 ×85 = 1,190

13 74 ×36 = 2,664

14 97 ×40 = 3,880

15 41 ×56 = 2,296

16 92 ×57 = 5,244

17 63 ×45 = 2,835

18 52 ×27 = 1,404

19 84 ×29 = 2,436

20 99 ×34 = 3,366

21 50 ×26 = 1,300

22 74 ×30 = 2,220

23 89 ×40 = 3,560

24 36 ×29 = 1,044

25 98 ×90 = 8,820

Multi-Digit Multiplication—Skills Practice

Name: _____

Form A

Multiply a 3-digit number by a 1-digit number.

1	513 × 2 ——— 1,026	2	120 × 3 ——— 360	3	612 × 4 ——— 2,448	4	711 × 5 ——— 3,555
5	460 × 3 ——— 1,380	6	325 × 7 ——— 2,275	7	940 × 5 ——— 4,700	8	518 × 3 ——— 1,554
9	105 × 9 ——— 945	10	862 × 4 ——— 3,448	11	728 × 5 ——— 3,640	12	429 × 6 ——— 2,574
13	123 × 7 ——— 861	14	256 × 8 ——— 2,048	15	908 × 9 ——— 8,172	16	381 × 2 ——— 762
17	712 × 3 ——— 2,136	18	923 × 3 ——— 2,769	19	752 × 7 ——— 5,264	20	310 × 6 ——— 1,860
21	304 × 6 ——— 1,824	22	502 × 5 ——— 2,510	23	837 × 6 ——— 5,022	24	604 × 8 ——— 4,832

Multi-Digit Multiplication—Skills Practice

Name: _____

Form B

Multiply a 3-digit number by a 1-digit number.

1	100 × 7 ——— 700	2	421 × 3 ——— 1,263	3	324 × 1 ——— 324	4	202 × 4 ——— 808
5	504 × 9 ——— 4,536	6	614 × 5 ——— 3,070	7	945 × 8 ——— 7,560	8	157 × 5 ——— 785
9	624 × 8 ——— 4,992	10	457 × 3 ——— 1,371	11	967 × 4 ——— 3,868	12	804 × 6 ——— 4,824
13	250 × 4 ——— 1,000	14	512 × 9 ——— 4,608	15	381 × 5 ——— 1,905	16	336 × 7 ——— 2,352
17	843 × 2 ——— 1,686	18	938 × 6 ——— 5,628	19	362 × 9 ——— 3,258	20	278 × 4 ——— 1,112
21	308 × 5 ——— 1,540	22	724 × 7 ——— 5,068	23	548 × 3 ——— 1,644	24	909 × 9 ——— 8,181

Multi-Digit Multiplication—Skills Practice

Name: _____

Form A

Multiply a 4-digit number by a 1-digit number.

1	5,213 × 2 = 10,426	2	6,120 × 4 = 24,480	3	5,332 × 3 = 15,996	4	5,201 × 4 = 20,804
5	4,360 × 5 = 21,800	6	7,025 × 3 = 21,075	7	1,945 × 6 = 11,670	8	3,518 × 7 = 24,626
9	2,075 × 9 = 18,675	10	4,208 × 6 = 25,248	11	7,528 × 2 = 15,056	12	5,299 × 3 = 15,897
13	1,234 × 7 = 8,638	14	2,048 × 5 = 10,240	15	9,088 × 3 = 27,264	16	8,301 × 8 = 66,408
17	7,302 × 4 = 29,208	18	9,423 × 2 = 18,846	19	7,526 × 4 = 30,104	20	4,610 × 6 = 27,660
21	3,604 × 8 = 28,832	22	5,902 × 9 = 53,118	23	8,637 × 6 = 51,822	24	6,804 × 5 = 34,020

Multi-Digit Multiplication—Skills Practice

Name: _____

Form B

Multiply a 4-digit number by a 1-digit number.

1	4,130 × 2 = 8,260	2	5,212 × 4 = 20,848	3	3,023 × 3 = 9,069	4	1,200 × 4 = 4,800
5	5,170 × 5 = 25,850	6	6,047 × 8 = 48,376	7	2,593 × 6 = 15,558	8	8,350 × 7 = 58,450
9	3,084 × 9 = 27,756	10	2,708 × 6 = 16,248	11	8,925 × 2 = 17,850	12	7,599 × 3 = 22,797
13	9,423 × 4 = 37,692	14	2,048 × 5 = 10,240	15	4,625 × 7 = 32,375	16	5,304 × 8 = 42,432
17	2,730 × 3 = 8,190	18	9,067 × 2 = 18,134	19	7,199 × 4 = 28,796	20	5,402 × 7 = 37,814
21	6,521 × 8 = 52,168	22	3,207 × 9 = 28,863	23	8,022 × 6 = 48,132	24	4,635 × 5 = 23,175

Multi-Digit Multiplication— Repeated Reasoning

Name: _____

Find place value patterns.

Set A

1. 6 × 11 = 66
2. 6 × 101 = 606
3. 6 × 1,001 = 6,006

4. 7 × 11 = 77
5. 7 × 101 = 707
6. 7 × 1,001 = 7,007

7. 8 × 11 = 88
8. 8 × 101 = 808
9. 8 × 1,001 = 8,008

10. 9 × 11 = 99
11. 9 × 101 = 909
12. 9 × 1,001 = 9,009

Set B

1. $\begin{array}{r} 22 \\ \times\ 3 \\ \hline 66 \end{array}$
2. $\begin{array}{r} 202 \\ \times\ 3 \\ \hline 606 \end{array}$
3. $\begin{array}{r} 2{,}002 \\ \times\ 3 \\ \hline 6{,}006 \end{array}$

4. $\begin{array}{r} 22 \\ \times\ 4 \\ \hline 88 \end{array}$
5. $\begin{array}{r} 202 \\ \times\ 4 \\ \hline 808 \end{array}$
6. $\begin{array}{r} 2{,}002 \\ \times\ 4 \\ \hline 8{,}008 \end{array}$

7. $\begin{array}{r} 22 \\ \times\ 5 \\ \hline 110 \end{array}$
8. $\begin{array}{r} 202 \\ \times\ 5 \\ \hline 1{,}010 \end{array}$
9. $\begin{array}{r} 2{,}002 \\ \times\ 5 \\ \hline 10{,}010 \end{array}$

Describe a pattern you see in one of the sets of problems above.

Answers will vary. Students may see that they can decompose the multi-digit factor to find and then add two partial products using mental math.

Multi-Digit Multiplication— Repeated Reasoning

Name: _____

Find patterns multiplying by 98 and 99.

Set A

1. $\begin{array}{r} 99 \\ \times\ 2 \\ \hline 198 \end{array}$
2. $\begin{array}{r} 99 \\ \times\ 3 \\ \hline 297 \end{array}$
3. $\begin{array}{r} 99 \\ \times\ 4 \\ \hline 396 \end{array}$

4. $\begin{array}{r} 199 \\ \times\ 2 \\ \hline 398 \end{array}$
5. $\begin{array}{r} 199 \\ \times\ 3 \\ \hline 597 \end{array}$
6. $\begin{array}{r} 199 \\ \times\ 4 \\ \hline 796 \end{array}$

7. $\begin{array}{r} 299 \\ \times\ 2 \\ \hline 598 \end{array}$
8. $\begin{array}{r} 299 \\ \times\ 3 \\ \hline 897 \end{array}$
9. $\begin{array}{r} 299 \\ \times\ 4 \\ \hline 1{,}196 \end{array}$

Set B

1. $\begin{array}{r} 98 \\ \times\ 2 \\ \hline 196 \end{array}$
2. $\begin{array}{r} 98 \\ \times\ 3 \\ \hline 294 \end{array}$
3. $\begin{array}{r} 98 \\ \times\ 4 \\ \hline 392 \end{array}$

4. $\begin{array}{r} 198 \\ \times\ 2 \\ \hline 396 \end{array}$
5. $\begin{array}{r} 198 \\ \times\ 3 \\ \hline 594 \end{array}$
6. $\begin{array}{r} 198 \\ \times\ 4 \\ \hline 792 \end{array}$

7. $\begin{array}{r} 298 \\ \times\ 2 \\ \hline 596 \end{array}$
8. $\begin{array}{r} 298 \\ \times\ 3 \\ \hline 894 \end{array}$
9. $\begin{array}{r} 298 \\ \times\ 4 \\ \hline 1{,}192 \end{array}$

Describe a pattern you see in one of the sets of problems above.

Answers will vary. Students may see that to multiply a number by 99 you can just multiply by a hundred and then subtract the number.

Multi-Digit Division—Skills Practice

Name: _____   Form A

Divide 2-digit dividends.

1 $3\overline{)81}$ — 27 **2** $4\overline{)52}$ — 13 **3** $5\overline{)90}$ — 18 **4** $2\overline{)78}$ — 39

5 $6\overline{)85}$ — 14 R1 **6** $9\overline{)63}$ — 7 **7** $3\overline{)92}$ — 30 R2 **8** $7\overline{)81}$ — 11 R4

9 $2\overline{)73}$ — 36 R1 **10** $5\overline{)70}$ — 14 **11** $8\overline{)99}$ — 12 R3 **12** $4\overline{)95}$ — 23 R3

13 $9\overline{)98}$ — 10 R8 **14** $3\overline{)99}$ — 33 **15** $6\overline{)38}$ — 6 R2 **16** $5\overline{)95}$ — 19

17 $7\overline{)87}$ — 12 R3 **18** $8\overline{)62}$ — 7 R6 **19** $4\overline{)82}$ — 20 R2 **20** $2\overline{)87}$ — 43 R1

Fluency Practice   **429**

Multi-Digit Multiplication—Repeated Reasoning

Name: _____

Find patterns multiplying by near-hundreds.

Set A

1 $101 \times 2 = 202$ **2** $102 \times 2 = 204$ **3** $103 \times 2 = 206$

4 $101 \times 3 = 303$ **5** $102 \times 3 = 306$ **6** $103 \times 3 = 309$

7 $101 \times 4 = 404$ **8** $102 \times 4 = 408$ **9** $103 \times 4 = 412$

Set B

1 $202 \times 2 = 404$ **2** $202 \times 3 = 606$ **3** $202 \times 4 = 808$

4 $203 \times 2 = 406$ **5** $203 \times 3 = 609$ **6** $203 \times 4 = 812$

7 $204 \times 2 = 408$ **8** $204 \times 3 = 612$ **9** $204 \times 4 = 816$

Describe a pattern you see in one of the sets of problems above.
Answers will vary. Students may see that they can decompose the multi-digit factor to
find and then add two partial products using mental math.

428 Fluency Practice

Multi-Digit Division—Skills Practice

Name: _____

Form A

Divide 3-digit dividends.

1 214 $\overline{3)642}$

2 82 $\overline{4)328}$

3 149 $\overline{5)745}$

4 281 R1 $\overline{2)563}$

5 102 $\overline{9)918}$

6 150 R5 $\overline{6)905}$

7 168 R4 $\overline{5)844}$

8 71 R1 $\overline{7)498}$

9 50 R7 $\overline{8)407}$

10 325 $\overline{3)975}$

11 208 $\overline{2)416}$

12 148 $\overline{4)592}$

13 115 R3 $\overline{6)693}$

14 91 R2 $\overline{5)457}$

15 286 R2 $\overline{3)860}$

Multi-Digit Division—Skills Practice

Name: _____

Form B

Divide 2-digit dividends.

1 27 $\overline{2)54}$

2 16 R2 $\overline{3)50}$

3 8 R2 $\overline{4)34}$

4 11 $\overline{5)55}$

5 12 R5 $\overline{6)77}$

6 13 $\overline{7)91}$

7 12 R1 $\overline{8)97}$

8 10 R5 $\overline{9)95}$

9 44 R1 $\overline{2)89}$

10 31 R1 $\overline{3)94}$

11 20 R3 $\overline{4)83}$

12 15 R3 $\overline{5)78}$

13 15 $\overline{6)90}$

14 7 R1 $\overline{7)50}$

15 10 $\overline{8)80}$

16 9 R6 $\overline{9)87}$

17 19 $\overline{2)38}$

18 31 R1 $\overline{3)94}$

19 24 R3 $\overline{4)99}$

20 18 R4 $\overline{5)94}$

Fluency Practice

Multi-Digit Division—Skills Practice

Form B

Name: _____

Divide 3-digit dividends.

1. 247
3)741

2. 127
4)508

3. 70 R4
5)354

4. 352 R1
2)705

5. 133 R5
7)936

6. 108
6)648

7. 164
5)820

8. 21 R2
7)149

9. 114 R4
8)916

10. 320
3)960

11. 305 R3
2)613

12. 221 R3
4)887

13. 123
6)738

14. 86 R2
5)432

15. 240 R2
3)722

Multi-Digit Division—Skills Practice

Form A

Name: _____

Divide 4-digit dividends.

1. 2,311
3)6,933

2. 326
4)1,304

3. 246 R4
5)1,234

4. 3,675
2)7,350

5. 227
7)1,589

6. 262 R2
6)1,574

7. 529 R3
5)2,648

8. 928 R1
3)2,845

9. 751 R6
8)6,014

10. 2,858
3)8,574

11. 2,659
2)5,318

12. 645 R3
4)2,583

13. 625 R4
6)3,754

14. 1,427 R3
5)7,138

15. 1,667 R1
3)5,002

Fluency Practice

Multi-Digit Division—Skills Practice

Name: _____   **Form B**

Divide 4-digit dividends.

1. $\begin{array}{r} 1{,}464 \\ 3\overline{)4{,}392} \end{array}$

2. $\begin{array}{r} 873 \\ 4\overline{)3{,}492} \end{array}$

3. $\begin{array}{r} 841\ R1 \\ 5\overline{)4{,}206} \end{array}$

4. $\begin{array}{r} 4{,}785 \\ 2\overline{)9{,}570} \end{array}$

5. $\begin{array}{r} 422\ R4 \\ 7\overline{)2{,}958} \end{array}$

6. $\begin{array}{r} 873\ R3 \\ 6\overline{)5{,}241} \end{array}$

7. $\begin{array}{r} 1{,}613 \\ 5\overline{)8{,}065} \end{array}$

8. $\begin{array}{r} 1{,}546\ R1 \\ 3\overline{)4{,}639} \end{array}$

9. $\begin{array}{r} 231\ R6 \\ 8\overline{)1{,}854} \end{array}$

10. $\begin{array}{r} 1{,}913\ R1 \\ 3\overline{)5{,}740} \end{array}$

11. $\begin{array}{r} 3{,}677\ R2 \\ 2\overline{)7{,}356} \end{array}$

12. $\begin{array}{r} 955 \\ 4\overline{)3{,}820} \end{array}$

13. $\begin{array}{r} 753\ R5 \\ 6\overline{)4{,}523} \end{array}$

14. $\begin{array}{r} 1{,}229\ R3 \\ 5\overline{)6{,}148} \end{array}$

15. $\begin{array}{r} 668\ R1 \\ 3\overline{)2{,}005} \end{array}$

Multi-Digit Division—Repeated Reasoning

Name: _____

Find patterns in quotients.

Set A

1. $404 \div 1 = 404$
2. $404 \div 2 = 202$
3. $404 \div 4 = 101$

4. $606 \div 2 = 303$
5. $606 \div 3 = 202$
6. $606 \div 6 = 101$

7. $808 \div 2 = 404$
8. $808 \div 4 = 202$
9. $808 \div 8 = 101$

10. $909 \div 1 = 909$
11. $909 \div 3 = 303$
12. $909 \div 9 = 101$

Set B

1. $\begin{array}{r} 1{,}212 \\ 1\overline{)1{,}212} \end{array}$

2. $\begin{array}{r} 606 \\ 2\overline{)1{,}212} \end{array}$

3. $\begin{array}{r} 404 \\ 3\overline{)1{,}212} \end{array}$

4. $\begin{array}{r} 303 \\ 4\overline{)1{,}212} \end{array}$

5. $\begin{array}{r} 202 \\ 6\overline{)1{,}212} \end{array}$

6. $\begin{array}{r} 101 \\ 12\overline{)1{,}212} \end{array}$

7. $\begin{array}{r} 606 \\ 4\overline{)2{,}424} \end{array}$

8. $\begin{array}{r} 404 \\ 6\overline{)2{,}424} \end{array}$

9. $\begin{array}{r} 202 \\ 12\overline{)2{,}424} \end{array}$

Describe a pattern you see in one of the sets of problems above.
Answers will vary. Students may see that they can decompose the dividend to find

and then add two partial quotients using mental math.

_____

Unit Game Teacher Resource
Table of Contents

Name: _____

Subtraction Action Recording Sheet

_____   _____

Player A Name   **Player B Name**

1. □□,□□□
   − □□,□□□

       1. _____ < _____

1. □□,□□□
   − □□,□□□

2. □□,□□□
   − □□,□□□

       2. _____ < _____

2. □□,□□□
   − □□,□□□

3. □□,□□□
   − □□,□□□

       3. _____ < _____

3. □□,□□□
   − □□,□□□

4. □□,□□□
   − □□,□□□

       4. _____ < _____

4. □□,□□□
   − □□,□□□

5. □□,□□□
   − □□,□□□

       5. _____ < _____

5. □□,□□□
   − □□,□□□

Name: _____

Digit Cards 0–9

✂

0	1	2	3	4
5	6	7	8	9
0	1	2	3	4
5	6	7	8	9
0	1	2	3	4
5	6	7	8	9

Name: _____

Factor Finder Recording Sheet

Two-Digit Numbers

☐0 ☐1 ☐2 ☐3 ☐4 ☐5 ☐6 ☐7 ☐8 ☐9

_____
Player A Name

1. Two-digit number: _____
   Factors: _____

2. Two-digit number: _____
   Factors: _____

3. Two-digit number: _____
   Factors: _____

4. Two-digit number: _____
   Factors: _____

5. Two-digit number: _____
   Factors: _____

_____
Player B Name

1. Two-digit number: _____
   Factors: _____

2. Two-digit number: _____
   Factors: _____

3. Two-digit number: _____
   Factors: _____

4. Two-digit number: _____
   Factors: _____

5. Two-digit number: _____
   Factors: _____

TR 4

Name: ______________________________

Factor Finder Game Board

2	8	7	6	5
3	6	5	8	11
12	2	10	4	12
6	9	8	3	4
5	4	3	9	2

Digit Cards 1–9

1	2	3	4	5	6
7	8	9	1	2	3
4	5	6	7	8	9

Name: _____

Multiplication Products Recording Sheet

_____   _____
Player A Name   Player B Name

Round 1: Multiply a two-digit number by a two-digit number. Circle the <u>greater</u> product.

1. _____ × _____ = _____   1. _____ × _____ = _____

Round 2: Multiply a two-digit number by a two-digit number. Circle the <u>lesser</u> product.

2. _____ × _____ = _____   2. _____ × _____ = _____

Round 3: Multiply a four-digit number by a one-digit number. Circle the <u>greater</u> product.

3. _____ × _____ = _____   3. _____ × _____ = _____

Round 4: Multiply a four-digit number by a one-digit number. Circle the <u>lesser</u> product.

4. _____ × _____ = _____   4. _____ × _____ = _____

Round 5: Choose Round 1, 2, 3, or 4 to repeat.

5. _____ × _____ = _____   5. _____ × _____ = _____

Final Score Player A _____   **Final Score Player B** _____

Name: _____

Fraction Sums Recording Sheet

Denominators
2   3   4   6   8

Denominators
2   3   4   6   8

_____
Player A Name

Denominator Choice	Equation
1. _____	_____
2. _____	_____
3. _____	_____
4. _____	_____
5. _____	_____

Final Score Player A [_____]

_____
Player B Name

Denominator Choice	Equation
1. _____	_____
2. _____	_____
3. _____	_____
4. _____	_____
5. _____	_____

Final Score Player B [_____]

Name: _____

Angle Sums Recording Sheet

Player A Name	**Player B Name**
_____	_____

1. _____ + _____ = _____   1. _____ + _____ = _____

            1. _____ > _____

2. _____ + _____ = _____   2. _____ + _____ = _____

            2. _____ > _____

3. _____ + _____ = _____   3. _____ + _____ = _____

            3. _____ > _____

4. _____ + _____ = _____   4. _____ + _____ = _____

            4. _____ > _____

5. _____ + _____ = _____   5. _____ + _____ = _____

            5. _____ > _____

Final Score Player A _____   **Final Score Player B** _____

Angle Sums Game Cards

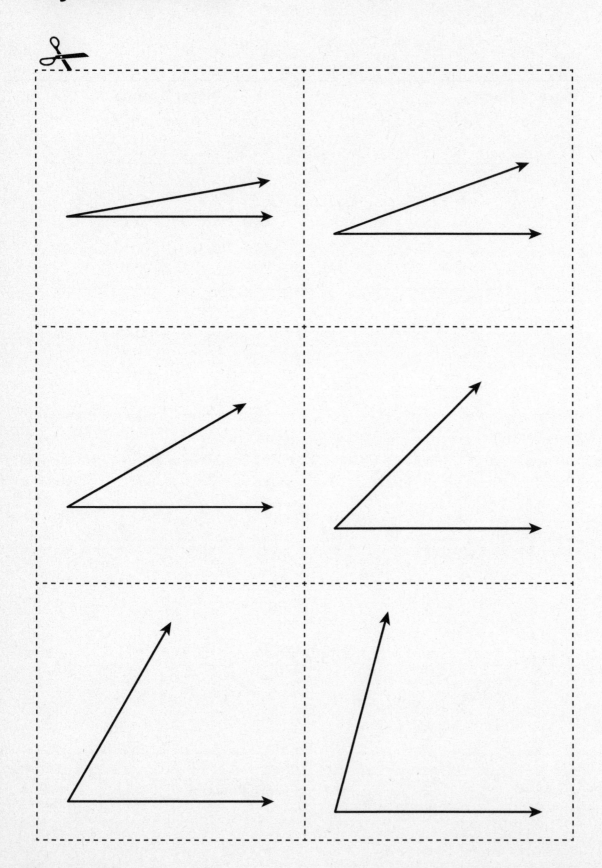

©Curriculum Associates, LLC   Copying is permitted for classroom use.

Angle Sums Game Cards (continued)

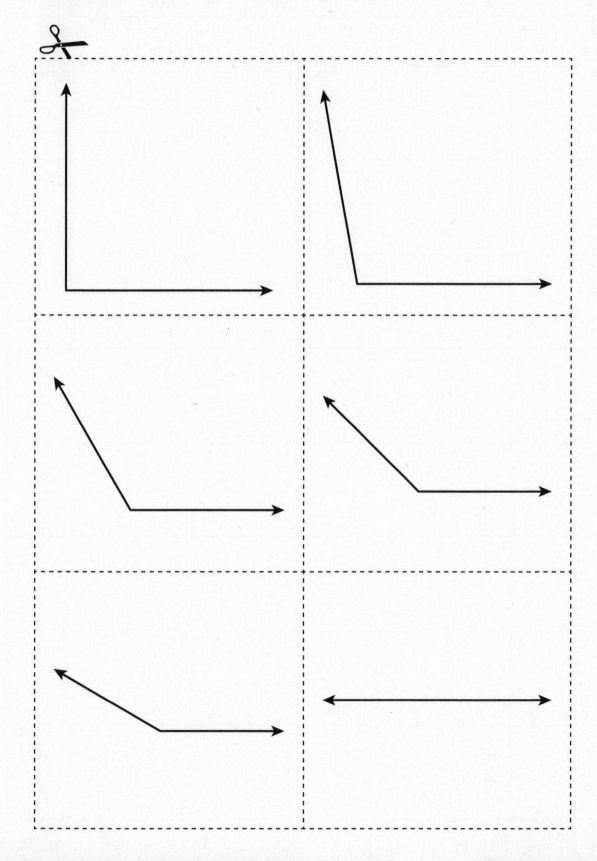

Name: _____

Shape Round-Up Recording Sheet

Description on Game Card	Shapes Covered on Game Board

Shape Round-Up Game Cards

✂

has acute angle(s)	has obtuse angle(s)	has right angle(s)	has more than one pair of parallel sides
has more than one pair of perpendicular sides	has acute angles and obtuse angles	has acute angles and right angles	has exactly one pair of parallel sides
has exactly one pair of perpendicular sides	acute triangle	obtuse triangle	right triangle
has more than 4 obtuse angles	has right angles and obtuse angles	has no sides that are parallel	has no sides that are perpendicular

Shape Round-Up Game Board

square	hexagon	triangle	trapezoid
pentagon	triangle	trapezoid	parallelogram
parallelogram	rhombus	pentagon	hexagon
hexagon	rectangle	triangle	triangle